IN THE PINE

Leonard Roberts, east Kentuckian by birth, earned his undergraduate degree at Berea College in English and Music. He studied at the State University of Iowa (MA), at the University of North Carolina, Indiana University, and took his doctorate degree at the University of Kentucky, concentrating on English Literature, folklore, and frontier history. He has taught in North Carolina, Georgia, West Virginia, and Kentucky.

Dr. Roberts discovered that he was of the folk when he went down out of the Cumberland foothills to the army and then to school at Berea and elsewhere. He was able to be among the first to "discover" and make known the rich heritage of folktale and legend in Appalachia. He has garnered thousands of items in most genres and has learned to perform the long tales and legends. Most of his published collections are still in print, such as **I Bought Me a Dog, South from Hell-fer-Sartin, Folk Tales of the Southern Mountains,** and two were combined to make up most of the book titled **Sang Branch Settlers.** At present he is Professor and Director of the Appalachian Studies Center at Pikeville College.

Calvin Buell Agey, now an Emeritus Professor and part-time teacher at West Virginia Wesleyan College, spent 25 years as chairman of Wesleyan's Music Department. He has been a graduate student at Peabody Conservatory, Cincinnati Conservatory, at Cincinnati College of Music and in 1955 was the first Ph.D. in Music Theory granted by Florida State University.

Over one hundred of Dr. Agey's compositions, editings, and arrangements of choral and instrumental music are presently distributed by major publishers throughout the United States and the British Commonwealth.

Dr. Agey's concern with folksong is directed toward the objective perception of its tonal attributes and their interrelationship with structural, rhythmic, modal, and cultural characteristics. His music analysis is ever alert to incidence of surprise, anomaly, and ethnic idiom so refreshingly revealed in the unsophisticated simplicity of folksong.

IN THE PINE
SELECTED KENTUCKY FOLKSONGS

Collected by
Leonard Roberts
Pikeville College

Music Transcriptions by
C. Buell Agey
West Virginia Wesleyan College

Consultant
Jan Philip Schinan
Duke University

Published by
Pikeville College Press
Pikeville, Kentucky
1978

First Edition

Second Edition, with corrections, 1979

Library of Congress Cataloging and Publication data

Roberts, Leonard Ward and Agey, Calvin Buell

In the Pine: Selected Kentucky Folksongs

1. Folksongs, Kentucky I. Title. II. Bibliography
2. History, Kentucky   Folklore, Appalachia
3. Music, oral transcriptions South, songs, hymns
    LC No. 78-56599   1978   784.4973

Manufactured in the United States of America

CONTENTS

PART I BALLADS

A. ENGLISH AND SCOTTISH BALLADS

PART II FOLKSONGS

A. LYRICAL AND LOVE SONGS

B. HYMNS AND HOMILETIC SONGS

C. HUMOROUS AND SATIRICAL SONGS

INTRODUCTION TO THE TEXTS

One of the first Child ballads I remember collecting was on Wooton's Creek in Leslie County, Kentucky, in the spring of 1949. Bill Baker, one of my students in the Foundation School of Berea College, was taking me up the long winding Cutshin Creek to his home on Baker's Fork. We had planned to stay at his aunt's house and then cross the hill to his home the next morning. Bill had brought me into the region the fall before on an adventurous trip of many miles up Greasy Creek. I had let the front end of the car slide over an enbankment, and we needed to find a place to stay the night and get the car pulled back on the road the next morning. Now we were playing it safer by planning the way.

We reached his aunt's cottage-like home on the hillside overlooking the winding valley in late afternoon. Dusk was setting over the region and the air was like ether along the creek banks. The aunt, Mrs. Luther York, and her youngest daughter of twelve welcomed us with the usual mountain hospitality. Her husband was away at a job. Since she had electricity, we lugged the heavy tape recorder up the hill to the living room. Within half an hour she had supper on the table and we sat down to one of the finest and most welcome feasts imaginable.

Mrs. York had not inquired about our mission into those parts, but the large case with the odd name had made her and the daughter anxious and quiet. They kindled a fire in the living room, where, after the dishes were washed, we sat around the circle. Bill had given them some hints about our collecting old tales and songs. Mrs. York began to name people up and down the creek who could tell tales and sing, and her daughter got closer to the business by mentioning stories that she had heard her mother tell, a subtle and welcome turn for us. Mrs. York finally agreed that she had heard some and yes, she could tell one or two of them yet. We readied the machine and I heard my first version of the Haunted House story and then one about the woman who turned herself into a witch in the shape of a hog in order to do meanness one night and got her foot cut off, and the next morning one of her hands was missing.

By this time we were closer to the fire, the daughter clinging to her mother's arm. Mrs. York didn't want to scare everybody to death, she said, so she volunteered to sing a song she learned while at Pine Mountain School. We turned the recorder back on and waited. She hummed the tune and went through the first stanza before she began in a plaintive and lonesome voice to sing

> There was a ship a-sailin, a-sailin on the sea
> Cryin' O the lonesome lowland low—

and on, carefully and inevitably unfolding the story to the end when the cabinboy

> Pitched upon his breast and away swam he
> Cryin' O the lonesome lowland low—

A cold shiver had run through me from the first stanza and by the end I had been strangely elevated by the tragic story (no. 34). I had not been more indelibly impressed by ballad singing before, and have scarcely been since. We went on our way warmly refreshed the next morning—but I don't remember any more of that weekend.

I do recall, however, many other trips up and down the creeks of Leslie and Perry counties. On a trip down Cutshin Creek in the spring of 1952 I made my first acquaintance with the Couch family. I went in a jeep with the nurse of Pine Mountain School, Miss Rood, fording the waters of the creek for several miles before turning up a steep incline into Guther's Branch. The valley opened out for a mile until we came to a typical pole cabin on a level flat high above the stream. Here lived Mandy Hendrix, oldest sister of Jim and Dave Couch. She did not keep on telling "them old lying tales" any more, she said, but told us that her brother Jim "had younguns swarming around the house every time he came over there." I pursued the members of the family for the next four years, until they had recorded some sixty long folktales and over a hundred ballads, songs, and hymns. This experience is recorded in my **Up Cutshin and Down Greasy.** The only ballad of theirs in the present collection is "Lord Bateman" (see no. 12), sung by Jim. All of their stories and songs are in **Sang Branch Settlers.**

Another trip worth recounting led Dr. William H. Jansen and me from the head to the mouth of Greasy Creek. I had been inquiring along the valley for descendants of Old Sol Shell, who had given some Munchhausen and other tall tales to Percy McKay in the 1930's (**Tall Tales of the Kentucky Mountains**). Old Sol had lived to be 131 years old, had hunted until he was over a hundred, and fathered a child at 101. Did anybody inherit his tall tales and legends? At last I found an elderly woman who knew Sol. She named others who might have learned some tales from him and who liked to sit up all night telling them. She agreed to set up a party of old timers for me on a certain Saturday night. I called the folklorist William H. Jansen at the University of Kentucky to come for the occasion.

We set out for Greasy Creek that Saturday morning and arrived in the early afternoon. The lady was at home but she soon became apologetic. One of the men could not come and another was away at the time. In short, the all-night session was called off.

Dr. Jansen and I decided to rough it on down Greasy, a distance of about twenty miles. With good luck we might have a session at the Howards (where Baker and I had stayed a year earlier) and then reach the highway at the mouth of the creek before night. At the Howards we found a grown son Anse, story teller and singer, back home from school. We lingered until supper, but then the session was delayed because of church services up the creek. Negotiating the walk-log across the thirty-foot stream was a test of balance. Those who were a little shaky on the quivering logs (Jansen and I) used a long pole for a crutch. In the churchyard we paused until the service was to begin. An elderly woman in an apron stood on the steps smoking an old clay pipe. Jansen said, when she had knocked the ashes out against the wall and had gone in, "Wasn't that a precious sight."

Rain fell lightly throughout the night, waking me from time to time to the louder and louder roar of the creek. Anse had mentioned a dozen songs and stories, but the house had no electricity. Early in the morning we hurried away with him and his guitar. A mile below the house we ran into a long ford of the swollen stream. At the foot of the hill, trying to climb out of the water, I turned on the gas too soon and stalled half out of the swirling water. The horn echoing up and down the valley brought the Howard truck to our assistance. A few miles farther on we stopped at a newly abandoned house and found the electricity still on. There in the rain above the roaring creek we recorded Anse's tales and some songs, including "The Farmer's Curst Wife" (no. 32).

Anse volunteered to accompany us on to the ford. When we arrived at the mouth of Greasy, behold, the Middle Fork of the Kentucky River was rising and floating foam and debris on its crest. The rocks outlining the lower terrace of the ford were now like gothic ripples. Anse said he guessed we could make it if I went slower than I did up yonder. Dr. Jansen didn't say a word. I put the car in low gear and nosed into the water. As we crept along, the muddy water slapping the car floor, Anse cheered the car on by crying, "Come on it ther, old Plymouth!" It did.

During my most active collecting, I found the most fertile area to be Grapevine Creek, Pike County, the home of my wife Edith and her people. I collected on visits there from about 1949 to 1955. As I asked for sources of their lore, most performers gave the name of Old Eli Sullivan. When his biography was finally pieced out, I learned that his people had come to the Left Fork of the Big Sandy in the 1860's (at the time Edith's grandfather Orlando Reynolds had walked with his widowed mother from High Point, North Carolina, to Kentucky). Old Eli, a red-headed Irishman, had furnished the fun for the shut-in community for decades. He wouldn't go to church, they said, "for love nor money," but when meetings broke on Sundays and the preachers had gone off to chicken dinners, Old Eli would appear on the grounds and tell a few yarns and sing some rowdy songs, dance the jig, and get all to clap hands for a square dance. His son, Eli Jr., still living and keeping a store on the top of Grapevine Mountain, would not record for me.

When I collected from Edith's parents they too cited Eli for such songs as "Little Matty Gross," "The House Carpenter," and "The Darby Ram." Mrs. Florence Lamb and Mary Rowe, who sang several songs in unison, cited him for "Lovin' Henry," "Lord Daniel's Wife," "Lonesome Scenes of Winter," and others. These songs are not typically Irish, but Eli had not come directly from the Old Sod; his forebears had married into the Scotch-Irish and the English, with whom they had swapped songs and play-party games in their westward migration.

In the same community lived Claude Reynolds and his wife, who received some songs from Eli, but Claude had picked up later pieces, especially early phonograph recordings. They sang "Lord Daniel," "Barbara Allen," "Drunkard Blues" (Child 278), and "The WPA." Farther up the Left Fork of the river Mrs. Louise Bertrand, mother-in-law of Zelda, Edith's sister, volunteered to sing all the songs she knew, enough to surprise us. Curiously, about half of her dozen songs were older British broadsides, such as "Molly Bond," "Dog and Gun," "If Mary's Alive," and "Selling the Cow," my only version of the broadside ballad related to Child 283.

Student collecting is a supplementary way for the folklore teacher to get materials into his archive. My going with students to their homes has been rewarding and instructive. A modification of the plan is to assign field work and research papers. After the students are well acquainted with definitions, field techniques, ballad classifications and lists, I have usually offered them free tapes and the loan of a recorder, and even a promise to go with them for recording sessions. The results of some of these projects are pleasant to summarize.

While I was teaching at Union College in southeastern Kentucky, Mrs. Eller Hensley from Bell County came to the college in-service courses, including my folklore class. After a few weeks she was reporting her success with a group of older folk up on the Cumberland River. We set a time for a visit and upon my arrival she had six or eight at her home above the river. They sang the tunes for songs she had already received from them, and some other folksongs not yet collected. Mr. Elbert Miracle sang the "Brown Girl" (Child 73), "The Devil's Curst Wife," and a parody of the "Darby Ram," substituting the hunting of a deer for the ram. His wife sang "Barbara Allen" and others. Mr. Henry Green sang "The Waterfall," the story of a woman with an exciting hair-do, and he told the story of "The Candy-Pulling," which I later discovered to be a short yarn from the pen of G.W. Harris. His sister sang my only version of "Jeremiah Beechum" (a ballad of a famous Kentucky tragedy; see KFR, 14: 14-19). The three-hour session gave the visitors some fun and recreation and it gave me some twenty-five tunes and additional folksongs.

Mrs. Ina Mae Enzor from farther up the Cumberland River in Harlan County came to the college for courses. She was already interested in the folksongs of her people. After a few weeks she was employing her disk recorder in the area around the town of Cumberland. She brought the results in and allowed me to transfer the songs to tapes. From her grandmother (Mrs. Cassie Scott) alone she had seven Child ballads, including "Lord Bateman," "Black Jack Davie," "The Kings' Daughters" (Child 4), and "The Three Babes" (Child 79). She also recorded some fine ballads and folksongs from Mrs. Rebecca Creech.

While teaching at Morehead State University in northeastern Kentucky from 1958 to 1961, I had both undergraduate and graduate students taking folklore courses. Some excellent projects and collections were completed by these more mature students. Jesse Stuart's oldest sister Sophie Keeney made a fine tape recorded collection, obtaining valuable folksongs from her husband. From Bill Williams (Negro) she recorded "In the Pine," and "Don't Let the Deal Go Down." From Orin Nelson, husband of her younger sister Mary, she secured about twenty-five songs. But then Mary came into the course a year later and between the two they collected about one hundred folksongs from Orin, some of which were "Barbara Allen," "The House Carpenter" (Child 243), "John Hardy," and "Bryan O'Lynn." From Wash Nelson (no relation) she obtained one of the rarest ballads in my collection, "The Three Brothers," an interesting form of "Henry Martyn" (Child 250).

Thus by living and collecting in three sections of the state I have garnered, however sporadically, some folk material from most of eastern Kentucky, including samplings from the region drained by the tributaries of its four rivers, the Cumberland, the Kentucky, the Big Sandy, and the Licking. In all of the areas I have found folk singing to be an important and meaningful tradition. The older people still know and on occasion still sing the imported folk ballads. Most of my well-preserved Child ballads (some three hundred variants) came from the memories of people from sixty to eighty years old. They likewise are the preservers of the British broadsides. The hundred or more variants collected are surprising in quality and variety. I have missed some of the older native American ballads, but still my archive contains about two hundred. On the other hand, the folksongs—the lyrical, the courting, the religious, the humorous—make up the bulk of the collection, perhaps a thousand variants. The serious ballad and the lyric seem to be the types most cherished by both men and women singers, except that some singers were more outspoken in favor of their homiletic pieces.

Since I am reversing chronology in introducing the present collection, the next step is to sketch, in a few paragraphs, the origin of our folksongs, who brought them, when, and to what purpose.

Virtually all of the imported folksongs in this or in any American collection have come from Britain, although some, traced by Child (and summarized in my notes), originated on the European continent. The English and Scottish peoples seem to have brough some ballads and folksongs (at least hymns) with them to the Eastern Seaboard in colonial times. Although these peoples continued immigration to America down to the Revolution and later, an increased flow of people westward developed among the Scotch-Irish, those who had settled in North Ireland in the seventeenth century and for various reasons broke away from their oppressive landlords and came to America by shiploads in the eighteenth century. Because these enterprising Scotch-Irish, mostly Presybterian, found the first frontier occupied, they were obliged, because of their poverty, to push on into the Piedmont frontier. Accordingly, after the Revoluntary War, their descendents joined in our greatest westward movement. They left their Piedmont homes in Pennsylvania, Virginia, and North Carolina and created the third, or Appalachian frontier. Along with their English, Irish, and German cousins, they were soon carving out new states beyond the mountains—Kentucky, Tennessee, Ohio, and others.

Today we look at conditions in parts of Appalachia and naively ask, "Why did they stop and stay in those rough mountains? Wagons break down?" No, wagons had to await completed roadways. They stopped in the mountains because the mountains were there! Because the mountains were somewhat like their earlier homes in the Piedmont, and like their still earlier homelands in Wales, Highland Scotland, North Ireland, and, for that matter, like the highlands of Germany and France. Their mountainous homes in Britain and in Europe had always represented freedom and independence—freedom from economic, political, and religious persecutions. And so Appalachia became their new home away from their ancestral homes.

And what did Appalachia offer that was so wonderful for homesteading? It offered all the rich resources needed in the New World for making a living, raising children, and replenishing the earth. It had an abundance of water courses for transportation and for fishing; great woodlands for housing, for furniture, and for fuels; an abundance of wild game for food and clothing; much rich bottomland for farming and for cattle raising. Boone and his followers thought the land west of the mountains "a paradise of a place." My grandfather used to sing a little song, one line of which ran: "There's wine and oil and fertile soil down in Tennessee."

A curious topic for discussion and even for cartoons today is regarding the long isolation of the mountain people. Their isolation overtook them somewhat recently and for a shorter period of time than the popular conception. Most of America, except the Eastern Seaboard, was sparsely settled down to the end of the nineteenth century, and most of the land was in forests and farms. All transportation was by foot, by horseback, and by river flatboat. Until the railroads fanned out over inland America after the Civil War, all the American people were comparatively isolated. The people of the mountains simply retained their self-sufficiency and personal independence after the rise of our industrial East and the improvement of communication and transportation across the Midwest and the South. People have lived in Appalachia for 150 to 200 years but their isolation lasted roughly from the Civil War to World War I.

The settlers of Kentucky were not living entirely alone during this time. They were making contacts with the "outside" throughout their most isolated period. They began to sell the produce of the mountains to the eastward and to the westward settlements soon after settling the highlands. They began to drive cattle and hogs over the Wilderness Road and later over Pound Gap to Virginia during most of the nineteenth century. They walked their livestock and droves of turkeys to market and floated their sawlogs by rafts down to the Bluegrass. On their return trips they carried needed goods from the stores and later from the nearest railheads to their homes in the highlands.

Of course this period of isolation was long enough for the people's cultural and traditional patterns to take root and to persist into the present century. The somewhat homogeneous settlers shared a common social and cultural background and language and, naturally, a common life cycle. All members of families worked from sunup to sundown in the spring of the year. During the summer they had some leisure—to visit and to attend social and church services. Religious gatherings often stretched through the day, with chain preaching and dinner on the ground. These meetings celebrated Easter and especially Decoration Day. A summer form of these all-day services developed into annual memorials to honor and eulogize those who had passed on during the winter. Some reporter, looking for quaintness, has labeled these sacred services "funeralizings."

In the fall of the year there was considerable work to be performed again to save the crops, to preserve the foods, and to make clothing and quilts. Many kinds of work swappings (bees) developed over the years, such as apple peelings, bean stringings, corn shuckings, and quiltings. When winter set in, with "falling weather," the church-going almost ceased and the socializing with it. Recreating, handicrafting, play-gaming and the like were conducted among families and in small community groups. The special holidays were celebrated in simple and humble ways. Thanksgiving called for table extras such as "holed-up" vegetables and fresh pork; Christmas, the most important and most noisy holiday, was a time for games in the homes, for shooting guns and firecrackers, for hanging stockings on the mantel for old Santa Claus. People visited one another early on the holiday morning calling "Christmas Gift" from the door.

In the spring the confinement of the long winter was broken with the resurrection of all vegetation. It was the return of the green to the hills, the first white to the sarvice (service) trees, and the red to the dogwods. The preacher usually showed up during the first warm days to baptize the young and to christen the newborn; to marry those who were ready, and those who had already started families and to announce the time and place of the annual associations and memorials.

During these cycles of the seasons the people learned to live with loneliness and with suffering and hardships. They set examples of self-sufficiency and independence and other virtues of democracy before their young. Outsiders have spoken of the mountain people's independence, but this was simply the normal way of life of a free people. To them it meant that they were not beholden to others for the essentials of life. To be dependent on others for jobs, for housing and land, and for services was indeed slavery. The mountain people usually felt pity and compassion for renters, for job-hunters, and for all who were without homes and means to provide for themselves.

The above remarks have been background and preamble to the people's folksongs. The present collection is a selection of about 150 texts drawn from an archive of material accumulated over a period of twelve years, from 1947 to 1955. My 85 tapes are a valuable treasury of the collection, preserving both the texts and tunes of several hundred folksongs. For transcribing the music I have been fortunate to have as collaborator the fine musician Dr. C. Buell Agey of the West Virginia Wesleyan College Music Department. From the beginning of the project we were interested in presenting a variety of Appalachian folksongs with the best texts and tunes. This plan has prevailed, except that in order to present versions of all Child ballads (and a few others) available, I have been obliged to enter some without tunes. The collection has been divided into two main parts— the ballads and the folksongs. These two divisions have been arranged into three sections each.

Only a few words need to be said about the material grouped by sections. We have included some thirty-four of the Child ballads, counting the floating stanzas of a few, such as Nos. 46 and 76, and a "member of the class" Child discusses at No. 283. Among my rarer ones in the Child canon are his Nos. 1, 3, 11, 138 (a Robin Hood ballad reported only once before it and probably from print), and 250. As for other British Ballads, I have found more broadsides in Kentucky than one would expect (as stated above), although all are not selected for this collection. A good variety of native American ballads is entered, but some of the categories of Laws (NAB) are lightly represented, or not at all, such as those of lumberjacks, cowboys, sailors—somewhat undersandable since these are not "native" to the Southern Mountains. The three sections of folksongs are rather evenly represented.

In selecting and transcribing, I have preserved the texts as found. A minimum of editing has been done in determining the stanza patterns, in punctuating (some left almost bare), and in other minor matters expected of the responsible editor. The headnotes have been made as concise and a usable as possible. For the English and Scottish ballads I have relied on Child's notes and texts. When the information on British, Continental, and American ballads that he and others give was enlightening to me and, hopefully, to others, I have paraphrased it and have given synopses of texts and of related folktales. I have traced the versions through collections in Britain and in America down toward the present time. I have not, however, encumbered the notes with all parallels and accumulated references that have already been done by previous collectors and editors. For American references I have indicated the regions where texts have been found in tradition, with fuller listings for Appalachia and for Kentucky. The collections most often used have been cited in the notes by abbreviations and placed alphabetically in the Bibliography and Key to the Notes.

In this appropriate place I wish to extend hearty thanks to the librarians of West Virginia University and West Virginia Wesleyan College for book loans and purchases and for duplication services over a long period of time. Finally, I wish to thank West Virginia Wesleyan College for two research grants and for encouragement to continue the task.

Leonard Roberts

Pikeville College
Pikeville, Kentucky

INTRODUCTION TO THE MUSIC

The one hundred and thirty-nine tunes to the ballads and folk songs of this volume have been transcribed by the editor from taped recordings of live performances. These songs have been selected from a large source of folk material collected over the years by my colleague, Dr. Leonard W. Roberts, during the sojourns of his numerous field trips throughout the rural Appalachian regions of Kentucky, Virginia, and Tennessee.

Folk music lives chiefly by virtue of its inherent charm and simplicity. During the long—and often vague—history of a ballad or folk song it is constantly undergoing a sort of metamorphosis which eventually proliferates into an amazing host of genetic variants—both of text and music. The promiscuous labelling of folk music as "authentic" may be reasonably questioned, and possibly disputed. In our day, when everything from a Child ballad to a Tin-Pan-Alley pop tune is called "folk music," plus the fact that no one has, to date, come forth with a mutually acceptable definition of the term, any such attempt on the part of this editor would be like carrying coals to Newcastle. However, there is little room for doubt concerning the authenticity of a non-cultivated type of song, passed on by oral tradition, with its roots grounded in the culture of a rural provenience. In this respect the authors claim authenticity for the material of this collection, as recorded on tapes, with pertinent historical and humanistic facts concerning the specific versions of the songs.

Scholars have directed their attention primarily toward the literary aspects of balladry to the neglect of the music. Actually both are concomitant aspects of the same art form—one having primary appeal to the intelligence and the other to the emotions. According to eminent authorities such as Bertrand Bronson, Phillips Barry, and others, there is justifiable evidence that, in tradition, folk tunes were not set to preexisting poetry, but the words of a poem were fitted to the metrical structure of a prevailing tune.

Only a few persons have undertaken a formal approach to the musical elements of folk song, and among these there seems to be little evidence of agreement in the technique and substance of their analyses. The analysis of the tunes of our collection, like the tunes themselves, is simple and objective, using the criteria of traditional theoretical principles. Concerning the method of analysis, the editor has elected to follow, with certain reservations, the analytical principles as set forth in the **Introductory Notes** of the **Frank C. Brown Collection of North Carolina Folklore, Volume IV,** by Jan Philip Schinhan. In this respect the editor is indebted to Dr. Schinhan, who, serving in an advisory capacity in this undertaking, tendered copious notes and valuable suggestions concerning various aspects of analysis.

Doubtless there are some facets of analysis left untapped—intentionally so, and for substantial reasons; but chiefly in order not to transcend the scope and explicit design of the presentation. The efforts in this behalf are purely in the nature of providing correlative data and comments on the respective songs. This portion of the work is not intended as a discourse on formal style elements of folk song in general.` In the representation of the more primary aspects of analysis the musical material has been examined from the following viewpoints and classifications:

1. Scale pattern
2. Mode
3. Range
4. Tonal Center
5. Structure
6. Melodic relationship
7. Other pertinent aspects, influences, idioms, etc.

SCALE: Classification of tonal material into scales is determined according to the number of different scale tones occurring in the tune, along with the quality, character, and organization of the tonal material. Scales are classified as Tetratonic or Tetrachordal, Pentatonic or Pentachordal, Hexatonic or Hexachordal, and Heptachordal. For instance, a five-tone scale may be classified as Pentatonic or Pentachordal. A Pentachordal scale embraces a diatonic succession of five tones, all of which are contained within the first five scale tones: 1 to 5. A five-tone scale not conforming to the foregoing, but containing one or more gaps or skips (exceeding a major second) is classified as Pentatonic. An analysis of scale occurrence among the 135 tunes of this volume, in the order of their greatest frequency, reveals:

Number of tunes

41 . . . . Pentatonic; Mode III
37 . . . . Heptachordal
20 . . . . Hexachordal
15 . . . . Hexatonic
10 . . . . Pentatonic; Mode II
4 . . . . Tetratonic
3 . . . . Pentachordal
3 . . . . Pentatonic, irregular
2 . . . . Pentatonic; Mode IV

Total 135

If a scale tone appears both in its diatonic position and also in its chromatic alteration the tonal series is qualified as an "Inflected" scale.

MODE: Granting the inevitable dichotomy of mode and scale, the mere classification into—for instance— Pentatonic and Heptachordal scales fails to reveal the specific modal pattern. With the exception of the classifications of the Pentatonic scale (see below) the scale material is categorized by mode in accordance with the traditional principles underlying the ecclesiastical (church) modes. Such modal designations are given only when the tonal material embraces a full seven-tone Heptachordal scale which strictly conforms to one of these modal patterns, with concern for the characteristic behavior and use of the tonal material. Only in a few sporadic and well-deserved instances has the editor used his prerogative to comment on the modal implication, or tendency of a six-tone scale. Herein the designation "major" is used for the mode historically known as "Ionian"; and the term "Plagal" is used in the traditional sense, when the tune descends below the tonal center. In this respect the melodies of our collection come within the following classifications:

28—Authentic
107—Plagal
30—Major
2—Mixolydian
1—Dichotomous; Dorian or Mixolydian, according
to scalar inflection.
1—Dichotomous: Major or Mixolydian, according
to scalar inflection.

Theoretically the Pentatonic scale—apart from its transpositions— conforms to the scale pattern: c-d-f-g-a; however, it is commonly recognized that by process of inversion, using different tones as tonic, five different modal classifications may be derived, as follows: [1]

Mode I   c-d-f-g-a
Mode II   d-f-g-a-c
Mode III   f-g-a-c-d
Mode IV   g-a-c-d-f
Mode V   a-c-d-f-g

[1] Willi Apel. **Harvard Dictionary of Music** 2nd Ed., p. 652. The Belknap Press, Cambridge, Mass., 1969.

Pentatonic scales not conforming to one of the above classifications are designated as "Irregular." In similar manner other tunes embracing scalar ambiguities may be classified as "irregular," or "mixed" mode.

RANGE: Ranges of tunes are set forth in the generally accepted manner of designating "octave letters." In view of the fact that the gamut extremities of our overall material do not exceed three octaves, the tones in the first octave below middle-C are indicated by small letters; the octave beginning on middle-C by c', d', e', etc.; and likewise the second octave by c", d", etc. The following table shows the ranges of our tunes, according to their intervallic compass and total incidence:

Number of tunes	Range
44	Perfect octave
33	Major 9th
14	Major 6th
15	Perfect 11th
8	Minor 7th
6	Minor 6th
4	Major 10th
3	Perfect 5th
2	Minor 9th
2	Major 7th
1	Major 13th
1	Minor 13th
1	Perfect 12th
1	Diminished 12th

Total 135

It is not unusual that the tunes encompassing the widest or the smallest ranges have the least frequency of occurrence, and that songs spanning the octave and major ninth are in predominance. Only one song extends the distance of a major 13th.

TONAL CENTER: Tonal center indicates the fundamental tone of the scale, and it is, with few exceptions, the final tone of the piece. The editor has made observations and comments respectively in the analyses concerning instances where a tone other than the tonic center has a particularly predominant frequency of iteration—occasionally greater than that of the tonal center; but he does not accept this as a valid criterion for determinig tonal center. [2] Also, in reference to the relative duration of certain scale tones, only sporadic analyses are included herewith, and only when the particular melodic organization seems to justify such comment.

A tune is classified as "Circular" when its final cadence ends on a note other than its tonal center, wherein there is an obvious assumption that the treatment of such cadence in the final stanza will be so modified as to effect a natural ending on the tonal center. In any event the final tone of a song must be weighed against the overall tonal organization of the complete tune, for this seemingly incomplete ending might possibly be the tonal center, in which case the tune could possibly belong to one of the traditional church modes. In this respect one has to consider the elements of tonal stress, and/or aspects of tonic-dominant relationship, as well as other factors involved. In our collection there are twelve instances of **circular** tunes—virtually eight percent of the total. There are relatively few examples of tunes falling purely within the category of the ecclesiastical modes, and of these most are of Mixolydian pattern.

STRUCTURE: Each tune is analyzed with primary regard for its smallest structural unit: the phrase of music which corresponds to the line of verse (or textual phrase). In accordance with customary procedure, the individual phrase units, or structural components, are represented by alphabetical letters, such as A, A1, A2, B, etc. Frequently an alternate, or secondary analysis of the overall structure is added alongside, to illustrate how the smaller structural components may be compounded into their larger structural entities, for example: A B C D E F (2, 2, 2, 2, 2, 2) equals A B C (4, 4, 4), etc. The professional is well aware of the varied possibilities in this respect. Not infrequently, in the analysis of these minute fragments of tonal and rhythmic material, the editor may feel that he is between Scylla and Charybdis in attempting to reach a categorical decision. There are inevitably ambiguous—sometimes equivocal—factors involved in this seemingly simple technical discipline which could challenge the most astute scholar. Particularly in these pieces of small dimension the process of compounding the small phrase units into larger structural entities frequently presents a choice of two, three, or more possiblibities. Such exigencies are met—in many instances—by an arbitrary value judgment on the part of the analyst; thus, any endeavor to set forth a definitive appendix of the multiplicity of forms of this collection—based on the final compounding alone—would be of questionable value. It would necessarily be omitting the juxtapositon and

---

[2] Aspects for consideration include the qualitative value of tones, varying emphases, tonic-dominant relationships, and the use of tonal material.

sequence of the smaller constituent, and it is in the light of such relationships that the true **Gestalt** and overall rhythmic flow of a piece is conceivable.

In view of the foregoing considerations, and in the interest of practicality for the reader, the author has elected to list (below) the total occurrences of all the formal structures found among the 135 melodies of this collection, including—except where inapplicable—the inherent formal variants of each basic structure.

STRUCTURE OF THE MELODIES

Structure	Incidence	Structure	Incidence
A A	48	A B C A	3
A B A C	21	A B A	3
A B C D	18	A B C	2
A B A B	19	A A B (Bar form)	2
A B	18	A B B (Inverted bar form)	2
A A B A (Reprisenbar)	10	A B C B	2
A A A B	9	A B A A	1
A B B C	8	A A A A	1
A B B A (Inverted reprisenbar)	6	A A A A B	1
A A B C	6	A B C D D	1
A A B B	6	A B C C	1
A A A	4	A A B A // C A (Reprisenbar plus strophe)	1
A B A C C	3		
A B A B	3		

Among the above table of forms it is not surprising that the simple variation form, A A, heads the list, with an incidence of 48, also, one might consider the eighteen occurrences of A B to be proportionately low. The patterns of A B A C, A B A B, and A B C D are commonly encountered. It is not unusual that only two melodies conform to A A B—**Bar** form,[3], however, its germinally related

---

[3] **Bar** form, of medieval origin, traditionally conforms to the pattern: A A B— two **Stollen** (section A) and an **Abgesang** (section B), which has its roots in the Grecian Ode: strope, antistrophe, and epode. Alfred Lorenz's designation for **Bar** form, i.e. mmn (**Bar** form) and nmm (inverted **Bar** form) has not been used in our analysis, chiefly because the few examples of A A B and A B B in this collection undoubtedly conform to the stylistic principles of the **Bar**.

structures of Inverted Barform, Reprisenbar, Inverted Reprisenbar, and Reprisenbar plus strophe account for 21 of the melodies.

MELODIC RELATIONSHIP: The texts of the ballads and folk songs are traditionally categorized into **plot** families. To date, however, there has been no traditionally established, or generally acceptable, academic discipline for indexing tonal material under **tune** families, although some creditable attempts have been made in this direction. The editor readily foregoes any effort in behalf of such a project, or in the matter of style analysis. Either of these would certainly transcend the scope and purpose of this volume. The citations of melodic relationship under the respective tunes are not intended to be comprehensive, but helpful.[4]   Comments on various aspects of the respective songs include significant characteristics, influences, correlations, idioms, etc., which could provide a useful basis for further study and research.

TRANSCRIPTION: No attempt has been made to rearrange, or in any fashion alter, the tunes from the manner in which they were originally performed and taped. However, the transcribing of folk music is not a simple task. The unsophisticated folk singer is prone to make extemporizations, embellishments and subtle changes from one stanza to another, and to have lapses of memory and other foibles that can perplex the most competent editor. Occasionally, prerogative has to be exercised, within the bounds of editorial ethics, of course. It has not been deemed necessary for the purpose of this work to indicate myriad performance idiosyncrasies, such as minor inflections or intonations, weak tones, strong tones, vague **glissandi,** etc. It is purposed, however, to set forth the music in a manner which will be clear and most readily understandable. For instance, the use of mixed meters has been frequently avoided wherever possible to do so without impairing the vitality of the rhythmic flow. Often the insertion of a **fermata** will obviate an otherwise disjunct metrical structure, and at the same time will designate more accurately what the performer is actually doing. The transcriptions show the use of grace notes in performance when used consistently in all stanzas. Particularly obvious instances of **glissandi** are indicated by the sign: /   or   \   ; and small-size notes are inserted for correlation with alternate stanzas of the text. The editor does not postulate key, in the sense of major-minor tonality; and although this may be a controversial point, it is the editor's premise that such a practice is both tonally irrelevant and theoretically anachronistic to the tradition of folksong. Thus, chromatic signs

4
  They are not necessarily considered to be statements of genetic relationship.

do not occur in the signatures when the scale tones they indicate do not appear in the tune itself.

Although the history of folk music transcends our present system of traditional harmony (the major-minor concept of tonal relationships) it has been deemed in the practical interest of this collection to suggest harmonic accompaniment to the tunes by superimposing chord symbols above the music. The purist may completely disregard them; however, it is improbable that twentieth century ears can avoid the implication of functional harmonic relationships from the melodic outlines of the music.

PERFORMANCE SUGGESTIONS:

1. Folk music is rendered traditionally in a objective manner, with no attempt toward variance of expression, or dramatization.

2. The tunes are not to be sung with precision necessarily, but in a free and natural fashion.

3. The music is transcribed with primary regard for the syllabic accent of the first stanza. Succeeding stanzas with varied syllabic patterns may easily be adapted by either crowding into the beat (or measure pattern), or eliding certain notes.

4. Traditionally, folk song is generally a monophonic form, that is, sung by a single unaccompanied voice. However, the use of accompanying instruments such as the guitar, banjo, autoharp, dulcimer, etc., is quite common. Harmonies are for the most part very simple ones, and any usage of chromatic, rich, or contemporary harmonies would be strictly anachronistic and in bad taste.

5. The tunes herein which begin with the chorus almost always end with the chorus.

6. It is customary for ballad singers to follow without pause from one stanza to the next; however, in the case of accompanied singing an occasional instrumental interlude is entirely proper, and tends to increase the effectiveness of the ballad.

C. Buell Agey
June 30, 1977

West Virginia Wesleyan College
Buckhannon, West Virginia

PART I - BALLADS

A. ENGLISH AND SCOTTISH BALLADS

1. THE DEVIL'S NINE QUESTIONS
(Child 1)

Riddles and vexing questions have come down out of mythology and religion (Oedipus, Samson) into the culture of Western civilization. In the Middle Ages they were used in the form of dialogues and debates between the Devil and Everyman. If the Devil was victorious in one of these battles of wits, he snatched the victim away; if he was not, he disappeared and left the man as victor. This kind of debate, for the study of this and other ballads, has been termed a **homily**. See Phillips Barry, editor, **Bulletin of the Folksong Society of the Northeast,** X (1935): 8-10, and XII (1937): 8-10, for extended discussions. Sets of these questions and answers, either in blocks of from four to fourteen, or alternating a question with an answer, have been handed down in folktale and folksong by oral and written transmission to the present time.

In the meantime, as these clusters of questions passed through the Renaissance and later centuries, they became adapted to more secular uses. With narrative beginnings and endings this kind developed into a **romance** (Barry, **Ibid.**). When Francis James Child began his collection of English and Scottish popular ballads, his first two versions of "Riddles Wisely Expounded," drawn from broadside collections of the eighteenth and nineteenth centuries, were **romances**: A knight visits the house of a mother and three daughters. The oldest serves his supper, the second makes his bed, the youngest sleeps with him. Next morning the youngest requests marriage. The knight will if she can answer three questions. He asks her six, which she answers to his surprise, and they marry.

Child's C, D and E (V, 205) versions are homilies. In his final additions to Volume V (283-84) Child inserted his oldest text of the ballad. It is a homily in Middle English of the 1440's. In his headnote to this oldest version Child revises the arrangement of his texts by saying: "The 'good ending' of A, B, is manifestly a modern perversion, and the reply to the last question in A, D, 'The Devil is worse than err woman was,' gains greatly in point when we understand who the so-called knight really is." Sargent and Kittredge label this text A* and enter it first in their one-volume edition (1904) of Child's collection.

Since clusters of riddles have been used in other ballads (see Child nos. 2, 3, 46, and 76 below), texts of the present ballad have been elusive and difficult to identify. Fragments in folktale, cante fable, poetry, and the like began to appear in America from 1899. In 1929 Davis published "the only complete, or nearly complete, version, recovered in America" in TBA. Close to Child D, his "Devil's Nine Questions" is a homily with eight alternating questions and answers, the verses also alternating with nonsense refrains: "Sing ninety-nine and ninety," and "And you are the weaver's bonny." A romantic form of the ballad was discovered in Maine in 1934 (Barry **Bulletin** referred to above, X, 8-10). It has four questions in a block, asked by a "gay young cavalier" who comes courting a "lady fair." The two texts published by Richard Chase (**Songs of All Time,** p. 11; **American Folk Tales and Songs,** p. 110-111) and the two of John Jacob Niles (**Ballads, Carols and Tragic Legends** p. 2; and **Ballad Book,** no. 1) have titles and alternating questions and answers close to the Davis text. These are from North Carolina and Virginia. Others from North Carolina are in NCF, IV, 12, 12C, and 316 (nine questions). See Coffin's complete list of Child no. 1 texts (BTBNA). The most recently published text of the ballad was found in Oklahoma (BFSSW) with four alternating questions ending in marriage. Lawless lists 3 in print.

The present text is again close to that of Davis's. It has these differences: The refrain is more incremental or commonplace than nonsense, and it does have the nine questions, as expected from the title. It was recorded by Marie Estep of Clay County, Kentucky, in 1958. She quoted her mother as saying, "It was sung by my father when I was a child." Marie further stated, "Since my mother did not know all of the ballad, I persuaded my great aunt (no name given) to sing this much of it." This seems to be the first text reported from Kentucky.

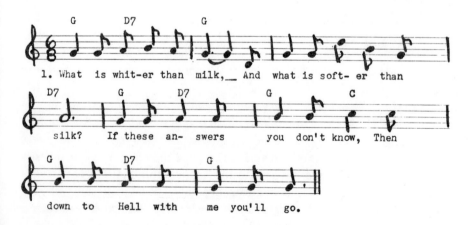

SCALE: Pentachordal (g a b c d). MODE: Plagal. RANGE: g' - d"
(Perfect 5th) TONAL CENTER: G. PHRASE STRUCTURE: A B C D
(2, 2, 2, 2). MELODIC RELATIONSHIP: This particular tune has not been
found as a tonal setting for any of the variants to Child No. 1 examined by the
editor.

The nursery-like tune doubtless has been superimposed on the text, and it seems
to convey quite appropriately the trochaic-like rhythm of the words.

2. Snow is whiter than milk,
   And down is softer than silk;
   Since these answers I do know,
   Then down to Hell I won't go.

3. What is louder than a horn,
   And what is sharper than a thorn?
   If these answers you don't know,
   Then down to Hell with me you'll go.

4. Thunder is louder than a horn,
   And a knife is sharper than a thorn,
   Since these answers I do know,
   Then down to Hell I won't go.

5. What is higher than a tree,
   And what is deeper than the sea?
   If these answers you don't know,
   Then down to Hell with me you'll go.

6. The sky is higher than a tree,
   And Hell is deeper than the sea;
   Since these answers I do know,
   Then down to Hell I won't go.

7. What is meeker than a lamb,
   And what is meaner than a woman?
   If these answers you don't know ,
   Then down to Hell with me you'll go.

8. A baby is meeker than a lamb,
   And the devil is meaner than a woman;
   Since these answers I do know,
   Then down to Hell I won't go.

9. This is the last of the nine,
   Are you God's or mine?

3

I'm God's I'll have you know,
And with you I won't go.

2. THE ELF IN KNIGHT
(Child 2)

The earliest text of this story in Mr. Child's collection is a broadside of about 1670. Child is convinced that the ballad evolved out of the many folktales found throughout Asia and Europe from early times. The general tale is as follows: A king has delayed marriage so long the people importune him to marry. He puts three questions to them, "What is the finest sound, the finest song, the finest stone?" A man, seeking the solution, talks it over with his daughter, who answers, "Bells, song of the angels, and the philosopher's stone." He reports to the king, who says, "That's right, but who told you?" He says he got them from his smart daughter. The king then tests **her** by asking for a shirt made of three inches of cloth. She counters by asking for an odd vessel in which to work. He returns one with the bottom out to be stitched. She returns it to be turned wrong side out for best sewing. He asks her to come to him neither naked nor clothed, neither riding nor walking, neither out of the road nor in the road. She puts on a fishing net, rides her goat with one foot stepping in the rut of the road, etc. She is such a clever lass that the king marries her.

These folktales from Germany, Scandinavia, Russia, Spain, Turkey, etc., reviewed by Child have been analyzed and indexed since Child's time by Aarne and Thompson (**Types of the Folktale**), and placed under Type 875 The Clever Peasant Girl, in ten forms. Of the tasks given under the Type number, none are parallel to the tasks in this ballad. Professor Child's study of influences is well taken, although he does not consider any direct relation of tale and ballad.

The ballad, in any case, has little more than a series of tasks set by a wooer, preconditioned by a set from the maiden. Even the narrative beginning is short and abrupt: A knight, an elf, or an old man is talking to a maid on a hill, or sends word over the hill to his lover to make his a sark, a smock, or a cambric shirt (A-E). Other texts of Child begin with the tasks. The supernatural element has disappeared from these, as well as from others found in England, Scotland, and North America. Almost every collection from Maine to Oklahoma has one or more examples of the ballad. Some forty-five are listed by Coffin (BTBNA). The most useful notes are given by Barry (BBM, no. 1), by Belden (BSM, no. 1), and by Belden and Hudson (NCF, II, no. 1). Professor Schinhan edits a text and tune in NCF, IV, no. 1B. Lawless lists 30 in print.

The nearest parallel to the present text is in **Northumbrian Minstrelsy**, pp. 79-80. The refrains are similar, as are most of the tasks. Another text given by

4

Child (II, 495,496, from Leeds, 1884) has exactly the same refrain. Both of his examples lack my unusual stanza 9, but I find the substance of the stanza in a text from Vermont (NGMS, pp. 8-11). The only other evidence of the ballad in Kentucky was found in Clay County (adjoining Breathitt, the origin of my text) and printed by SharpK, no. 1. My text was recorded by Mrs. Stella Byrd Brooks, Breathitt County, in 1961. She had moved at an early age from Virginia and had learned this and other songs from her parents in about 1920.

SCALE: Hexachordal (f g a b♭ c d).   MODE: Plagal.   RANGE: a - c"
(Minor 10th).   TONAL CENTER: F. Circular tune.   PHRASE STRUCT-
URE: A B C D (2, 2, 2, 2).   MELODIC RELATIONSHIP: This tune is con-
spicuous for its jagged melodic contour, embracing wide intervallic skips. A comparison of measures 4 and 8 reveals a rather interesting tonal and rhythmic relationship (note the inversion of the tones C and A). Cf. NCF, IV, 1B, first phrase
only. The above tune has not been encountered in any of the variants of Child
No. 2 examined by the editor. It is conceivable that the singer of this tune
arbitrarily augmented what would normally be a measure of 4/4 meter in measure
4.

2. Go tell her to buy me a cambric shirt
    Savory, sage, rosemary, and thyme,
    And make it so fast she can't see her own needle work,
    And she shall be a true love-yer of mine.

3. Go tell her to wash it in yondo well
    Savory, sage, rosemary, and thyme,
    Where never a drop of water fell,
    And she shall be a true love-yer of mine.

4. Go tell her to hang it in yonda tree
   Savory, sage, rosemary, and thyme,
   Betwixt the saltwater and the sea,
   And she shall be a true love-yer of mine.

5. Go tell her to iron it with a cold rock iron
   Savory, sage, rosemary, and thyme.
   Which never has been since Adam and Eve was born,
   And she shall be a true love-yer of mine.

6. As you go over yondo hill
   Savory, sage, rosemary, and thyme,
   Go take this message to that young lad,
   And he shall be a true love-yer of mine.

7. Go tell him to plant him an acre of corn
   Savory, sage, rosemary, and thyme,
   And plow it in with an old ram's horn,
   And he shall be a true love-yer of mine.

8. Go tell him to cut it with sickle and leather
   Savory, sage, rosemary, and thyme,
   And bind it up with a peacock's feather,
   And he shall be a true love-yer of mine.

9. Go tell him to thresh it on the cold stone wall
   Savory, sage, rosemary, and thyme,
   And let never a grain of it fall,
   And he shall be a true love-yer of mine.

10. Go tell him when he has done his work
    Savory, sage, rosemary, and thyme,
    To come and call for his cambric shirt,
    And he shall be a true love-yer of mine.

3. THE DEVIL AND THE SCHOOL CHILD
(Child 3)

Professor Child printed only three texts of this rare ballad, all from
Scotland. He printed related items from Sweden, and from Scottish nursery
rhymes. As with nos. 1 and 2, this ballad has almost no narrative element: A

schoolboy meets a false knight (i.e. the Devil in disguise) on the road and by a contest of wits bordering on name-tabu, the lad is able to escape the Devil. The ballad is almost non-existent in later British collections.

In America it has had somewhat more vitality in tradition. Two texts have been recorded from Nova Scotia (BSNS, no. 1, and BFSSNE, XI, 89); two in Maine (BBM, pp. 11-14) from Scotland; one each from Indiana (BSI, no. 2), Virginia (TBV, no. 2), North Carolina (SharpK, no. 2-A), Tennessee (SharpK, no. 2-B), Missouri (BSM, p. 4), and Oklahoma (BFSSW, no. 3, from Scotland). These and a few in JAF and some reprints make up the 18 entries in Coffin (BTBNA). It seems that the homiletic theme of the ballad appealed to the Scottish people and that they carried many texts to their New World settlements in Nova Scotia, Appalachia, and the Ozarks. Lawless lists 10 in print.

The tenor of the debate between the boy and the Devil remains fairly constant in the texts: Where are you going? To school. What do you carry? My books or my dinner, etc. The text from Maine helps to explain one exchange in my text. If the (fiddle) bow would break? May the end stick in your throat. The fence rail was easier to recall—and to use in Kentucky. See Barry's note on the ballad as religious homily (BFSSNE, **Ibid.**).

This seems to be the only text recorded in Kentucky. It was sung to me by Jim Couch, Harlan County, in 1953. It was printed in UCDG, pp. 147-149, in TSCF, no. 1, and in SBS, no. 1.

SCALE: Pentatonic (g a b d e).   MODE: III; Plagal.   RANGE: d' - e" (Major 9th).   TONAL CENTER: G.   PHRASE STRUCTURE: A B C D (2, 2, 2, 2).   MELODIC RELATIONSHIP: This song has the familiar ring of a host of jingle settings and prevalent tunes, including "The Girl I Left Behind Me" (final four measures). Also, Cf. SharpK I, p. 212, No. 28F for a similarity of melodic contour in a setting of Child No. 28.

*The anacrusis was alternated by the performer between the notes G and D.

2. "What do you have in your bucket?" said the proud porter gay,
   "All alone by the wayside lone?"
   "It's vittles for my dinner," said the child gentleman,
   And the game feller's walking along.

3. "O won't you give me some?" said the proud porter gay
   "All alone by the wayside lone?"
   "No, not a bite o' crumbs," said the child gentleman,
   And the game feller's walking along.

4. "I wished I had you in the woods," said the proud porter gay,
   "All alone by the wayside lone,"
   "With a good gun under my arm," said the child gentleman,
   And the game feller's walking alone.

5. "With your head broke in two," said the proud porter gay,
   "All alone by the wayside lone,"
   "O a fence rail jobbed down your neck," said the child gentleman,
   And the game feller's walking alone.

6. "Wished I had you in the sea," said the proud porter gay
   "All alone by the wayside lone,"
   "Good board under me," said the child gentleman,
   And the game feller's walking alone.

7. "Your head turned bottom up," said the proud porter gay,
   "All alone by the wayside lone,"
   "Yes, and you under the bottom," said the child gentleman,
   And the game feller's walking alone.

8. "I wished I had you in the well," said the proud porter gay,
   "All alone by the wayside lone,"
   "But the Devil's chained in Hell," said the child gentleman,
   And the game feller's walking alone.

4. THE KINGS' DAUGHTERS
(Child 4)

Child begins his study of this ballad with six versions in twelve variants, most of them from the rich collections of Scotland. He adds half a dozen more as additions in successive volumes. He begins his discussion by saying "of all ballads this has perhaps obtained the widest circulation." His notes too are

8

perhaps the longest for any ballad in his collection—some forty pages. After comparing the texts (A-F) he plunges into the widespread collections in Europe, beginning with the Dutch and on to the German, Scandinavian, Polish, French, Italian, Spanish, Turkish. Though the details of the ballad vary greatly, the bare narrative remains recognizable: A stranger (lover, elf-knight) is wished for and appears and woos the beautiful daughter. By promises of wealth, to be lady of his many castles, or by magic he persuades the girl to take money, jewels, fine clothes, horses and elope with him. They ride to deep woods or to the seaside and he orders her to dismount, telling her that he has slain five (six, seven) kings' daughters here and she is the next. She asks him to let her pray, to let her have his sword and pull off his coat so the blood won't spatter it (of course in these versions she kills him), or to avert his eyes (and she throws him into the sea), or to grant her three calls (she calls for God, Mary, and her brother). The brother rides up in time to slay the false lover, sometimes before, sometimes after she has been slain.

Since Child's time the ballad has had extensive studies, especially by Ivar Kemppinen (**The Ballad of Lady Isabel and the False Knight**, Helsinki, 1954), and by Holgar Nygard (**The Ballad of Heer Halewijn**, Knoxville, 1958).

Professor Nygard locates the source of the ballad in the Netherlands, from whence it was carried into Germany and Scandinavia; it was carried directly to France and later to England and America. Mr. Kemppinen included among his more than 1800 variants the English broadside, "The Cruel ship's Carpenter," because it had a related story of a sailor murdering his compromised sweetheart in the woods (see 53A below). We also trace our so-called native American murder ballads, such as "Pretty Polly," "The Jealous Lover," and "The Knoxville Girl," back to this broadside and others such as "The Wexford (Oxford) Girl." See summaries of these studies by Coffin (BTBNA) and by D. K. Wilgus (AFSS, pp. 308-311).

In passing, Mr. Child notices the folktales of Europe with closely related narratives. He is led to analyze a study of the ballad in relation to the Judith-Holofernes story in the Apocrypha, only to reject it as too remote. But other plots that throw light on our eroded ballad and suggest the motivations for the murder of fair maidens are mentioned. In a German story, a robber kills women "to obtain blood for magical purposes." In another German story a rich man becomes a leper from lewd living. "The devil put it in his head that he could be cured by bathing in the blood of twelve pure maidens." Another young man has power from the devil to spirit young maidens into the woods for sexual gratification, the devil to have the soul of every twelfth one. Child, finally, compares the ballad narrative to the "large class of Bluebeard tales." This tale has since been studied and indexed as Type 312 **The Giant Killer and his Dog (Bluebeard)**. A more closely-related group of stories comes under Types 950 ff., especially Type 955, **The Robber-Bridegroom.**

Concurring with Child's opening remark about wide distribution, this ballad has been reported by most serious ballad collectors in America. It has been collected in the Maritime Provinces (BSNS, BSSH), in most states of New England (BBM, VFB), in several states of Appalachia (FSS, FSSH), in Florida, Michigan, Missouri, Oklahoma, and Colorado. Coffin itemizes about 65 texts, including 17 from JAF. The many texts have essentially the same story, as found in Child C-E. It is the elopement of Polly with William, the attempt to murder the seventh daughter, the fake modesty of Polly, the throwing of the lover into the sea, her return home, and the talkative parrot. The most useful notes are given by Davis (MTBV, 3 texts), Belden (BSM, 10 texts), Cox (FSS, TBFWV, 11 texts), Belden, Hudson and Schinhan (NCF, II, IV, 6 tunes), SharpK, 10 texts, four from Kentucky. Lawless lists 83 in print.

Two other texts have been reported from Kentucky: Shearin and Combs in **KySyll** and Wyman and Brockway in **Lonesome Tunes,** p. 82. I have one other text, collected in Harlan County. The present, "The Kings' Daughters," was recorded by Ina Mae Enzor, Harlan County, from the singing of her grandmother, Cassie Scott, in 1957.

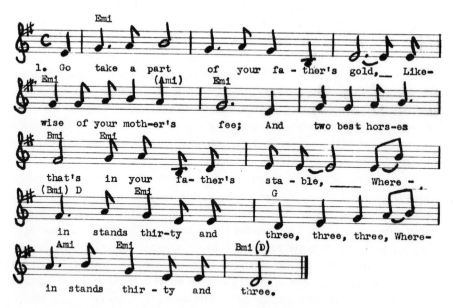

SCALE: Hexatonic (e f# g a b d).   MODE: Plagal.   RANGE: b - b'
(Perfect octave).   TONAL CENTER: E; Circular tune.   PHRASE STRUC-
TURE: A B A^1 C C^1 (3, 2, 3, 2, 2).   MELODIC RELATIONSHIP: Compare
final four measures above with bars 9 to 16 in "House Carpenter" of this collection.   Also Cf. SharpK I, Nos. 3A and B "Lady Isabel and the Elf Knight"–
final four measures of each.

10

2. She brought some of her father's gold
   And some of her mother's fee
   And two of the best horses
   Wherein the stable stood thirty and three, three, three
   Wherein the stable stood thirty and three.

3. She jumped on the pony black
   And he on the dapple gray
   They rode to the banks of the river
   Three long hours before it was day, day, day
   Three long hours before it was day.

4. Light ye down, light ye down, my pretty Colin
   Light ye down, light ye down, said he
   Six Kings' daughters I've drowned here
   And the seventh ye shall be, be, be
   And the seventh ye shall be.

5. O take off that new silk gown
   O take it off of thee
   It cost too much of your father's gold
   To lie rottin' in the salt sea, sea, sea
   To lie rottin' in the salt sea sand.

6. Turn your body around about
   And look upon a tree
   To keep from seeing an undressed woman
   On the banks of the salt sea, sea, sea
   On the banks of the salt sea shore.

7. He turned his body round about
   And looked upon the tree
   She picked him up by the stren'th of her arms
   And throwed him in the deep sea, sea, sea
   And throwed him in the deep sea.

8. Give me your hand, my pretty Colin
   Give me your hand, my dear
   I'll be your servant so long as I live
   And wait upon thee both night and day, day, day
   Wait upon thee both night and day.

9. Lie there, lie there, you false-hearted wretch
   Lie there in stead of me

Six Kings' daughters you've drowned here
And the seventh has drowned thee, thee, thee
And the seventh has drowned thee.

10. She jumped on the pony black
And leading on the dapply gray
She rode to her father's gate
One long hour before it was day, day, day
One long hour before it was day.

11. Then up spoke the little parrot
. . . .
What made you stray, my pretty Colin,
So long before it's day, day, day
So long before it's day?

12. Hold your tongue, hold your tongue, my little parrot
And tell me tales on me
Your cage shall be of gold yeller beat
And locked with a silver key, key, key
And locked with a silver key.

13. Then up woke the old man
. . . .
What made you raise, my little parrot
So long before it was day, day, day
So long before it was day?

14. The old puss come close to my cage
Waylaying to take my life
And I called on my pretty Colin
To scare the old puss away, 'way, 'way
To scare the old puss away.

15. Well done, well done, my little parrot
Well done, well done, said he
Your cage shall be of the gold yeller beat
Doors of the finest ivory, 'ry, 'ry
Doors of the finest ivory.

5. THE DOUGLAS TRAGEDY
(Child 7)

Child begins his study of this old elopement tragedy with ten texts in six versions (A-F). In addition to these he adds G, H, I (I, 489, 493) and other variants and notes throughout his collection. He is immediately struck by the corresponding story in the Scandinavian ballad of "Ribold and Guldborg," of which his Danish friend Grundtvig had twenty-seven versions. To throw light on the interesting plot of the abrupt English story, Child gives a synopsis of "Ribold and Guldborg" and related ballads: Guldborg is betrothed to an absent gentleman and is under the watchful eye of the guard. Ribold, a visiting king's son, wooes her in secret and promises her heaven on earth if she will elope. To escape, he disguises her in a cloak and rides with her into the heath. They are accosted; the disguise and a bribe are to no avail. As he prepares to fight, Ribold bids Guldborg to hold the horses and "though you see me fall, name me not at all." In the fight, six or eight are slain, until only her youngest brother remains. She calls to Ribold, "Spare him, to carry tidings to my mother." Ribold is mortally wounded and rides with Guldborg toward his home, with blood staining his cloak. He and his mother die, and Guldborg kills herself. Child traces this ballad back to a story in the Hilda Saga.

The ballad that has come to America is almost entirely parallel to Child B, taken from Scott's **Minstrelsy.** It is not too widespread, but it has been collected in Nova Scotia (BSHS), Maine (BBN), Vermont (SSSA, FSSH), and down Appalachia from Pennsylvania and West Virginia (FSS), North Carolina (NCF, II, IV, 7 texts, 8 tunes), to Mississippi and the Ozarks. The five previous texts found in Kentucky are in SharpK (4) and in the **KySyll.** Lawless lists 34 in print. I have hesitated to include the present text because it is very close to Child B. It has more Scottish dialect than does Scott's. For instance, my text says **doun** throughout for his **down.** I include it, however, for a few reasons: all American texts are close to Child B; the present text leaves out an occasional word or phrase hinting at traditional usage. My text changes a line and other phrases in stanza 6, making for better singing and scansion. Child B has

> She held his steed in her milk-white hand,
> And never shed one tear,
> Until she saw her seven brethern fa,
> And her father hard-fighting who loved her so dear.

The present text was turned in to me without tune by Dorothy Major, Greenup County, from a copy belonging to Matthew Warnock and Annelle McCullin, also of Greenup County. I had no opportunity to find out more about Mrs. McCullin, but Mr. Warnock sang several modern songs for another student collector.

1. "Rise up, rise up, now Lord Douglas," she said
   "And put on your armour so bright,
   Let it never be said that a daughter of thine
   Was married to a lord under night.

2. "Rise up, rise up, my seven bold sons,
   And put on your armour so bright,
   And take better care of your youngest sister,
   For your eldest's awa the last night."

3. He's mounted her on a milk-white steed,
   And himself on a dapple gray,
   With a bugelet horn hung doun his side;
   And lightly they rode away.

4. Lord William look'd o'er his left shoulder,
   To see what he could see,
   And there he spy'd her seven brethren bold,
   Come riding over the lea.

5. "Light down, light doun, Lady Margret," he said,
   "And hold my steed in your hand,
   Until that against your seven brethren bold,
   And your father, I make a stand."

6. O, there she stood, and bitter she stood,
   And never did shed one tear,
   Until that she saw seven brethren fa',
   And her father, who lov'd her so dear.

7. "O hold your hand, Lord William!" she said,
   "For your strokes they are wondrous sair;
   True lovers I can get many ane,
   But a father I can never get mair."

8. O she's ta'en out her handkerchief,
   It was o' the holland sae fine,
   And aye she dighted her father's wounds,
   That were redder than the wine.

9. "O chuse, O chuse, Lady Margret," he said,
   O whether will ye gang or bide?"
   "I'll gang, I'll gang, Lord William," she said,
   For ye've left me no other guide."

10. He's lifted her on a milk-white steed,
    And himself on a dapple gray,
    With a bugelet horn hung doun by his side;
    And slowly they baith rade away.

11. O they rade on, and they rade on,
    And a' by the light of the moon,
    Until they came to yon wan water,
    And there they lighted doun.

12. They lighted doun to take a drink
    Of the spring that ran sae clear,
    And doun the stream ran his guide heart's blood,
    And sair she gan to fear.

13. "Hold up, hold up, Lord William," she says,
    "For I fear that you are slain."
    " 'Tis naething but the shadow of my scarlet cloak,
    That shines in the water sae plain."

14. O they rade on, and on they rade,
    And a' by the light of the moon,
    Until they came to his mother's ha' door,
    And there they lighted doun.

15. "Get up, get up, lady mother," he says,
    "Get up and let me in!
    Get up, get up, lady mother," he says,
    For this night my fair lady I've win.

16. "O make my bed, lady mother," he says,
    "O make it braid and deep,
    And lay Lady Margret close at my back,
    And the sounder I will sleep."

17. Lord William was dead lang ere midnight,
    Lady Margret lang ere day,
    And all true lovers that go togither,
    May they have mair luck than they!

18. Lord William was buried in St. Mary's kirk,
    Lady Margret in Mary's quire;
    Out o' the lady's grave grew a bonny red rose,
    And out o' the knight's a brier.

19. And they twa met, and they twa plat,
    And fain they wad be near;
    And a' the warld might ken right weel
    They were twa lovers dear.

20. But bye and rade the Black Douglas,
    And wow but he was rough!
    For he pulled up the bonny brier,
    And flang 't in St. Mary's Lough.

6. THE TWO SISTERS
(Child 10)

Child had twenty-one versions (A-U), many with two to four variants, for his original headnote, plus four more, V-Y (I, 493-496), and an additional three variants at IV, 447-449. This is one ballad that Child knew to be still in tradition in Britain. His texts were drawn largely from the many collections in Scotland, one, R, from the renowned folktale collection of J. F. Campbell, PTWH, and even one (U) from W. W. Newell, GSAC, found in New York. His earliest text (Aa) is a broadside from **Notes and Queries** of 1656. Most of the versions have refrains: Hey down, or bow down; Edinburgh, Edinburgh; Binoria, O Binoria. And as he says, most of the complete ballads have a consistent story of the courting, the choosing of the youngest with gifts, and the drowning of the girl by the oldest sister. The variations begin with the weird adventures of this youngest's body. She struggles in the water to the Miller's dam. In some texts she is pulled out dead and parts of her body are used in a musical instrument, which, singing, reveals the murderer. In others she is robbed of jewels while still alive and pushed in again.

Child traces the ballad in European tradition, especially in Scandinavia, Iceland, and the Faroes. He also notices the story in folktale tradition, citing the Danish collection of Grundtvig and the German of the Grimm Brothers. This is folktale Type 780, **The Singing Bone**. Another tale in which the murder of a boy is revealed by singing bones or hair is Type 720, **My Mother Slew Me; My Father Ate Me. The Juniper Tree**. I have found this tale in the Kentucky Mountains **(South from Hell-fer-Sartin**, no. 27).

The ballad has also been in vigorous tradition in America (Coffin has about 75 entries in BTBNA). It is found in the major collections from Newfoundland, Maine, Vermont, New York, and down Appalachia from West Virginia (FSS, no. 3, WVCS, no. 56, TBFWV, no. 2, 5 texts), Kentucky (SharpK, no. 5, 4 texts, DD, SG), Virginia (TBV, no. 5, MTBV, no. 6, 23 texts), North Carolina (NCF,

II, IV, 7 texts, 6 tunes), Tennessee (ETFS, p. 29), to Mississippi and Florida across the Midwest to Michigan, Iowa, Missouri (BSM, pp. 16-24, five), the Ozarks, and Oklahoma. Lawless lists 70 in print.

The many variations of the ballad have fascinated research students (See Coffin BTBNA for an excellent summary). In general the conclusions are that the ballad began in Norway or in England and was early carried to Denmark; the folktale originated in Poland.

About ten texts have been collected in Kentucky plus this one and another in my files. All that I have seen follow Child's R-V, Y. They do not include the making of the musical instrument from her hair, or breast-bone. My text was sung in 1954 by Buell Kazee, earlier Brunswick recording artist, who grew up in Magoffin County. He had learned this and other old ballads from his mother.

MODERATELY

1. There was an old man___ lived by the sea,
Bow - ie down,_____ There was an old man ___lived
by the sea, His bows were bent __ to me, ____ There
was an old man__ lived by the sea, And he had daugh -ters
one, two, three, I'll___ be true, true to my love,
If my love will be true ___ to me.

SCALE: Heptachordal (g a b c d e f#). MODE: Major; Plagal. RANGE: d' - d'' (Perfect octave). TONAL CENTER: G. PHRASE STRUCTURE: A B A¹ A² A A² B¹ C (2, 2, 2, 2, 2, 2, 2, 2) or A A¹ A² B² (4, 4, 4, 4). MELODIC RELATIONSHIP: Cf. SharpK I, No. 5C, p. 28, phrase 3 ff. Of the several hundred variants of this Child 10 ballad tune the above seems (to this editor) one of the most lyrically beautiful of all. Note the overall basic affection, the diatonic scalewise movement, and the frequent treatment of the short melismatic figures.

2. There came a young man a-courting there,
   Bow—ie down
   There came a young man a-courting there,
   His bows were bent to me,
   'There came a young man a-courting there,
   And he took choice of the youngest fair.
   I'll be true, true to my love,
   If my love will be true to me.

3. He brought the youngest his beaver hat,
   Bow—ie down,
   He brought the youngest his beaver hat,
   His bows were bent to me,
   He brought the youngest his beaver hat,
   And the oldest sister didn't like that,
   I'll be true, true to my love,
   If my love will be true to me.

4. As they walked down to the water's brim,
   Bow—ie down
   As they walked down to the water's brim,
   His bows were bent to me,
   As they walked down to the water's brim,
   The oldest pushed the youngest in.
   I'll be true, true to my love,
   If my love will be true to me.

5. O sister, O sister, lend me your hand,
   Bow—ie down,
   O sister, O sister, lend me your hand,
   His bows were bent to me,
   O sister, O sister, lend me your hand,
   And you may have my houses and land.
   I'll be true, true to my love,
   If my love will be true to me.

6. She floated down to the miller's dam,
   Bow—ie down,
   She floated down to the miller's dam,

His bows were bent to me,
She floated down to the miller's dam,
The miller drew her safe to land.
I'll be true, true to my love,
If my love will be true to me.

7. And off of her fingers took five gold rings,
Bow—ie down,
And off of her fingers took five gold rings,
His bows were bent to me,
And off of her fingers took five gold rings,
And into the water he plunged her again.
I'll be true, true to my love,
If my love will be true to me.

8. The miller was hanged on the gallows high,
Bow—ie down,
The miller was hanged on the gallows high,
His bows were bent to me,
The miller was hanged on the gallows high,
The oldest sister there close by.
I'll be true, true to my love,
If my love will be true to me.

7. THE CRUEL BROTHER
(Child 11)

Child prints fourteen texts of this ballad, some of them fragments (I, 144 ff, 497-498; IV, 449). His A-E versions have one lover (knight, gentleman) coming and courting three sisters and choosing the youngest. This plot is older (Child's oldest text is from Herd, 1776) and more suitable for the tragedy than the others having three men coming to see one woman. The motivation for the bride-murder by her brother is founded in ancient familial mores of rank and other rights belonging to the men of the house.

There have been conjectures by later students of the Child and other ballads that the jealousy implies incest. For instance, Professor Child, in tracing the ballad to other European countries, gives the plot of the one from Italy as follows: "Rizzardo is conducting his bride home and on the way embraces and kisses her. Her brother witnesses this and thrusts his sword into the happy bridegroom's heart." Other ballads summarized from Germany, Denmark, and France are not so plain—the bride is accidentally wounded and dies in the German and Danish texts.

Although the ballad was reported to Child as being in living tradition in Scotland, it has been reported only in seven or eight localities in America. Some of those that I have seen have three men wooing three women. Except for a text from Vermont (ABTSNE) and one from Massachusetts (JAF, 28; 300-301, reprinted in BBM), the remainder have been collected in or near Appalachia. There are two texts from North Carolina in SharpK (no. 6), and two with tunes in NCF, II, IV, no. 5; one from Tennessee (Haun, **Cocke Co.**), and one from Kentucky (Niles, BB, no. 8). Lawless lists 6 in print.

The present text, with its one knight, belongs among the fuller versions of Child's A-E, especially C. It does not have the almost omnipresent refrain, but it does have a telltale line resembling the one in C: "My silken snood and golden fan." Another line in the present text is very close to one in his E: "Sing Annet, an Marrat, an fair Maisirie." My version was recovered in 1957 without music by Katherine Tompkins, who lived for a time in Virginia before moving to Harlan County. She says of it, "This was given to me by Mrs. Sylvia Hall, 55 or 60. She would not sing it. She heard it when she was a little girl." The faulty quatrains indeed imply that the text has been handed down as a song ballet, often copied but seldom sung.

1. There were three sisters whose lives were gay,
   They were happy from day to day.
   Pretty as a rose were the sisters three,
   Their names being Annett, Marrett, and Marie.

2. A knight came riding along their way,
   And courted them all so fair and gay.
   Annett, he held her in great pride,
   He whispered softly, "Will you be my bride?"

3. Marrett wearing a gown of green,
   He softly said, "Will you be my queen?"
   Marie, the youngest, dressed in white,
   Holden her in his arms so tight,
   "Oh, Lady Fair, be my heart's delight."

4. "Sir, Knight, my heart you win,
   First you must ask all my kin.
   First you must ask my father the king,

Next you must ask my mother the queen,
Then you must ask my sisters each one.
Make sure you ask my brother John."

5. Soon the wedding day did come.
The knight was proud of the girl he had won.
Many a lord and many a knight
Come to attend their wedding that night.

6. Her father led her down the aisle,
Her mother so hard to smile.
Her sisters standing so very close,
Her brother John sat on her horse.

7. She was now ready with her groom to depart,
Stooping over to her brother,
He stabbed her through the heart.

8. As she started riding through the town,
She soon saw the blood had stained her gown;
Slowly she turned to her groom so gay,
And slowly these words to him she did say,

9. "I love you, dear, but with you I cannot stay,
For the Master above has called me today,
Hold me gently in your arms,
I will tell you my will, it won't take long.

10. "To my father I leave my silk white steed that carried me here,
My mother my clothes for to wear,
My sisters I leave my snood and fan,
To keep them cool in the sun.

11. "The last thing I wish to leave,
This being for my brother John,
The gallows tree to hang him on,
The gallows tree for to hang him on.

8. JIMMY RANDAL
(Child 12)

For his headnote and in Additions Child prints twenty-four texts of the ballad. He also traces it on the continent, especially in Germany and Scandinavia. The story of a young man poisoned by his sweetheart is fairly consistent throughout the concise texts, varying only in details, such as his name, the poisoned dish, and the bequests. Many of the Child texts came from Scotland and the remainder from England except one (I) from Boston.

Coffin (BTBNA) lists about a hundred references and classifies them in six story types. Almost all, containing the normal narrative, are found under Type A. It has been found in most states where there has been collecting: Nova Scotia, Maine, Vermont, Pennsylvania, West Virginia (FSS, no. 4, 12 texts; TBMWV, no. 3; WVCS, no. 60; WVF, 1955, 22); Virginia (TBV no. 6, 14 and a fragment, and two from New York and Oklahoma, MTBV, 6); North Carolina, (NCF, II, IV, no. 6, 6 texts and 6 tunes; SharpK no. 7, 5 texts); South Carolina, Georgia, Florida, Mississippi, Michigan, Missouri, Ozarks, Oklahoma, and Utah. Lawless lists 70 in print.

In Kentucky the ballad is not so widespread. There are two texts in BB, one in SharpK, one each in FSKM and KySyll, and I have seven in my collection. The present one was turned in to D. K. Wilgus of Western Kentucky University in 1952 by Blanche Dingus from Mrs. Amy Begley, both of Floyd County (printed in KFR, 2(1956), p. 56).

1. Where have you been, Jimmy Randal, my son?
   Where have you been, my handsome young one?
   I've been to my true love, Mama,
   I've been to my true love, Mama,
   O make my bed soon,
   Cause I'm sick to the heart
   And I fain would lie down.

2. Where are your hounds, Jimmy Randal, my son?
   Where are your hounds, my handsome young one?
   They swelled up and died, Mama,
   They swelled up and died, Mama,
   O make my bed soon
   Cause I'm sick to the heart
   And I fain would lie down.

3. What did you eat, Jimmy Randal, my son?
    What did you eat, my handsome young one?
    Some fried eels and onions, Mama,
    Some fried eels and onions, Mama,
    O make my bed soon
    Cause I'm sick to the heart
    And I fain would lie down.

4. I fear you are poisoned, Jimmy Randal, my son,
    I fear you are poisoned, my handsome young one.
    O yes I'm poisoned, Mama,
    O yes I'm poisoned, Mama,
    O make my bed soon,
    Cause I'm sick to the heart
    And I fain would lie down.

9. HOW COME THAT BLOOD ON YOUR SHIRT SLEEVE?
(Child 13)

For this ballad Child had only two full texts and one fragment, and even the text B from Percy's **Reliques** he considered a literary re-working of the original. In it the son has killed the father and implicates the mother in the last line: "Sic counseils ye gave to me." This is the finding of Archer Taylor in his **Edward and Sven I Rosengard,** where he traces the ballad from Britain to Scandinavia and concludes that it was originally a British ballad of fratricide as in Child A and in others in Britain and America.

As with so many of these ballads, this one has come into most major collections in America. Although there seems to be no evidence of it in Canada and only a few texts recovered in New England (Flanders, ABTNE and BMNE), it has appeared in most states touching Appalachia: West Virginia (TMBWV, no. 4); Virginia (TBV, no. 7, 5 printed of 6; MTBV, no. 8, 3 texts; SCSM, pp. 180-184, 3); North Carolina (NCF, II, IV, no. 7, 2 texts and tunes; Niles, BB no. 10; SharpK, no. 8); also in Mississippi, Florida, Texas, the Ozarks, and surprisingly in abundance in Oklahoma (BFSSW, no. 8, 22 recovered, one printed). Lawless lists 30 in print.

Except for the listing in the **KySyll,** this is the only text I am able to find from Kentucky. It has the same stanza form and other identifying elements as most of the ten in SharpK, Scarborough A, B (from South Carolina), and the

Oklahoma text. It was sung by Martha Roberts Beddow, age about 40, Knox County, in 1956. She had grown up in Leslie County and learned a number of songs from her parents.

SCALE: Pentatonic (d f g a c).   MODE: II Plagal.   RANGE: c' - d" (Major 9th).   TONAL CENTER: D.   PHRASE STRUCTURE: A B C D D^1 A^1 D D^1 (2, 2, 2, 2, 2, 2, 2, 2) or A B A^1 (4, 6, 6).   MELODIC RELATIONSHIP: Cf. SharpK, p. 47, No. 8D "Edward" - very close. NCF, IV, p. 23, No. 7C - close except for phrase 1. Also, Bronson TTCB I, p. 238 "Edward," almost identical tune.   There is an obvious ambiguity of motivic elements in this tune; notwithstanding the structure A B A it is not a rondo type.

2. How come that blood on your shirt sleeve?
    O dear love tell me.
    It is the blood of the old grey mare
    That plowed that field for me, me, me,
    That plowed that field for me.

24

It is too pale for the old grey mare
That plowed that field for thee, thee, thee,
That plowed that field for thee.

3. How come that blood on your shirt sleeve?
    O dear love tell me.
    It is the blood of my brother-in-law
    That went away with me, me, me,
    That went away with me.

4. And what did you fall out about?
    O dear love tell me.
    About a little bit of bresh
    That soon would've made a tree, tree, tree,
    That soon would've made a tree.

5. And what will you do now my love?
    O dear love tell me.
    I'll set my foot on yonder ship
    And sail across the sea, sea, sea,
    And sail across the sea.

6. And when will you be back my love?
    O dear love tell me.
    When the sun sets yonder in a sycamore tree,
    And that will never be, be, be,
    And that will never be.

10. TWO CROWS
(Child 26)

This ballad was so rare in tradition in Europe that Child did not trace it. He even placed the stark tragedy of the "Twa Corbies" of Scott's **Minstrelsy** in his headnote as a counterpart to the true ballad. His text, a variant printed in 1611, has the hounds and hawks protecting the knight until a fallow doe carries him away and buries him. The other full text (Additions, V, 212, from **Notes and Queries**, 1892) presents a touchingly human drama:

> Then comes a lady, full of woe,
> As big wi' bairn as she can go, etc.

The ballad has been sung throughout America, Coffin making about fifty-five entries in his bibliography, and arranging them into five story types. Its variations extend all the way from tragic and lyric to quartet parody. It has been collected in Nova Scotia, Maine, Vermont, and down Applachia in Pennsylvania, West Virginia (FSS, no. 6), Virginia (TBV, no. 10, 17 printed of 27; MTBV, no. 13, 3 texts; SharpK, no. 11, 3 texts); North Carolina (NCF, II one), Mississippi, Missouri, Ozarks, Oklahoma. Lawless lists 20 in print.

The present text, without music, I hesitated to include until I noticed others of about the same length and of infinite variety in other collections. Not one has this "chewing gum" motif. The only other versions I have seen from Kentucky are two in Niles (BB, no. 17) and one in KFR, 6(1960):127. This one was turned in by Georgia Lloyd in 1955 from the singing of J.T. Bingham, who heard it from his father in about 1888, all of Knox County.

1. There were two crows a-sittin' in a tree,
   These two crows were as hungry as two crows could be,
   Said one old crow to his chum,
   "What shall we do for chewing gum?"

2. There's a horse in yonder lane,
   For chewing gum we will use his mane,
   We will fly upon his bare back bone,
   Pick his eye balls out one, one by one.

11. THE RIDDLE SONG
(Child 46)

The riddle ballads in the English and Scottish tradition go back to the Middle Ages. Child began his collection with some in which riddles are used to stump the Devil, to test the wit of women for marriage, and many others (see Child nos. 1, 2, 3, and 76). When Child came to his no. 46, "Captain Wedderburn's Courtship," he found another series of riddles used by a keeper of the game to woo a coy maid. But this ballad had appeared as late as 1785. Since the clusters of riddles were older than the ballad, Child returned to earlier uses of riddles and printed a set from the 15th century similar to the present one, known by its Latin refrain "Perri Merri Dictum Domine."

Thus, recent collectors have related "The Riddle Song" to Child 46; some scholars have tried to point out that if any borrowing was done it was by the no.

46 ballad singer. The best statements of this problem are given by Henry (FSSH, no. 311), by Barry (TBM, pp. 93-99), and summarized by Coffin (BTBNA, pp. 59-60).

Child traces the analogues of riddle contests over Europe, not so much in ballads as in folktales. He cites a story in the **Gesta Romanorum**, no. 70; a stanza from Chambers's **Popular Rhymes of Scotland** that seems to be a fragment of "The Seven Blessings of Mary" (see below no. 116); a Greek tale, now known under Type 853 A, **NO**; and other folktales from Persia, Russia, Germany (Grimm, no. 22), and Scotland (PTWH), no. 22). These are found under Types 851, **The Princess Who Cannot Solve The Riddle**, and 753, **The Hero Catches the Princess With Her Own Words**. Although they are related to the ballad, no direct borrowing can be documented. Child printed only three late copies of no. 46 and referred to an Irish version (V. 216).

Needless to say, the complete courtship ballad is quite rare in America. Some references are Maritime Provinces (SBNS), Maine (BBM), Vermont, Pennsylvania (Korson, PSL, no. 35), Michigan (BSSM, no. 48B, BSSM, no. 48A), North Carolina (NCF, II, 2 texts, IV, 3 tunes), West Virginia (WVCS, no. 25), Tennessee (ETFS, p. 88). The related "Riddle Song" and "Perrie Merrie" are found pretty well over Appalachia and in the Ozarks (see Coffin, BTBNA, p. 54, for separate listings). The riddle song seldom varies the gifts from a cherry, a chicken, a ring, a baby. The "Perrie Merrie" hardly differs from the one in Child's footnote: a bird, cherry, blanket, book. Lawless lists 8 in print.

"The Riddle Song" was sung by Marie Estep, Whitley County, in 1958, from the singing of her oldest sister Irene. The "Perrie Merrie" was given to me without music in 1955 by Mary Lipps, Clay County.

A

MODERATELY

1. I gave my love a cher-ry that had no stone, I
gave my love a chick-en that had no bone, I
gave my love a ring, that had no end, I

gave my love a ba — by with no cry — in'.

SCALE: Pentatonic (f g a c d).   MODE: III. Plagal.   RANGE: c'-d''
(Major 9th).   TONAL CENTER: F; greatest frequency on C; scale steps
1 and 5 are focal points of emphasis.   PHRASE STRUCTURE: A B A A[1]
(2, 2, 2, 2).   MELODIC RELATIONSHIP: Cf. NCF IV, No. 12A, and 12C;
Also, SharpK, II, 144A on opening phrase and general melodic contour. Also
Bronson TTCB I, No. 46, Appendix, version 8, close identity in rhythm, pitch
and meter.

2. How can there be a cherry that has no stone,
   How can there be a chicken that has no bone,
   How can there be a ring that has no end,
   How can there be a baby with no cryin'?

3. When a cherry is pitted it has no stone,
   When a chicken is an egg it has no bone,
   When a ring is rolling it has no end,
   When a baby is sleeping there's no cryin'.

B

PERRIE MERRIE DIXIE DOMINIE

1. I had four brothers over the sea
   Perrie merrie dixie dominie.
   And they each sent a present unto me
   Petrum patrum paradise temporie,
   Perrie merrie dixie dominie.

2. The first sent a chicken without any bones,
   Perrie merrie dixie dominie.
   The second sent a cherry without any stones
   Petrum partrum paradise temporie
   Perrie merrie dixie dominie.

3. The third sent a book which no man could read
   Perrie merrie dixie dominie.
   The fourth sent a blanket without any thread.

Petrum partrum paradise temporie,
Perrie merrie dixie dominie.

4. How could there be a chicken without any bones?
   Perrie merrie dixie cominie
   How could there be a cherry without any stones?
   Petrum partrum paradise temporie,
   Perrie merrie dixie dominie.

5. How could there be a book which no man could read?
   Perrie merrie dixie dominie
   How could there be a blanket without any thread?
   Petrum partrum paradise temporie,
   Perrie merrie dixie dominie.

6. When the chicken's in the eggshell there are no bones,
   Perrie merrie dixie dominie.
   When the cherry's in the blossom there are no stones,
   Petrum partrum paradise temporie
   Perrie merrie dixie dominie.

7. When the book's in the press no man can read it
   Perrie merrie dixie dominie
   When the wool is on the sheep's back, there is no thread
   Petrum partrum paradise temporie
   Perrie merrie dixie dominie.

12. LORD BATESMAN
(Child 53)

Child had fifteen versions (A-N) of the ballad for his headnote, all except one from Scotland. He traces it over Europe, from Spain to Scandinavia, and, because it has an old romance narrative, he finds it popular in southern Europe as well. In his Additions (II, 508) he prints a text to substitute for his L. This, a broadside, has influenced the later English and American texts.

Coffin has about seventy-five references (in two story types) for the ballad in North America. Most complete ballads come under his Type A. His Type B is based on variations in the ending, such as the marriage of the Turkish Lady to another of Bateman's family.

The ballad has been found in all sections of the country, from the Maritime Provinces, Maine (BBM, p. 106), Vermont, West Virginia (FSS, no. 8, TBMWV, no. 7, WVCS, no. 53); Tennessee (ETFS, p. 81); Virginia (TBV, no. 12, nine printed of twelve; MTBV, no. 16, three texts; SharpK, 4); South Carolina, Florida, Michigan, the Ozarks, and Oklahoma. Lawless lists 57 in print.

More texts have been found in Kentucky than in any other state. There are five in SharpK, five in my collection, and one or more in **KySyll**, DD, BB, KMFS, and LT. The present one was sung with banjo in 1952 by Jim Couch, age about 50, Harlan County (printed in TSCF, no. 2).

SCALE: Pentatonic (g a b d e).   MODE: III. Plagal.   RANGE: d'-e"
(Major 9th).   TONAL CENTER: G.   PHRASE STRUCTURE: A B C A[1]
(2, 2, 2, 2).   MELODIC RELATIONSHIP: Opening phrase is reminiscent of the "Come all ye" tunes. See "Silver Dagger" and "Some have Fathers Gone to Glory" in this collection for melodic similarity.

2. He sailed the east and he sailed west
    He sailed over to the Turkish shore,
    And there he was caught and put in prison
    And he never expected his freedom any more.

3. That Turkish had a lovely lady,
    She was of some high degree,
    She stoled the keys from her father's castle
    And said, "Lord Batesman, I'll set you free."

4. "Have you houses and rich land?
   Are you of some high degree?
   Will you will it all to the Turkish lady
   If out of this prison she'll set you free?"

5. "I have houses and rich land
   I am of some high degree
   I'll will it all to the Turkish lady
   If out of this prison she'll set me free."

6. She took him down to her father's hall
   She drew a glass of the strongest wine
   And there she gave and drink unto him
   And said, "Lord Batesman, you are mine."

13. THE CHERRY TREE CAROL
(Child 54)

This is the most popular of three Carols Child includes in his collections. The story itself is probably derived from Pseudo-Matthew, Chapter XX, wherein is related Joseph's flight into Egypt. On the third day the little family pauses under a palm tree for shade and rest. While Joseph goes seeking water, Mary observes fruit high in the palm and has a craving for it. She asks Joseph to get her some. He rebukes her for such a request when the waterskin is empty. The infant Jesus from her lap performs the first miracle by bidding the tall tree to bow down to His mother's feet. Lloyd (FSE, pp. 119-120) quotes dialogue from a Coventry play, **The Miraculous Birth and the Midwives,** which reveals a 15th century source.

The final stanzas of most English versions are concerned with the prophecies of Jesus from the womb, as the couple are going to Bethlehem. He relates that His birth will be a lowly one at Christmas, and that at His death on Good Friday the very stones in the street will moan, and that He will rise on Easter Day. In most American versions Jesus announces His birth to be on January 5 or 6. This is because the folk kept Old Christmas after the English adopted the new calendar in 1752.

Although the carol has had some currency in English and Scottish tradition (Notes to no. 15 in SharpK list nine), and in Ireland (BFSSNE, vol. 6, pp. 6-7, gives a text learned in Ireland about 1863), it has been in more active tradition in

America (Coffin gives some 35 entries in BTBNA). It has been collected in Canada, in Maine, Vermont, and down Appalachia, but not so abundantly as expected: Virginia (TBV, 3 texts; C, a fragment, was the first reported in America); West Virginia (WVCS, no. 74); North Carolina (2 in SharpK and 2 in NCF, II, no. 15, no tunes); Florida (FSF, p. 262); the Ozarks (OFS, I, 88); and Oklahoma (BFSSW, no. 16, 2 texts, one probably from Virginia). Lawless lists 17 in print.

Kentucky seems to have yielded more texts of this ballad than any other state. There is a text collected by Miss Wheeler in KMFS (pp. 3-8), and she sent one to Henry for FSSH, no.10; one in McGill's FSKM (from JAF, 1929: 293); one in Niles's **Seven Kentucky Mountain Tunes;** three in Thomas's BMMK (pp. 223-232); four in SharpK; and I have three other texts (one printed in TSCF, no. 3). The present text was contributed to Mrs. Marie S. Gick, Rowan County, in 1959. Her husband recorded the tune. The couple had lived for a time in Westchester, Ohio.

SMOOTHLY

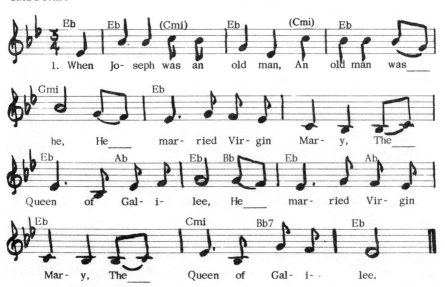

SCALE: Pentatonic (e^b f g b^b c).   MODE: III. Plagal.   RANGE: b^b - c" (Major 9th).   TONAL CENTER: E^b; with strong emphasis on B^b. PHRASE STRUCTURE: A B B^1 (4, 4, 4) Inverted barform.   MELODIC RELATIONSHIP: For close melodic relationship Cf. SharpK, I, pp. 90 ff, No. 15; also, Cf. Bronson II, Nos. 15 and 19, for close relationship.

2. Then Mary spoke to Joseph,
   So sweet and so mild,
   "Joseph, gather me some cherries,
   For I am with child.
   Joseph, gather me some cherries,
   For I am with child."

3. Then Joseph flew in anger,
   In anger flew he,
   "Let the father of the baby
   Gather cherries for thee.
   Let the father of the baby
   Gather cherries for thee."

4. Then Jesus spoke a few words,
   A few words spoke he,
   "Let my mother have some cherries,
   Bow down low cherry tree.
   Let my mother have some cherries,
   Bow down low cherry tree."

5. The cherry tree bowed low down,
   Bowed low down to the ground
   And Mary gathered cherries,
   While Joseph stood around.
   And Mary gathered cherries,
   While Joseph stood around.

6. Then Joseph took Mary
   Upon his right knee,
   "What have I done, Lord?
   Have mercy on me.
   What have I done, Lord?
   Have mercy one me."

7. Then Joseph took Mary
   Upon his left knee,
   "Oh tell me, little baby,
   When will thy birthday be?
   Oh tell me little baby,
   When will thy birthday be?"

8. "The sixth day of January
    My birthday will be,
    When the stars in the heavens
    Shall tremble with glee.
    When the stars in the heavens
    Shall tremble with glee."

14. LOVIN' HENRY
(Child 68)

Child prints eleven texts, some fragments, of this ballad, all from Scotland (two reworked by Sir Walter Scott). He finds that the few related ballads found in Scandinavia have parallel stories to his oldest versions and some of the more ancient folklore motifs found in ballads, such as the brightening of a candle over a corpse in the water; the body of a victim bleeding when touched by the murderer; trial by fire; and a talking bird. All except this last motif have disappeared from American texts. The ballad it seems has not been collected in Britain since Child's time and has rarely been recovered in the Maritime Provinces.

It has a rather active tradition in the United States. Coffin lists over fifty references, divided into seven story types. The many variants have a persistent narrative: a jilted girl stabs her lover when he rides up to tell her of another lover. Then she and sometimes a helper throw the body into deep water. A bird (usually a parrot) begins to reveal the murder and will not be bribed by the girl. Here the texts usually end. They have been found in Maine (BBM, a trace), and one each from New Brunswick and New York; many have been found in the Appalachian states: West Virginia (FSS, no. 9); 20 in Virginia (TBV, no. 17, MTBV, no. 17, BB, no. 27, SharpK, no. 18); North Carolina (NCF, II, no. 18, one, IV, 2 tunes, one with different text; SharpK, no. 18, 7); Tennessee (**Bulletin,** 8:72); South Carolina, Georgia, Mississippi, Florida, Missouri (BSM, pp. 34-37); Ozarks (OFS, I, 92-93); Oklahoma (BSFFW, no. 17); Texas, and Jamaica. Lawless did not tabulate this one.

The ballad has a modest distribution in Kentucky. There are two texts in SharpK, three in JAF, 20: 252-53, 30: 298-99, and 52: 30; and I have six other texts. The present one was sung in 1949 by Florence Lamb and Mary Rowe, both of Pike County.

1. Look___ down, look___ down, lov-in' Hen-ry, she__ said, And___ stay all night with___ me. You___ bed shall be made of___ dia-monds of gold, And your doors of i - vo - ry, And your doors of i - vo - ry.

SCALE: Pentatonic (g a b d e).   MODE: III. Plagal.   RANGE: d'-d" (Perfect octave).   TONAL CENTER: G.   PHRASE STRUCTURE: A B A¹ C C (2, 2, 2, 2, 2).   MELODIC RELATIONSHIP: Cf. Bronson, TTCB II, p. 68 "Young Hunting," variant 12, for a remote relationship; also, MTBV, p. 115, No. 17BB, some resemblance.

2. I can't get down nor I shan't get down,
   Nor I won't stay all night with thee,
   For I have another girl in the ivy cliff
   And tonight she's a-lookin for me.
   And tonight she's a-looking for me.

3. He leaned over from his saddle stirrup
   For to kiss her snow white cheek,
   And in her hand she held an awful knife
   And she stobbed him both wide and deep,
   And she stobbed him both wide and deep.

4. O shall I ride east or shall I ride west,
   Or anyways under the sun
   To bring a doctor here
   For to cure this wounded one,
   For to cure this wounded one.

5. You needn't to ride east,
   You needn't to ride west,
   Nor no ways under the sun,
   There's just one good God above us all
   That can cure this wounded one,
   That can cure this wounded one.

6. He gave a few more dying groans,
   Said, Little girl, you've treated me wrong,
   I'm going to a better world
   Where you can never come,
   Where you can never come.

7. She took him by his brown curly locks,
   And her sister by his feet,
   They carried him down to the deep stonewall well
   Where the water was so cold and deep,
   Where the water was so cold and deep.

8. Lay there, lay there, Lovin Henry, she cried,
   Till the meat drops off of your bones,
   For that girl that you have in the ivy cliff
   Thinks you're a long time comin home,
   Thinks you're a long time comin home.

9. As she return-ed to go back home,
   A little bird set on a limb,
   Said, Go home, go home, you cruel-hearted girl,
   There's another boy for thee,
   There's another boy for thee.

10. Fly down, fly home, you purty little bird,
    And rest upon my knee,
    Your cage shall be made of yaller-beaten gold,
    And hung on a willow tree,
    And hung on a willow tree.

11. I can't fly down, nor I shan't fly down,
    Nor I won't rest upon your knee,
    For you just have murdered your old truelove
    And perhaps you'll murder me,
    And perhaps you'll murder me.

12. Said, If I had my cedar bow,
    My arrow and my string,
    I'd shoot you right through the heart,
    And no more would you sit there and sing,
    And no more would you sit there and sing.

13. If you had your cedar bow,
    Your arrow and your string,
    I would fly to the top of some tall tree,
    And there I would sit and sing
    And there I would sit and sing.

15. LORD THOMAS
(Child 73)

This is the second most popular of all the English and Scottish ballads sung in England and America. The most popular is "Barbara Allen." In his notes to no. 73 Child calls it "The most beautiful of our ballads, and indeed of all ballads." Although a poignant love triangle in our version, it has some fierce and primitive conflicts in other lands. It has been collected in Scandinavia, in a version in which the jilted girl is the young man's wife in all but name. He abandons her for another. She attends the wedding feast and even bears the torch that lights the newlyweds to bed. Then in one variant she sets fire to the house and laughs as the bride burns in the bridegroom's arms. This fierce revenge is an echo from the Norse sagas.

The stories in the English (Lloyd in FSE cities broadside influence, p. 29) and American texts stay fairly close to one conflict. The man chooses between a poor but pretty woman and a rich ugly one. The brown girl in a fit of jealousy stabs Eleanor. The man, who has been of two minds all along, now destroys the brown girl and himself.

Of the nine versions (A-I) printed by Child, the version D (nine variants, three found in America by way of Ireland) seems to be the source of virtually all texts in America. It is found in abundance here and its details are catalogued in many headnotes. Coffin (BTBNA) lists about 100 bibliographical items, without, as he says (xiii), eliminating reprints or counting the number of texts included in each citation.

The ballad has been found in Nova Scotia, Newfoundland, Maine, Vermont, Massachusetts, in all the states touching Appalachia, and down the Midwest: Michigan, Iowa, Nebraska, Missouri, the Ozarks, Oklahoma, and Texas. The number found in Appalachia is hard to count, but with eleven mentioned by Cox (FSS, no. 10), forty-seven by Davis (TBV, no. 18; MTBV, no. 18), thirty-one in SharpK, no. 19, fourteen in NCF, II, IV, no. 19, and about fourteen from Kentucky (BKH, FSKM, DD, TKMS), plus seventeen in my collection, we can see that it is second only to "Barbara Allen" in popularity. Lawless lists 140 in print.

The present text was recorded on a disk in 1957 by Ina Mae Enzor of Cumberland, Harlan County, from her grandmother, Cassie Scott.

SCALE: Pentatonic (d f g a c). MODE: II. Plagal. RANGE: c'-d" (Major 9th). TONAL CENTER: D*. PHRASE STRUCTURE: A A¹ B C (2, 2, 2, 2) MELODIC RELATIONSHIP: The editor has been unable to locate this particular musical setting in any of the available sources. For another version Cf. "The Brown Girl," next tune. Also, Cf. NCF, IV, 17, pp. 30ff. for close resemblances: A(1), E(1), G, I, and O; Bronson's 147 variants, TTCB - closest relationship is No. 124 "The Brown Girl", p. 143, vol. II.

*The editor recognizes the possible justification for an alternate analysis of the tonal center as F, in which case this would be a circular tune, Mode III, Plagal.

2. I riddle you down, my oldest son,
    I riddle you both as one,
    I grant you as my dearest blessing
    To bring the brown girl home.

3. The brown girl has a house and home,
   Fair Ellender she has none,
   I grant you as my dearest blessing
   To bring the brown girl home.

4. Go saddle up my old gray mare,
   Go saddle him up for me,
   Go saddle up my old gray mare,
   Fair Ellener I'll go and see.

5. He rode till he come to Fair Ellender's hall,
   He knocked all at the ring,
   No one was so ready as Fair Ellender herself
   To rise and let him in.

6. What news, what news, Lord Thomas? she said,
   What news you come bringing to me?
   I've come to ask you to my wedding,
   Tomorrow it shall be.
   * I've come to ask you to my wedding,
   The brown girl my bride shall be.

7. Come riddle me down, my own dear mother,
   Come riddle us both as one,
   Whether I must go to Lord Thomas' wedding
   Or stay at home and mourn.

8. I riddle you down, my oldest daughter,
   I riddle you both as one,
   I grant you as my dearest blessing
   To stay at home and mourn.
   * To Lord Thomas' wedding I would go
   If I knew I would never return.

9. She dressed herself in scarlet and white
   And bound her head in green,
   And every town that she rode round
   They took her to be some queen.

10. She rode till she come to Lord Thomas' hall,
    She knocked all at the ring,
    No one was so ready as Lord Thomas himself,
    To rise and let her in.

11. He took her by the lily white hand
    And led her across the hall,
    And set her down in a chair of gold
    Among the ladies all.

12. Is this your bride, Lord Thomas? she cried,
    I think she looks wonderfully brown;
    You once could have married as fair a lady
    As ever the sun shone on.

13. The brown girl having a pen-knife in her hand,
    It being both long and sharp,
    Between the long ribs and the short,
    She pierced Fair Ellender's heart.

14. Are you sick, Fair Ellender? said he,
    I think you look wonderful pale,
    You once did have as fair a color
    As ever I'd wish to see.

15. Are you blind, Lord Thomas, she said,
    Or can't you very well see?
    I think I feel my own heart's blood
    Come trickling down my knee.

16. Lord Thomas having a sword close by,
    It being both sharp and tall,
    He hacked the brown girl's head off her shoulders
    And kicked it against the wall.

17. A grave, a grave, Lord Thomas he cried,
    A grave both wide and deep,
    Go bury Fair Ellender in my arms
    And the brown girl at my feet.
    * Go bury Fair Ellender in my arms
    The sounder we may sleep.

*Same music as for previous two lines.

40

16. SWEET WILLIAM
(Child 74)

In the previous ballad about Lord Thomas, three lovers die of jealousy and revenge; in this one and the following, "Lord Lovel," two lovers die of unfulfilled love and remorse.   As usual, Child traces these ballads to Germany and Scandinavia where the stories are somewhat clearer.   In most of them the man (sometimes husband) abandons the girl to her grief or disgrace, and returns before or just after she dies in childbirth. He orders a wider and deeper grave, and falls on his own sword. The rose-brier (sometimes tree) endings occur in many of the Germanic versions. Child had only broadsides to work with, the earliest from the end of the 17th century, and Ac, d and B, C from the Percy papers of 1765. But he notes the fragments recited in **The Knight of the Burning Pestle** of 1611.

With some fifty entries, Coffin does not list so many printings of this ballad as for no. 73 or 75. Yet it has been recovered in Nova Scotia, Newfoundland, Maine (BBM, 134-139); Vermont (VFB, ABTSNE, 7 texts and two fragments); Massachusetts (Child V, 293-294); and in most Appalachian states: West Virginia (Cox FSS, seven texts); Virginia (TBV, fifteen printed of twenty-eight; SharpK, seven texts; MTBV, three printed of seven); North Carolina (NCF, II, no. 20, seven printed of eight, IV, 5 tunes; SharpK, five); Michigan, Ohio, Illinois, Missouri, the Ozarks, and Oklahoma. Lawless lists 87 in print.

Some nine texts have been printed from Kentucky (JAF 1910:381; KFR, 1957:89; 1960:127; FKM, p. 71; SharpK, no. 20, three texts; KySyll, LT, p. 94). My collection contains twelve texts. The present one was collected by Mrs. Mary Ellen Stamper, Knox County, in 1956, from the singing of Mrs. Elma Mitchell, who said she had heard it sung by Molly Garland.

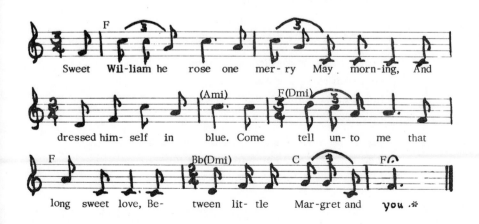

SCALE: Pentatonic (f g a c d). MODE: III. Plagal. RANGE: c'-d"
(Major 9th). TONAL CENTER: F. PHRASE STRUCTURE: A B A^1 C
(2, 2, 2, 2) or A A^1 (4, 4). MELODIC RELATIONSHIP: The editor has
found no resemblance to this tune in any of the numerous variants of Child 74.

Note the angularity of the melody with wide intervallic skips.

*Sung "me" instead of "you".

2. I know nothing about little Margret's love,
   I know she doesn't love me,
   But tomorrow morning at eight o'clock
   Little Margret my bride shall see.

3. Little Margret standing in her own hall door,
   Combing back her hair,
   Just then she spied Sweet William and his bride
   As they the church drew nigh.

4. She threw away her ivory combs
   And quickly did up her hair,
   Out of the hall this fair lady went
   Never to return again.

5. The day was spent and the night came on
   When all men were asleep,
   Sweet William he spied Little Margret's ghost
   Standing at his bed's feet.

6. The night was spent and the day came on
   When all men were awake,
   And Sweet William was troubled in his head
   For the dream he dreamed last night.

7. Sweet William he called to his merry maids all,
   He called them one, two, and three,
   But the last of all he called his bride:
   Little Margret may I go see?

8. What are you going to do with little Margret, my love?
   And what are you going to do with me?
   I'll go see little Margret, my love
   And then I'll return to thee.

9. He rose, he went to his own love's house
   And he tingled on the ring,
   No one was so ready but her brother
   To rise and let him in.

10. - - - - - - - - - - - - - - - - - -
    Is she in the kitchen, is she in the hall?
    Is she in her chamber
    With her merry maids all?

11. She is neither in the kitchen,
    She is neither in the hall
    But there she lies in her coffin
    That sits against the wall.

12. Fold up, fold up those highland sheets
    That are made and lined so fine,
    And let me kiss little Margret's lips,
    For often she has kissed mine.

13. Fold down, fold down those highland sheets,
    For they are lined so fine,
    And today they hang over little Margret's corpse
    And tomorrow they shall hang over mine.

17. LORD LOVEL
(Child 75)

In this ballad (as in 74) two lovers lose their lives, she from hope long deferred and he from remorse and grief. Child prints ten versions of the ballad and traces it to Germany and Scandinavia. In some of the Continental stories the man abandons the girl in trouble, or they quarrel and part until the man dreams that something has befallen the girl.

Most of the American texts follow Child H, a London broadside. Well over a hundred references are listed by Coffin (BTBNA), in only two story types, attesting to the consistency and simplicity of the ballad, and to the many reprintings in pre-Civil War songbooks. It has been found in Nova Scotia, Maine (BBM, 139-149, four texts and an excellent study); Vermont, New York, Pennsylvania, and most Appalachian states: West Virginia (FSS, no. 12, 5 texts;

TBMWV, no. 8, 3 texts; SharpK, no. 21, 2 texts); North Carolina (NCF, II, no. 21, 7, IV, 6 tunes; SharpK, two); Mississippi, Florida, and in the Midwest from Michigan, Nebraska, Missouri (BSM, seven), the Ozarks, Oklahoma, and Utah. Lawless lists 61 in print.

The number of Kentucky texts is rather modest, one each in SharpK, **KySyll, FSKM,** Thomas' **Singin' Gatherin',** and five in my collection. The present text without tune was turned in by Clifton Beam, Montgomery County, in 1960.

1. Lord Lovel he stood at his castle gate,
   A-combing his milk-white steed,
   When along came Lady Nancy Bell,
   A-wishing her lover good speed, speed, speed,
   A-wishing her lover good speed.

2. "Oh, where are you going, Lord Lovel?" she said,
   "Oh, where are you going?" said she.
   "I'm going, dear Lady Nancy Bell,
   Strange countries for to see."

3. "When will you be back, Lord Lovel?" she said,
   "When will you be back?" said she.
   "In a year or two or three at the most
   I'll return to my Lady Nancee."

4. He'd not been gone but a year and a day,
   Strange countries for to see,
   When languishing thoughts came into his mind,
   Lady Nancy Bell he would see.

5. He rode and he rode on his milk-white steed,
   Till he reached fair London Town,
   And there he heard St. Varney's bell,
   And the people all mourning around.

6. "Is anyone dead?" Lord Lovel he said,
   "Is anyone dead?" said he.
   "A lady is dead," the people all said,
   "And they call her the Lady Nancy."

7. He ordered the grave to be opened forthwith,
   The shroud to be folded down,

And then he kissed her clay-cold lips
Till the tears came trickling down.

8. Lady Nancy she died as it might be today,
   Lord Lovel he died tomorrow,
   Lady Nancy she died of pure, pure grief,
   Lord Lovel he died of sorrow.

9. Lady Nancy was laid in St. Clement's churchyard,
   Lord Lovel was buried close by her,
   And out of her bosom there grew a red rose,
   And out of his backbone a brier.

18. WHO WILL SHOE YOUR FEET?
(Cf. Child 76)

The main motivation in this pathetic love story is that of a lass looking for the father of her child. She arrives at her lover's door and someone within (presumably his mother) hears her pleas and love tokens, only to turn her away. She sets sail again. When her lover hears of her visit he hastens to the shore only to find her drowned. He kills himself. Two or more of the stanzas are given over to her questions: "Who will shoe my foot?" etc. Child had eleven versions (A-K) for his headnote, mostly from Scotland, but as a whole the ballad has not appeared very often in Britain or in America since his time. For Canada see Fowke, TSSO, no. 42. For American references, see FSS, no. 13, and NCF, II, IV, no. 22.

America has the "shoe-my-foot" stanzas, either alone, or as part of various love lyrics. These make up most of the bibliography by Coffin (BTBNA) under his Types B and C. He questions whether these stanzas in other lyrics should be used to identify Child 76. Davis (TBV, no. 21) prints twenty-one texts under the number and an additional nine in an appendix of love lyrics containing the "shoe-my-foot" stanzas. Belden (BSM, p. 55) puts none under the number, but discusses the problem under other songs, especially under "Blue-Eyed Boy" (A, pp. 478-479) and under "The False True-Lover" (pp. 480-482). SharpK and Karpeles have none under the number but recognize the floating stanzas in some of the variants of their no. 94, "The False Young Man," and no. 114, "The True Lover's Farewell". They feel that this latter song is derived from "Young Hunting," Child no. 68. For all mixtures of no. 76 Lawless lists 64 in print.

The present text likewise is made up of floating stanzas: the pastourelle opening is similar to SharpK, no. 94, B, C, D, H; two stanzas are from Child no. 68; the final turtledove stanza is similar to versions of SharpK, no. 114, etc. It was turned in by Charles Doll in 1957 from the recitation of John Stealy, both of Whitley County.

1. As I walked out one merry May morn
   To hear the little birds sing sweet,
   I lay my head in a true lover's door
   To see true lovers meet.

2. Come in, my own true love,
   Come in, come in, said she,
   It's been a year and a half or more
   Since you returned to me.

3. I can't come in my own true love,
   I have but a moment of time,
   You have another true love hear I,
   I fear he has beaten my time.

4. Oh, don't you remember that rocky mountain top
   Where we sat side by side,
   And you promised me to marry me
   And to be no other man's bride.

5. Oh, who will shoe your feet, my love
   And who will glove your hands,
   And who will kiss your red rosy cheeks
   When I am in a far away land?

6. My father will shoe my feet, my love,
   My mother will glove my hands,
   My baby will kiss my red rosy cheeks
   When you are in a far away land.

7. Oh, don't you see that turtle dove
   Flying from pine to pine,
   Mourning over its own true love
   Like I am over mine?

19. LADY GAY or THE THREE LITTLE BABES
(Child 79)

Professor Child had only one text (from Scott's **Minstrelsy**) and a fragment from G. R. Kinlock for his original entry. His note is brief but he says, "Nothing that we have is more profoundly affecting." His C text (III, 513-514) is from Shropshire, and he prints another (V, 294-295) from North Carolina which is nearer in particulars to other American texts. According to Belden (BSM, 55-57, two texts), "One suspects some printed source as an explanation of the likeness in the American texts . . . ." The ballad is almost nonexistent in present British collections.

Likewise, it has had little currency in eastern North America. There is a trace of it in Maine (BBM, 449-451), and one text each in Vermont (related to Child A) and in New Hampshire (ABTSNE, 187-194). It has been found in some abundance in Appalachia, in the South, and in the Middle West. Eight variants have been recorded in West Virginia (FSS, no. 14; WVCS, no. 58); 23 have been found in Virginia (TBV, no. 22, and MTBV, no. 23); 19 in North Carolina (SharpK no. 22 and NCF, II, 7 texts, IV, 7 tunes); and scattered appearances in Mississippi (FSM), Florida, Ohio, Indiana, the Ozarks, Texas, and Oklahoma (BFSSW, 2 texts). Lawless lists 68 in print.

Kentucky has yielded several instances of the ballad. There are four texts in SharpK, a text in BKH, one in FSKM, one in the **KySyll,** one in KMFS, three in the booklets of Niles, plus one in his BB. My collection contains 7 texts. The present one was sung to me by Buell Kazee in 1954. He had heard it in Magoffin County and recorded it for Brunswick in the 1920's.

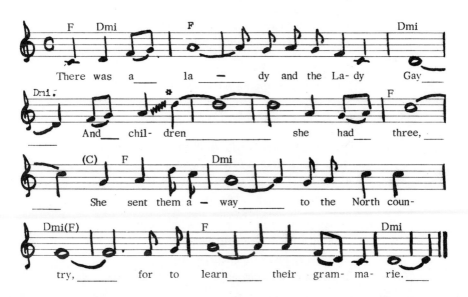

There was a___ la — dy and the La- dy Gay___
And___ chil- dren___ she had___ three,
She sent them a — way___ to the North coun-
try,___ for to learn___ their gram- ma- rie.

SCALE: Pentatonic (d f g a c).   MODE: II. Plagal.   RANGE: c'‑d"
(Major 9th).   TONAL CENTER: D.   PHRASE STRUCTURE: A B C A¹
(4, 4, 4, 4). Although the phrase structure works out consistently there probably
has been internal incrementation in the usage of the semibreves.   MELODIC
RELATIONSHIP: Cf. NCF IV, pp. 49ff, No. 25C, E, E(1): Cf. Bronson, TTCB
II, p. 260, version 38: "The Wife of Ushers Well" for close variant; MTBV, pp.
162‑163, very close, with metrical deviations; OFS II, p. 250, No. 210: "Manassa
Junction," for first two and final phrases especially: There is an interesting,
though unknown, association here between this Civil War song and our tune.

2. They had not been there very long,
    Scarcely six months and a day,
    When death, cold death came hasting along
    And took those babes away.

3. It was about old Christmas time,
    The nights were long and clear,
    She looked and she saw those three little babes
    Come running home to her.

4. She set a table both long and wide
    And on it she put bread and wine,
    Come eat, come drink, my three little babes,
    Come eat, come drink of mine.

5. We want none of your bread, Mother,
    Neither do we want your wine,
    For yonder stands our Saviour dear,
    And unto Him we must resign.

6. She made a bed in a little back room
    And over she spread white sheets,
    And over it that golden spread,
    Where the three little babes might sleep.

7. Take it off, take it off, cried the oldest one,
    Take it off, take it off, cried he,
    For yonder stands our Saviour dear
    And unto Him we must resign.

8. Green grass grows over our head, Mother,
    Cold clay lies under our feet,
    And every tear you shed for us,
    It wets our winding sheet.

20. LITTLE MATTY GROVES
(Child 81)

Child had fourteen versions of this ballad (A-N) for study, many variants from English broadsides such as **Wit Restored** (1658), Pepys, Roxburghe, and the added O from Gypsies (IV, 478). He also reveals that it had been entered in the Stationers' Registers in 1630, and that fragments were sung in **The Knight of the Burning Pestle** (1611) and in later 17th century plays. The story varies in details, such as the meeting-place: at the church, on a holiday, or at a ball. The footpage hears of the planned tryst in secret, or is threatened or bribed to keep still; or a friend of the lord's carries the news. The lord kills the two in various ways, and bemoans the loss of one or the other, and in some texts slays himself or is hanged. But throughout all complete texts the essential tragedy remains constant. The ballad has been found in later British tradition.

It has had vigorous currency in America (Coffin enters some 60 references). It is in the collections of Nova Scotia, Maine (BBM, 9 texts with study and praise of more vigorous and purer texts in America), Vermont, and in most Appalachain states—Pennsylvania, West Virginia (FSS, no. 15), Virginia (TBV, no. 23, 7; MTBV, no. 24, 5), North Carolina (SharpK, no. 23, 4; NCF, II, IV, no. 26, 5 texts, 6 tunes; BB, no. 34, 2); and South Carolina, and in the Midwest from Michigan, Missouri, Ozarks, and Oklahoma. It has been found also in Jamaica. Lawless lists 51 in print.

More texts have been recovered in Kentucky than in any other state. There is one version in BKH, one in JAF (1917:309), on in "Notes from Pine Mountain School," one in SFC, KySyll, and TKMS. There are 9 texts in SharpK and my collection contains 7, one printed in TSCF, no. 4. The present version was sung for me by Florence Lamb and Mary Rowe, Pike County, in 1949.

SPRIGHTLY

One day, one day, one hol-ly hol-ly day, On the first day of the year, __ We all went down to the church-house, French El-len for to hear, To French El-len for to hear.

SCALE: Hexachordal (c d e f g a).   MODE: Plagal.   RANGE: e'-e"
(Perfect octave).   TONAL CENTER: C.   *PHRASE STRUCTURE: A B
C D D¹ (2, 2, 2, 2, 2).   MELODIC RELATIONSHIP: Cf. NCF IV, Nos. 26A
and B, quite close in phrases 1 and 2; versions F and G show slight resemblances.
Also, Cf. SharpK, "Little Musgrave and Lady Barnard," versions L and N. Cf.
Bronson, TTCB II, p. 297, variant 43, chiefly in phrases 1 and 2.

*This version is probably marked by some structural erosion; note internal
incrementation in phrase B.

2. The first come in was little Mattie Groves,
   Next one in was the girl,
   The very next to come in was Lord Darnell's wife,
   O, a thirst among them all.

3. The little foot page was standing there
   To see what he could hear,
   He carried the news away to Lord Darnell,
   He carried it far and near,
   There he carried it far and near.

4. Little Mattie Groves was a-standing there
   On him she cast her eye,
   Saying you must go home with me tonight,
   This live long night to lie,
   Now this live long night to lie.

5. I can't go home with you tonight,
   I cannot by you lie,
   For by the rings that you wear on your finger,
   You must be Lord Darnell's wife,
   Looks like you must be Lord Darnell's wife.

6. If I am Lord Darnell's wife,
   Lord Darnell hain't at home,
   He's gone away to the high King's gate,
   French Ellen for to learn,
   Where French Ellen for to learn.

7. This may be a lie you brought unto me,
   This may be the truth,
   And if it's a lie you brought unto me,
   To the highest tree you'll hang,
   And never be cut down.

8. He gathered his men all in the band,
   And a bugle and a horn,
   And every time the horn did blow,
   Said Get up Little Mattie and go, go,
   Get up Little Mattie and go.

9. I must rise up, Little Mattie says,
   I must rise up and go,
   I hear Lord Darnell blowin' his trumpet,
   Blowing for me to go, go
   Blowing for me to go.

10. Lie still, lie still, Little Mattie, she said,
    Lie still in the bed with me,
    It's nothing but my father's shepherds,
    To summon their sheep to the food,
    To summon their sheep to the food.

11. From that they fell to hugging and kissing,
    From that they fell asleep,
    And when Little Mattie Groves awaked,
    Lord Darnell was at his bed feet,
    Seed Lord Darnell was at his bed feet.

12. Rise up, rise up, Little Mattie, he says,
    Rise up and put on your clothes,
    Fight me like a man, for I hate to have it said
    That I slew a naked man,
    That I slew a naked man.

13. I can't rise up, Little Mattie says,
    I cannot for my life,
    You have two brand new swords hanging by your side,
    And me not as much as a knife,
    And me not as much as a knife.

14. If I have two brand new swords,
    They cost me deep in the purse,
    And you may have the best one,
    And I will take the worst,
    And I will take the worst.

15. You may have the first lick
    And kill me if you can,

And if you don't the next lick's mine,
As sure as you're a man,
As sure as you're a man.

16. The very first lick Little Mattie struck,
    He made a dreadful sore,
    The very first lick Lord Darnell struck,
    Little Mattie couldn't fight no more,
    Little Mattie couldn't fight no more.

21. BARBREY ALLEN
(Child 84)

"Barbrey Allen" is used by folklorists to introduce students to the old English and Scottish ballads. There are so many texts of the three fairy distinct versions that the items collected in America alone run into the hundreds. Davis had 118 items to edit in Virginia alone (TBV, no. 24; MTBV, no. 25). Some comments on the ballad are as follows:

It is a Scottish story, but was first mentioned by Pepys in his **Diary** for January 2, 1666. Pepys was a ladies' man and loved to go to plays. He said he was in perfect pleasure to hear Mrs. Knipp (an actress) sing her little Scotch song of Barbrey Allen. On the strength of this remark some say that the song might have been a stage piece. Barry tries to go a step further and consider it a libel on Charles II and his mistress Barbrey Villers. See the note in NCF, II, IV, no. 27, 18 texts, 18 tunes by different contributors. See also Barry BBM, pp. 195-200, and BFSSNE, 10, 23-24.

The second historical fact about the ballad is its appearance in Ramsay's **Tea-Table Miscellany,** 1740 edition. And the third is an allusion by Oliver Goldsmith when in an essay of 1765 he says: "The music of the finest singer is dissonance to what I felt when an old dairymaid sang me into tears with 'Johnny Armstrong's Last Goodnight' and 'The Cruelty of Barbrey Allen'."

Child admitted only three faulty short versions into his collection, those that he felt were authentic. Two have the tavern slighting, all have Barbara's remorse, but none have the rose-briar motif.

In the great number of American texts we have interesting but not vital details. In some the lover dies cursing Barbrey, or in heaping on her most of his possessions (these details are listed by Child in his headnote but he does not print full texts). In some, Barbrey does not die of remorse, but is still cruel; she curses the lover, or her parents for interfering. See Coffin's ten types in BTBNA, 82-85, where he lists over a hundred references.

Without listing, we find the ballad in virtually all collections. This wide distribution was aided by the songsters, magazines, and bulletins that have printed it. Kentucky has produced its share of texts: SharpK (5 texts), BB, BKH, FKM, **KySyll**, KFR, DD, SG, KMF, LT. There are 67 texts in my collection. Lawless lists 83 in print. The present text was recorded by Catherine Nickels, Charles Patton, and Beulah Patrick in 1961 from "Banjer" Bill Cornett of Hindmen, Knott County, who said he had learned it and about two hundred other songs from his people, "Barbrey Allen" in about 1898. (See the recordings issued by the Folksong Archive of the Library of Congress.) The other variant titled "Barbara Allen" was collected in 1959 by Mary S. Nelson from the singing of her husband Orin, both of Greenup County.

A

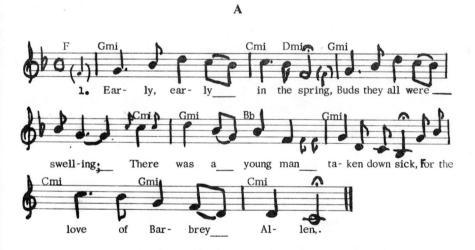

SCALE: Pentatonic (c d f g b♭).   MODE: IV. Plagal; leans toward Dorian mode.   RANGE: c' - d" (Major 9th).   TONAL CENTER: C. The harmonic type motive in measures 1 and 3, plus its inversion in measure 5, give a temporary impression of G as the final (tonic center).   PHRASE STRUCTURE: A A¹ B C (2, 2, 2, 2).   MELODIC RELATIONSHIP: Close relationship with NCF IV, No. 26A6; less in Sl. Cf., SharpK I, 24L, M, N, and P, for partial relationship of tonal material. MTBV, No. 34AA shows close tonal correlation in first two phrases, although metrically different. TTCB II, p. 378, No. 155, phrase A, closest of 198 variants to this tune.

2. He put his waitress on his horse,
   Sent him to her dwelling,
   Saying, "Master dear said for you to come here,
   If your name's Barbrey Allen."

3. Slowly, slowly she got up,
   Slowly she went to him,
   But all she said when she got there,
   "Young man, I hear you're dying."

4. "Yes, I'm sick and very sick,
   And death is on me dwellin',
   No better will you ever get,
   Till I get Barbrey Allen."

5. "If you are sick and very sick,
   And death is on you dwellin,
   No better will you ever get,
   You'll never get Barbrey Allen.

6. "Don't you remember in yonder town,
   The ladies all were dwellin',
   You drank a health to them all around,
   But you slighted Barbrey Allen."

7. "Yes, I remember in yonder town,
   The ladies all were dwellin'
   I treated a health to them all around,
   But my love was for Barbrey Allen."

8. He turned his pale face to the wall,
   Turned his back upon her,
   Said, "Adieu, adieu to this wide world,
   Be kind to Barbrey Allen."

9. She had not gone more than half way home,
   She heard a death bell ringin'
   Rang so clear they seemed to say,
   Hard-hearted Barbrey Allen.

10. She looked to the east and looked to the west,
    She saw the corpse a-comin',
    Said, "Hand me down that cold clay corpse,
    And let me look upon him."

11. The more she looked the more she blushed,
    She bursted into cryin'
    Said, "I once could have saved his sweet little life."
    She was all in the want of cryin'.

12. Like sweet William died today,
    And Barbrey died tomorrow,
    Sweet William died for his own true love,
    And Barbrey died for sorrow.

13. Sweet William was buried in the new church yard,
    And Barbrey in the old one,
    From the new church yard there sprung a rose,
    From the old one there sprung a briar.

14. They grew and grew and rose so tall,
    They could not grow any higher,
    They linked and tied in a true love knot,
    The rose around the briar.

B

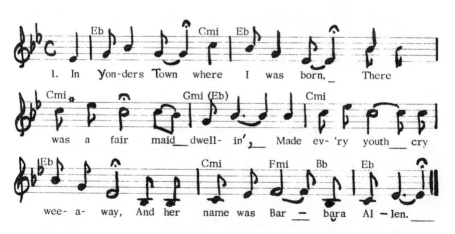

1. In Yon-ders Town where I was born, There was a fair maid dwell-in', Made ev-'ry youth cry wee-a-way, And her name was Bar — bara Al — len.

SCALE: Pentatonic (e^b f g b^b c). MODE: III. Plagal. RANGE: b^b - e^{b}" (Perfect 11th). TONAL CENTER: E^b. PHRASE STRUCTURE: A B B^1 C (2, 2, 2, 2). MELODIC RELATIONSHIP: Of the eighteen versions of this tune in NCF, IV, and sixteen in SharpK, there are none that exactly duplicate the above version in its initial motive; see NCV IV, No. 27A and A3 for some tonal relationships. Cf. also, Bronson TTCB III, No. 39, p. 217, "The

Gypsy Laddy" in phrases 2 and 3, almost identical. Cf. also TTCB II, p. 363, No. 115, in second and third phrases. In most versions verse 1 begins: "In Scarlet Town." Note the use of the "Scotch snap," an idiom present also in American Negro music and in jazz.

*Most probably the rhythm in measure 3 is a corruption of that in measure 1.

2. It was all in the month of May,
   When the rose buds they were swellin'
   Sweet Willie came from a western state,
   And he courted Barbara Allen.

3. It was all in the month of June,
   When the roses they were bloomin'
   Sweet Willie on his death bed lay
   For the love of Barbara Allen.

4. He sent his servant to the town,
   To the place where she was dwellin',
   "My Master's sick and sent for you,
   If your name be Barbara Allen.

5. "And death was painted on his face,
   And o'er his heart is stealin,'
   Go haste away to comfort him,
   Oh, lovely Barbara Allen."

6. Slowly, slowly she got up,
   And slowly she came to him,
   And all she said when she got there,
   "Young man, I think you're dying."

7. "Oh, yes, I'm sick, and very sick,
   And death is on me dwellin',
   No better, no better I'll never be,
   If I can't have Barbara Allen."

8. "Oh, yes, you're sick, and very sick,
   And death is on you dwellin,'
   No better, no better you never will be,
   For you can't have Barbara Allen."

9. He turned his pale face to the wall,
   And his back upon the dear ones,
   "Adieu, adieu, my friends, adieu,
   Be good to Barbara Allen."

10. As she was on her highway home,
    She heard the birds a-singin'
    And every one did seem to say
    Hard-hearted Barbara Allen.

11. She looked to the east, she looked to the west,
    She saw his corpse a-comin,'
    "Lay down, lay down that corpse of clay,
    That I might look upon him."

12. The more she looked, the more she weeped,
    She bursted out to cryin,'
    "Oh, take me up and carry me home,
    For I surely think I'm dyin.'

13. "Oh, Father dear, go dig my grave,
    Go dig it long and narrow,
    Sweet Willie died for my pure love,
    And I shall die for sorrow."

14. They buried them both in the old church yard,
    They buried them both together,
    On Willie's grave there grew a red rose,
    And Barbara's grew a briar.

15. They grew so high, they grew so tall,
    They reached the old church tower,
    They fell and tied in a truelove's bow,
    The rose and the briar.

22. LADY ALICE
(Child 85)

Child wrote a headnote of only six lines for his two texts (similar one, C, V, 225-226) to say that this ballad was a counter-part to "Lord Lovel." In three texts

(A-C), the boy Giles Collins takes sick and dies. Lady Alice, an old lover, stops the funeral procession, kisses the corpse, and dies. A lily grows from his grave until it touches her breast.

Versions found later in England (JFSS, III) give more motivation for the death of (now) Johnny Collins. He is fleeing from an unrequited, jealous, vengeful lover, connecting the story with Child's no. 42, "Clerk Colvill." See the studies relating Child no. 85 to 42 by Miss Barbara C'raster (JFSS, IV: 106-109), S. P. Bayard (JAF, 58:73-103), and summarized by Coffin (BTBNA, no. 85) and Davis (MTBV, no. 26).

The appearance of the ballad in America is almost totally confined to Appalachia and the South. Gardner and Chickering (BSSM, no. 9) give two floating stanzas of "A Lover's Farewell" learned in Virginia. Texts of the ballad have been recovered in West Virginia (FSS, no. 17, 5 items); Virginia (TBV, no. 25, 18 texts; MTBV, no. 26, 13 collected); North Carolina (SharpK, no. 25, 5 texts or tune stanzas; NCF, II, no. 28, 15 texts, IV, 9 tunes); Mississippi (FSM, FTM); Florida, the Ozarks, and Oklahoma. Other Appalachian texts are found in SharpK, Henry (FSSH and SSSA), Scarborough (SSM, pp. 117-122, 6 texts), Haun (CC), and Niles (BB, no. 37, 2 texts). Lawless lists 42 in print.

Only one other instance of the ballad, it seems, has been collected in Kentucky—Combs FKH, p. 8. I have five in my collection. Two of them have the opening stanza about the hobo (one mentioned by Davis, MTBV, but not printed). None suggest the cause of Collins's sickness (girlfriend, mermaid of Coffin's Type A), or the lily from the grave motif (Type C). Three contain the mother's attempt at consolation (Coffin's Type B); some have the turtle-dove ending (Type D). The present A text was collected in 1957 without music by Rosella Shaw, from Josh Sharp, both of Whitley County. B, "The Dying Hobo," was collected by Ardy Wright in 1957 from Lestle Wright, both of Pike County. The C text of two stanzas was recorded in 1957 by Mrs. Fanny Bright, Knox County, age about 50. She said this about it: "My sister, age now 85, played and sang this on the organ when I was a little girl." It has the only tune available.

A
GEORGE COLLINS

1. George Collins rode home one cold rainy night
   George Collins rode home so fine
   George Collins rode home one cold rainy night
   And taken sick and died.

2. Little Hattie was sitting in her mother's room
   A-sewing on silk so fine
   When she heard poor George had died,
   She laid her silk aside.

3. She followed him up, she followed him down
   She followed him to his grave;
   And there upon her knees she fell,
   She wept, she moaned, she prayed.

4. She sat down on the coffin, Take off the lid,
   Fold back the linen so fine
   That I may kiss his cold, pale lips,
   For I know he'll never kiss mine.

5. The happiest hours I ever spent
   Were by George Collins' side;
   The saddest news I ever heard
   Was that George Collins had died.

6. O, don't you see the turtle-dove,
   As he flies from pine to pine?
   He weeps, he moans for his own true love
   Just as I wept for mine.

B
THE DYING HOBO

1. Out on a western hobo trip
   On one cold December day
   In an empty boxcar
   A dying hobo lay.

2. Can't you see that pretty little girl
   Sewing her silks so fine?
   And when she heard her sweetheart was dead
   She laid her silks aside.

3. O daughter, O daughter, why do you weep?
   There's many more boys than George.
   O Mother, O Mother, he's the one that I love
   He's the one I always agreed.

4. She traveled up and she traveled down
   Till she came where poor George was laid,
   And when she came to where he was laid
   This is what she said.

5. Lay back, lay back his coffin lid
   Lay back the linen so fine,
   And let me kiss his pale blue lips,
   I know he'll never kiss mine.

6. Can't you see that turtle-dove
   A-flying from pine to pine
   Pining for its own true love
   So why not pine for mine?

C
GEORGE COLLINS

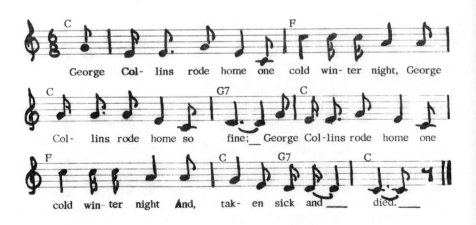

George Col-lins róde home one cold win-ter night, George
Col-lins rode home so fine;__ George Col-lins rode home one
cold win-ter night And, tak-en sick and___ died.___

SCALE: Pentatonic (c d e g a).   MODE: III.   RANGE: c' - c" (Perfect octave).   TONAL CENTER: C.   PHRASE STRUCTURE: A A^1 A B (2, 2, 2, 2) or AA^1 (4, 4).   MELODIC RELATIONSHIP: This version shows a harmonic type melody. Cf. SharpK, I, No. 25D for similarity in melodic contour. Note the "Scotch snap" in measures 1, 3, 5, and 7. One senses a bit of word painting in the final phrase, with its descending line; and this is generally applicable to most all the final lines of the various stanzas.

2. Set down the coffin, take off the lid,
    Lay back the linen so fine,
    And let me kiss those pale cold lips,
    I know they'll never kiss mine.

23. HANGS-A-MAN
(Child 95)

Child based his lengthy headnote upon eight versions of the ballad (A-H), most from England, the oldest from the Percy papers of 1765. His F is a children's game, and C and H, he says, are set to a popular tale in which the girl has lost a golden key or a golden ball. His E is from Scotland as well as his I (IV, 481). The end of this last is unique in that the freed girl hurls curses on her stingy kin. J and K are from England, the latter involving a man rather than a girl on the gallows. In V, 296, Child prints the earliest American text, recited by a North Carolina woman who said that her forebears brought it to Virginia before the Revolution.

In his scholarly way Child traces the ballad in European collections, such as Sicilian, Spanish, Faroe, Icelandic, Swedish, German, Russian. What he finds is a consistent story with infinite details: A wife in one, but girls in most, are seized by pirates (corsairs), usually from their ship, and are held for ransom. Father will not give up the household goods required, mother will not give up her silver trinkets, brother his hats, coats, swords, sister her shoes, etc. The husband or lover gives up all asked for and frees the victim. In the Wendish, Slovenian, and Russian versions the prisoner is a man.

The game played and the story told about the loss of a key or ball (G, H) precede the recitation or singing of the stanzas. This type of text (cante-fable) has been collected among Negroes of the West Indies and of Missouri—reprinted by Barry in BBM, pp. 210-213. I have collected tales with similar motifs in Kentucky (**South from Hell-for-Sartin**, no. 6) titled "The Little Blue Ball" and "The Golden Ball." I classified them as Type 311, **Three Sisters Rescued From the Power of an Ogre**. Further collecting and study may reveal the nature of story and ballad kinship.

In America the ballad has not yet been recovered north of Maine (BBM, pp. 206-213). It has been collected in Vermont and New York; in most Appalachian states such as West Virginia (FFS, no. 18; WVCS, no. 63); Virginia (TBV, no. 27; MTBV, no. 29); North Carolina (SharpK, no. 28, NCF, II, no. 30, 8 texts, IV, 8 tunes); South Carolina (SCB); Tennessee (ETFS, p. 85); Mississippi (SMF, no. 15); Florida, Michigan, Missouri, the Ozarks, Oklahoma, and Texas. In Kentucky it has appeared in BKH, p. 113; KFR, 1960, 127; SFC, 122; DD, 164, LT, 44; SharpK, no. 28 (2 texts); TSCF, no. 6; and I have ten texts in my collection. Lawless lists 73 in print. This variant was sung for me by Floyd Hall, Pike County, in 1950.

FLOWING

Slack your rope, hangs a-man, Oh, slack it for a-while, I think I see my fa-ther com-in', rid-ing man a mile. Oh, fa-ther, have you brought me gold, or have you paid my fee, Or have you come to see me hang-in' on the gal-lus

62

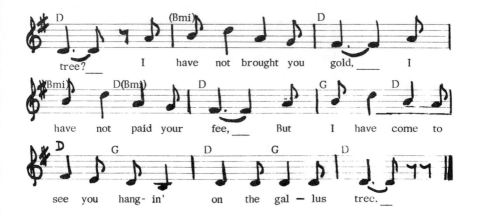

tree? I have not brought you gold,___ I

have not paid your fee,___ But I have come to

see you hang- in' on the gal — lus tree.___

SCALE: Hexachordal (d e f# g (g#) a b); Inflected scale.　　MODE: Plagal.
RANGE: b - d" (Minor 10th).　　TONAL CENTER: D.　　PHRASE STRUC-
TURE: A B C C^1 C^2 C^1 (4, 4, 4, 4, 4, 4) or A B B^1 (8, 8, 8) Inverted barform.
MELODIC RELATIONSHIP: Cf. Bronson, TTCB, variant 23, p. 457, for very
close relationship, excepting initial intervallic skip; NCF IV, No. 30N, p. 78, 79,
"Hangman, Hangman," our phrase 3 with their phrase 2 in pitch relationship.
Note the long iteration of D's in phrase C^1, associated with the Irish cadence.

2.　Slack your rope, Hangs-a-man,
　　Oh, slack it for awhile,
　　I think I see my mother comin'
　　Ridin a many a mile.
　　Oh, Mother, have you brought me gold,
　　Or have you paid my fee,
　　Or have you come to see me hangin'
　　On the Gallus tree?
　　I have not brought you gold,
　　I have not paid your fee,
　　But I have come to see you hangin'
　　On the Gallus tree.

3.　Slack your rope, Hangs-a-man,
　　Oh, slack it for a while,
　　I think I see my brother comin'
　　Riding a many a mile.
　　Oh, brother, you have brought me gold,

Or have you paid me fee,
Or have you come to see me hangin'
On the Gallus tree?
I have not brought you gold,
I have not paid your fee,
But I have come to see you hangin'
On the Gallus tree.

4. Slack your rope, Hangs-a-man,
   Oh, slack it for a while,
   I think I see my sister comin'
   Ridin many a mile.
   Oh, sister, have you brought me gold,
   Or have you paid my fee,
   Or have you come to see me hangin'
   On the Gallus tree?
   I have not brought you gold.
   I have not paid your fee.
   But I have come to see you hangin'
   On the Gallus tree.

5. Slack your rope, Hangs-a-man,
   Oh, slack it for a while.
   I think I see my lover comin',
   Ridin many a mile.
   Oh, lover, have you brought me gold.
   Or have you paid my fee.
   Or have you come to see me hangin'
   On the Gallus tree?
   Yes, I have brought you gold.
   And I have paid your fee.
   Nor have I come to see you hangin'
   On the Gallus tree.

24. MY NAME IS ALLAN-A-DALE
(Child 138)

Professor Child had three broadside variants of the 17th century (Pepys, Davis) for his study and acceptance of this among his many Robin Hood ballads. The prose narrative about Scarlock in the life of Robin Hood had appeared in the Sloane Manuscript nearly a century earlier. This one and about forty other Robin Hood ballads labored over by Child (nos. 117-154) have not often been found in oral tradition. Very few scattered titles have been reported in Britain, and Coffin can report only ten or twelve recovered in America.

For the present ballad he can cite only one appearance, that in JAF, 1956:28-38. In this article, Child no. 138 is one of seven Robin Hood ballads John Greenway collected from Aunt Molly Garland Jackson of Clay County, Kentucky. I never met her but have heard of her fantastic repertoire of traditional and protest songs, and occasionally a student cites her as source (see my Child no. 74). Professor Greenway inquired of another collector and learned that she had lent Aunt Molly a copy of Sargent and Kittredge (ESPB). When Greenway studied her Robin Hood texts he came to the conclusion that she had followed the Child text in general and had telescoped, expanded, and added stanzas to sing the ballad, even to improve it with more logical transitions and smoother rhyme and meter. With this ballad, for instance, containing 27 quatrains, she had altered almost every stanza, and had come out with exactly 27 stanzas. Not included by Lawless.

The present text has a few half lines identical with the Child and the Aunt Molly variants, but in no case does it have so much as a half stanza identical to either. My text tries to do in 31 lines what the Child and Molly texts do in over a hundred. Greenway says (p. 24): "I doubt that any Robin Hood ballads found in America have been received through purely oral channels." This is a safe assertion because so few have been received at all. But here is one that shows a good bit of wear and erosion, forgetting, and amending. It, along with several other interesting ballads, was turned in to me without music in 1957 by an in-service teach, Katherine Tompkins, age about 45 years, taking courses at Union College in Southeastern Kentucky. Her childhood was spent in Virginia, some years in Kentucky, and she is presently living in Tennessee. She says of it: "He knew no tune, could not remember all the verses. Sam Whitaker, Oak Ridge, Tennessee, age about 45."

1. As Robin Hood in the Greenwood stood,
   A young man he did spy.
   As the man slowly lifted his head
   He looked Robin in the eye.

2. Robin politely said, as he had said before,
   "Do you have any money to spare?"
   "I have but five shillings and a ring.
   For seven long years I have kept this in wait.

3. "I thought yesterday I would be wed.
   On arriving I found I was too late,
   For tomorrow another's bride she will be."

4. "What will you give," said Robin Hood,
   "If your true love I will set free?"
   "I have no money to pay a fee,
   But your servant I will always be."

5. Then swiftly rode Robin Hood
   To where the little church stood.
   As he drew nigh, he soon did spy
   A wealthy knight in glistening gold.

6. When Robin to the knight did say,
   "Might this be your wedding day?"
   With an answer the knight did say,
   "Get out, get out, you beggar, you,
   Before I have you beheaded today."

7. Then Robin did whistle,
   His men come like a thistle,
   And carried the knight away.

8. Robin took off the preacher's coat
   And put it on Little John,
   Then the real wedding begun,
   And the bride looked fresh as a queen.

25. THE JEW'S DAUGHTER
(Child 155)

Counting additions, Child reports twenty-one versions of the ballad (A-U), from England, Scotland, Ireland, and America. Most of his headnote is given over to tracing (and deploring) the supposed sacrifice of Hugh of Lincoln by Jews in 1255, and how the story was caught up in the Chronicles and in an Anglo-French ballad of ninety-two stanzas. Since this history is summarized by Davis (TBV) and by Coffin we need only say here that the story and ballad have persisted in tradition because of its three strong motifs: ritual murder, miracles of Our Lady, and the pathetic death of an innocent schoolboy. This last motif has kept up the interest to the present time. It has been collected in Britain only occasionally since Child's time.

In America it has been found in Nova Scotia, Vermont, Pennsylvania, and in all Appalachian states: West Virginia, Virginia, North Carolina, (NCF, II, 4, IV, 2 tunes), South Carolina (SCB), Florida, Alabama, Tennessee (ETFS, p. 1), Mississippi, Michigan, Ohio, Indiana, Missouri, the Ozarks, Oklahoma, and Utah. Most texts have been collected in Virginia (TBV, no. 33, 16; SharpK, no. 31, 1, and MTBV, no. 30, 7). West Virginia is probably second (FSS, no. 19, 14 texts and WVF, III, V, IX, XI, 4). Lawless does not include this one.

Kentucky has yielded a goodly number: JAF, 1906: 292; KFR, 1957: 92, and 1960, 127; SharpK, no. 31, 6 texts, and four in my collection. The present text was given to me without music by Angie Ward in 1957 from Mrs. Tandy Branham, both of Johnson County. It has many details in common with Child F and N, both of which came from Ireland. See the study of an unusual Kentucky version by F.T. Stamper and Wm. H. Jansen, JAF, 1958: 16-22.

1. It happened all on one cold day,
   The drops of dew did fall,
   And every scholar at that school
   Got lief to play the ball.

2. They knocked it high, they knocked it low,
   They knocked it to the Jew's gate.
   "Come in, come in, my little boy Hugh.
   And get your ball again."

3. "I can't come in, I dare come in,
   You would tell the school master on me.
   And if the school master knew of all,
   He would cause my blood to fall."

4. Then up stepped the Jew's daughter
   With apples in her hand,
   "Come in, come in, my little boy Hugh,
   And get you two or one."

5. She took him by the little white hand
   And led him through the hall.
   She took him to that stone well
   Where none could hear him squall.

6. She set him down in a silver chair
   And pricked him with a pin.
   And in her little basin clear
   She let his heart's blood spin.

7. She wrapped him in a sheet of lead
   From two and two enfold,
   She took him to that Dross Well
   Where it is both deep and cold.

8. Day going off, and night coming on,
   All children going home,
   Every mother had her son
   But Hugh's mother she had none.

9. She broke her a switch off yonders birch
   And ran up through the town
   Saying, "If I meet my little boy Hugh,
   I vow I'll whip him home."

10. She ran till she came to the Jew's gate,
    The Jews were all asleep.
    She ran till she came to the Dross Well,
    Where it was both cold and deep.

11. "Are you in here, my little boy Hugh?
    Oh, yes, I'm afraid you are,
    Speak one word to your mother dear,
    Who has been so tender to you."

12. "Oh, yes, I'm in here, dear Mother," he cried,
    "I've been lying here so long,
    With a little pen knife pierced through my heart,
    The blood it ran so strong.

13. "Oh, help me out, dear Mother," he cried.
    "And bury me by yonder church.
    Help me out, dear Mother," he cried,
    "And make my coffin of birch."

26. BLACK JACK DAVEY
(Child 200)

Of the twelve texts and fragments Child used in his study of the ballad, most were from Scotland (the oldest of 1740), with some from England, Ireland, and two from America (J, K). L is from Gypsy tradition. Child does not trace the story to Europe but confines his headnote to toleration and presecution of Gypsies in England and Scotland and to the possible historical background of the Earl of Cassilis, who is mentioned in several texts and whose wife is implicated in the elopement. This would have been in the 1640's. Since the Earl's wife died "a dear bed-fellow" in 1642, Child dismisses the connection. The ballad has continued in tradition in northern England and Scotland (FSNE, CX 2 texts) to the present.

It came to America also with some vigor, and, except for some minor episodes, has remained consistent. Coffin lists some 65-70 references in ten story types, though the majority of full texts seem to conform to his Type A, following in substance the rollicking, non-glamourizing lines of Child's H,I, J. It has been found in Newfoundland (BSSN), Nova Scotia, Maine (BBM, 269-277, 7 texts), Vermont (VFB); and in the Appalachian states: West Virginia (FSS, TBWV), Virginia (TBV, MTBV), North Carolina (NCF, II, 7, IV, 13 tunes); and through the Midwest from Michigan to Ohio, Indiana, Illinois, Iowa, Tennessee (ETFS, p. 97), down to Missouri, the Ozarks, Oklahoma, Texas, and west to Utah. Lawless lists 68 in print.

About a dozen texts have been printed from Kentucky: **Kentucky Counties Ms.**, KFLP (II, 7-8), KFR, 1956:58, and by Kincaid, McGill, Sharp K (no. 33, 1 text); Niles (BB, no. 52); FSSUS (2 listed, one printed, pp. 205-206); and there are seven texts in my collection. Two of them have the "How old are you, my pretty little miss?" lines (Coffin's Type H). The present text was recorded by Ina Mae Enzor in 1957 from the singing of her grandmother Cassie Scott, age about 70, both of Harlan County.

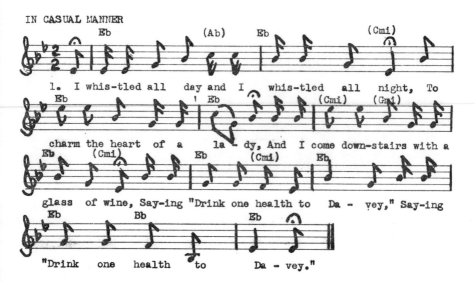

SCALE: Pentatonic (e^b f g b^b c).   MODE: III. Plagal.   RANGE: b^b-e^{b}" (Perfect 11th).   TONAL CENTER: E^b.   PHRASE STRUCTURE: A B B^1 C C^1 (2, 2, 2, 2, 2).   MELODIC RELATIONSHIP: Cf. NCF IV, pp. 84ff, motivic relationship at beginning and end of A B B (1), and E; also, Bronson TTCB III, p. 246, No. 119 "Black Eyed Davy" - closest melodic relationship of 128 variants; MTBV No. 33AA, p. 256, - first phrase only.

The consistent use of the fermata at the close of each line (except in C) seems to be a quite common practice with folk singers, as it is also observed in Gospel hymn singing.

2. It's late in the night when her husband come home,
    Inquiring for his lady,
    She's gone with Black Jack Davey,
    She's gone with Black Jack Davey.

3. Go saddle up my old gray horse,
    The black one hain't so steady,
    I'll ride all day and all night too
    Till I overtake my lady,
    Till I overtake my lady.

4. He rode till he come to the riverside,
   It being deep and muddy,
   He rode till he come to the other side,
   And there he overtaken his honey,
   And there he overtaken his honey.

5. Come go back, my dearest dear,
   Come go back, my honey,
   I'll lock you up in a chamber so high,
   Where the Black Jack can't come nigh you,
   Where the Black Jack can't come nigh you.

6. I can't go back, my dearest dear,
   I can't go back, my honey.
   For I'd ruther have a kiss from the Black Jack's lips
   Than you and all your money,
   Than you and all your money.

7. I once had a feather bed to lay upon,
   A waitin' girl to wait upon me,
   But now I come to the old straw tick,
   The Black Jacks begging all around me,
   The Black Jacks begging all around me.

27. GEORDIE
(Child 209)

Child had fourteen texts and fragments of this traditional ballad, all from Scotland. In the first three (A-C) there is an historical setting in which Geordie is sentenced for a crime, and, although his lady tries to pay a ransom, he is killed. In several others the lady is liberal with money and fees and rescues him. In an appendix (IV, 140-142) Child prints two English broadsides containing the essential story but he points out, as do later students, that one cannot tell which set was prior to the other. In any case, the Pepys broadside "The Life and Death of Oxford" (pp. 141-142, **circa** 1671 to 1692) has the opening first person narrator ("As I went over London bridge") and many of the motifs, including the hanging with a silken string, common to later British and American texts.

In America the ballad is fairly consistent and has been eroded down to an average of eight stanzas, many leaving off the climactic last stanza. In many that do have it the lady is wishing for pistols to fight for Georgy even though he is supposed to be dead. In a few, such as the present text and the one in BB, the calling for a dagger or blade to die with her lover is more "appropriate."

Coffin has about thiry references to ballad collections in America, arranged in four story types. The present text is nearest to story Type A, except for the unusual ending, possibly calling for another story type. It has been collected in the Maritime Provinces and in Vermont. In Appalachia it has appeared inPennsylvania, West Virginia (FSS, no. 23, WVCS, no. 65); in Virginia (TBV, no. 3, 2 and 2 fragments; SharpK, no. 34, 2 texts; MTBV, no. 34; BB, no. 53); in North Carolina (SharpK, no. 34, 4 texts; NCF, II, IV, no. 38, 1 text, 4 tunes ; SCSM, pp. 213-215); in the Midwest it has been found in Missouri (BSM, 76-78, 1 and 2 fragments); the Ozarks, and in Oklahoma. Lawless lists 24 in print.

This version may not have originated in Kentucky. It was turned in without music in 1957 by Betty Hackler of Harlan County, who said that she learned it at Pine Mountain Settlement School, same county. An almost identical variant is in a PMSS mimeographed booklet of 40 pieces titled simply **Ballads.** The text is quite close to the one in BB. Since Niles says that he collected his in Virginia thirty-seven years earlier and had been singing it ever since, I suspect that he sang it at the boarding school or in the hearing of teachers who were active in collecting in the region after the founding of PMSS in 1913.

1. As I walked over London Bridge
    One morning that was foggy,
    I overheard a fair one say,
    "Pray, save the life of Geordie!"
    I overheard a fair one say,
    "Pray, save the life of Geordie!"

2. "Go saddle up my milk white steed,
    For I must ride mile forty,
    Far over and away to Lonecastle fair
    To plead for the life of Geordie."
    (Repeat the last two lines throughout.)

3. She rode all day and she rode all night,
   Till she come wet and weary,
   A-combing out her golden locks,
   And a-pleading for her deary.

4. Then out of her pocket came a purse,
   The likes I ne'er saw any,
   Sayin': "Lawyers come and fee for yourselves,
   For I'll spend every penny."

5. Then Geordie in dock was standin' by,
   Said: "I ne'er did kill nobody,
   But I stole sixteen of the King's white steeds,
   And sold'em to Gohoody."

6. The oldest lawyer at the bar
   Said, "Geordie, it is a pity,
   By your own words you're condemned to die,
   You ought to've been more witty."

7. Now Geordie walked through the lined streets,
   And bid farewell to many,
   He bid farewell to his own true love
   And it grieved him more than any.

8. Geordie was hanged by a mighty chain
   Of gold that was so weighty
   'Cause he was from a noble line
   And he courted a noble lady.

9. "I wish I was on yonder hill
   Where kisses I had often,
   I'd stab myself with a pointed blade
   Beside my lover's coffin."

28. HOUSE CARPENTER
(Child 243)

Child had eight broadside versions of the ballad, the oldest (A) from Pepys of 1685 and the remainder from Scotland (F from Scott's **Minstrelsy**). Only his A has the full story and helps to explain the title. Jane Reynolds is betrothed to James Harris, a seaman. He is impressed as a sailor and is reported dead after three years. Jane marries a ship-carpenter and they live for four years and have children. James (like a man, but really his ghost) returns and persuades Jane to run away with him and he will support her with his seven ships. They are seen no more (other texts explain how the ship struck a rock and sank), and when the carpenter returns and finds his babies alone, he hangs himself. The other Child versions begin where James returns, B with the line that characterizes almost all later British and American texts: "Well met, well met, my own true love." The demonic character of the lover is lost, even in Child's texts, except for mention of his cloven foot and the "hills of heaven and hell" lines.

In America the ballad is wide-spread. It is close to Child's B and some variants retain the demonic allusions. But it also has been helped in American tradition by appearing in printed broadsides from Philadelphia and New York before the Civil War. It is second only to "Barbara Allen" in the number of texts found in several states. It seems not to have been collected in Canada, but has been found in Maine, Vermont, New York, West Virginia (FSS, no. 25, 21 texts; TBFWV, no. 12, WVCS, no. 61); Virginia (TBV no. 40, 52 texts; SharpK, no. 35, 2); North Carolina (SharpK, II, 2 texts; NCF, II, no. 37, 24 texts, IV, 8 tunes); Mississippi, Ohio, Indiana, Illinois, Missouri, Nebraska, the Ozarks, Oklahoma, Texas, and Utah. Lawless lists 173 in print.

The number of Kentucky texts runs a weak third to those of Virginia and North Carolina. There are two in JAF (1907: 257; 1939:46); two in KFLP (II: 7, 17), and one or more in KFR (1960:127), SCSM (158, from Jean Thomas), KySyll DD, BB (no. 55), SFQ (1938:75), TKMS, SharpK (no. 49, 6). I have seventeen texts in my collection. The present one was collected by Mrs. Meta Back in 1960, from Mrs Jessie Gevedon, who learned it from her dulcimer-playing father in about 1910. They all lived in Morgan County.

met, well met," said she ___ " I've just re- turned from the salt, salt ___ sea, And it's all for the sake of thee, ___ I've just re — turned from the salt, salt ___ sea, And it's just for the sake of thee."

SCALE: Hexachordal (g a b c d e).   MODE: Plagal.   RANGE: d'-d"
(Perfect octave).   TONAL CENTER: G; circular tune.   PHRASE STRUC-
TURE: A B C D E D^1 (4, 4, 4, 4, 4, 4) or A B C (8, 8, 8).   MELODIC RELA-
TIONSHIP: Cf. TTCB, pp. 433ff, Bronson gives 145 variants of this Child Ballad
No. 243, most of them bearing in contour and pitch levels to ours; closest tune
variant is probably "House Carpenter" No. 85, p. 467; also Cf. measures 9 to 16
here with the "The King's Daughters" in this collection, final bars.

2. "I could have married a king's daughter
    And think she would've married me,
    But I refused that crown of gold
    And it's all for the sake of thee."
    (Repeat the last two lines of each stanza.)

3. "If you could've married a king's daughter,
    I'm sure you are to blame,
    For I have married a house carpenter,
    And I think he's a fine young man."

4. "If you will leave your house carpenter
    And go along with me,
    I'll take you where the grass is ever green
    On the banks of sweet Italy."

75

5. "If I should leave my house carpenter
   And go along with thee,
   What have you got to support me upon
   And to keep me from poverty?"

6. "I have three hundred armored men
   And seven ships at sea,
   And that's enough to support you upon
   And to keep you from poverty."

7. They had not been at sea two weeks,
   I'm sure it was not three,
   Until she began to moan and weep,
   And she wept most bitterly.

8. "Oh, is it for my gold you weep,
   Or is it for my store,
   Or is it for your poor little babes
   That you never will see any more?"

9. "It is not for your gold I weep,
   Neither is it for your store,
   But it is for my poor little babes
   I never will see any more."

10. They had not been at sea three weeks,
    I'm sure it was not four,
    Until the ship sank in the deep,
    And it sank to rise no more.

29. THREE BROTHERS FROM OLD SCOTLAND
(Child 287)

With two short texts and a fragment Child enters this ballad, saying that it "must have sprung from the ashes of 'Andrew Barton'" (no. 167). No. 167 is a long sea story in epic detail of Scottish pirates and their capture and hanging by the King of England. It is told from the English point of view. No. 250, told from the Scottish viewpoint, begins with three brothers drawing lots, and moves swiftly to the one encounter and the escape of the Scottish pirate. Child's no. 287, "Captain Ward and the **Rainbow**," has a rover by the name of Captain Ward (probably English), who attempts to surrender to the King of England (probably James I) but is denied and attacked by the King's ship **Rainbow.** Captain Ward fights off the **Rainbow** and escapes, saying, "If he reigns king of all the land, I will reign king at sea."

Thus we see probably the same pirate and sea story treated thrice by the ballad muse. Barry (BBM, 253-258) follows Child's suggestion and his own study of American texts and argues for one ballad—no. 167. Coffin reviews his and other studies, including that of Davis (MTBV, no. 57), and places his references under no. 167. Davis, however, suggests separate ballads and, by studying the crossings of them and no. 287, he finds three forms for the American texts: the Martyn, the Ward, and the Bardan forms. The present text (before we go any farther) is the Ward form. Mr. Davis's conclusion therefore is to count all of the some thirty references by Coffin at no. 167 as "Henry Martyn" texts.

Twenty-nine texts have been collected in America: Nova Scotia, Maine, Vermont, New York, West Virginia (FSS, no. 26); Virginia (MTBV, no. 37); Michigan (BSSM, no. 81); Missouri (BSM, pp. 87-89, printed in JAF, 25: 171-173 and in BBM, 212-213—learned in Kentucky from Charlie Simms, who was of Kentucky stock but was brought up in Indiana); Oklahoma, the Ozarks, Colorado, and Utah. Not included by Lawless.

If the Missouri Barton form may ultimately have come from Indiana, the present (Ward form) is the only text collected in Kentucky. It was turned in to me in 1959 without music by Mary Stuart Nelson from Wash Nelson, age 71, both of Greenup County. Through curiosity I wrote to Mrs. Nelson in 1959 about the ballad and about the singer. Mr. Wash Nelson (no kin to Mary) sang the version again and changed a few words and added what there is here of stanza 5. He said he had learned this piece when he was very small from his grandmother Nancy Redwine Gilbert, who had moved from Virginia to Oldtown, Kentucky, in the late 1800's. Her family moved to Stump Run on Tygart's Creek (Greenup County) where Wash was born in 1888. The ballad therefore might have been learned in Virginia.

1. There was three brothers in old Scotland
    Three brothers, three brothers were they
    They all cast lots to see who'd go robbin'
    Go robbin' upon the salt sea.

2. The lot fell on the young Andrew Brattan
   The youngest of the three
   That he'd set sail and he'd go robbin'
   Who'd go robbin' upon the salt sea.

3. "Who is this, who is this?" said Captain Charles' son,
   "Who is this we're sailin' so nigh?"
   "We're a rich merchant ship from old Scotland
   Please won't you let us pass by?"

4. "Oh, no, oh, no," said Captain Charles' son
   "Oh, no, that never can be
   Your ship I'll capture, your gold take away
   And all of your merry men drown."

5. "Hey, hey," said Andrew Brattan,
   "Oh, no, this never can be
   For my lot is to rob . . . . . .
   . . . . upon the salt sea."

6. O now and then the battle began
   So loudly the cannons did roar
   They'd not been fightin' over an hour and a half
   Till Captain Charles' son gave o'er.

7. "Go home, go home, you cowardly dogs
   And tell your king for me
   That he can rule king all over dry land
   And I shall rule king on sea."

30. THREE NIGHTS' EXPERIENCE
(Child 274)

Child prints two versions of this humorous ballad, A, Scottish, from Herd of about 1776, and B, a London broadside. In tracing the ballad abroad he finds Gaelic and Flemish forms seemingly derived from his A. The B he says was turned into German in a very happy style, furnishing an ending in which the man gives his wife a beating ". . . as caresses which her mother has sent her." Child also identifies other European forms (Scandinavian, Magyar, French, Italian) but does not trace influences. The slight difference in the story elements is that in A (Coffin's A) the man returning finds one horse, hat, sword, etc., where his ought to be; in B (Coffin's B) the man finds three men's suspicious items. Coffin has a Type C (perhaps more recent and nearer most American forms) in which a man, usually drunk, returns home on three or four successive nights; hence, the local titles "Three Nights' Experience" and "Drunkard Blues."

The ballad has been dispersed over America, as was said, by late broadsides and then by phonograph records, radio, and television. But it is not so omnipresent in collections as expected, no doubt due to its bawdiness, versions of which are still unprinted in archives. The ballad has not been often found in Canada. It has appeared, however, in Maine (BBM, 2 texts), Vermont (AB, IV), and in most Appalachian states, including West Virginia (FSS, no. 28, 3 versions of Child A, WVCS, no. 68); Virginia (TBV, no. 43 and MTBV, no. 38, 12 texts); North Carolina (SharpK, no. 38, 2 texts; and in NCF, II, IV, no. 42, 4 and a fragment and 10 tunes); Mississippi (FSM); Florida (FSF); South Carolina (SCB); and a few in the Midwest and Far West: Missouri, Ozarks, Oklahoma, Texas, Iowa, Utah, and Oregon. Lawless lists 35 in print.

The Kentucky list is very modest. There are two texts in SharpK (D begins with the usual opening, "Old man came home. . . ."); two texts in KFR (1957:94 and 1960:127); one in Nile's BB, no. 57; one in TSCF, no. 7; and nineteen in my collection. The present one, sung by Oscar McKinney, was collected in 1961 by Betty Salisbury, both of Floyd County.

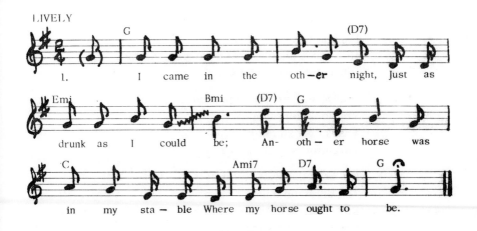

79

SCALE: Hexatonic (g a b d e f#). MODE: Plagal. RANGE: d'-d"
(Perfect octave). TONAL CENTER: G. PHRASE STRUCTURE: A B
C D (2, 2, 2, 2). MELODIC RELATIONSHIP: Cf. NCF, IV, No. 42B and B
(3) ff; also MTBV, No. 38BB, p. 303, "Our Goodman"; BFSS, No. 50, p. 120,
"Our Goodman" bears moderate resemblance.

2. Come here, my pretty little miss,
   Explain this thing to me,
   How come there's a horse in my stable
   Where my horse ought to be?

3. You blind fool, you dumb fool,
   You fool you cannot see,
   That's only a milk cow
   That Mommy sent to me.

4. I've been this wide world over,
   Ten thousand miles or more,
   But a milk cow in a horse's stable
   Well, I never did see before.

5. I came in the other night
   Just as drunk as I could be,
   Another coat was hanging on the rack
   Where my coat ought to be.

6. Come here, my pretty little miss,
   Explain this thing to me,
   How come another coat a-hanging on a rack
   Where my coat ought to be?

7. You blind fool, you dumb fool,
   You fool you cannot see,
   That's only an old bed quilt
   That Mommy sent to me.

8. I've been this wide world over
   Ten thousand miles or more,
   But a bed quilt on a coat rack
   Well, I never did see before.

9. I came in the other night
   Just as drunk as I could be,
   Another head was lying on the bed
   Where my head ought to be.

10. Come here, my pretty little miss,
    Explain this thing to me,
    How come another head a-lying on a piller
    Where my head ought to be?

11. You blind fool, you dumb fool,
    You fool you cannot see,
    That's only a cabbage head
    That Mommy sent to me.

12. I've traveled this world over
    Ten thousand miles or more,
    But a mustache on a cabbage head
    Well, I never did see before.

31. RISSELTY RASSELTY
(Child 277)

Child's headnote is based upon five late texts (earliest of 1803) from Scotland, all except E having refrains. C and D have refrains something like the present text: "Nickity, Nackity (Rifty Rafty) now, now, now." In additions (V, 304-305) Child has two more variants. One is Newell's Massachusetts text from JAF, VII: 23 (labeled F by Sargent and Kittredge). The other one, from Suffolk, has the Linko Clashmo refrain. These three refrains persist in America. Child traces the narrative back to an old tale, "The Wife Lapped in Morrill's Skin." A man finds himself coupled with a very cross and restive wife. He kills his horse Morrill, salts the hide, beats his wife in the cellar till she swoons, and then wraps her in the hide. On her recovery she is perfectly reformed. Child does not trace the ballad on the Continent.

Coffin lists about fifty references to the balad in America under three types. In A is the full story, including the reform of the wife; in B the man runs away to his father's house, declaring that his wife has lice; and in C the wife is beaten, sometimes without the dodge of the wether's skin. The ballad has been found in Nova Scotia, Maine, Vermont, Pennsylvania, West Virginia (FSS, no. 29, 5 texts; TBFWV, no. 13, 3); Virginia (TBV, no. 45, 12 texts; and MTBV, no. 39, 7); North Carolina NCF, II, IV, no. 44, 4 texts); Mississippi, Florida, Indiana, Missouri (BBM, pp. 92-94, 2 texts); Ozarks, Oklahoma, Texas, Colorado, and Utah. Lawless lists 6 in print.

Kentucky has not yielded very many versions of the ballad. There is one listed in the **Kentucky Syllabus,** Niles has one in BB, no. 59, and I have four texts. There is a related ballad in Appalachia called by my informant "The Bachelor Boy" (TSCF, no. 12) and by SharpK "The Holly Twig" (no. 53, 3 texts from Virginia). Miss Karpeles in her note (II, 397) cites four other appearances, three from England and one from JAF, 39:156.

The present (A) song, "Risselty Rasselty," was recorded by Bertram Draughn in 1961 from the singing of Mildred Creighton, both of Floyd County. The following (B) piece, "Nickety Nackety," is more obviously Child 277. It was collected without music in 1959 by Bonnie Ruth Lewis from the recitation of Lolita Ratliff Riggsby, both of Morgan County.

A

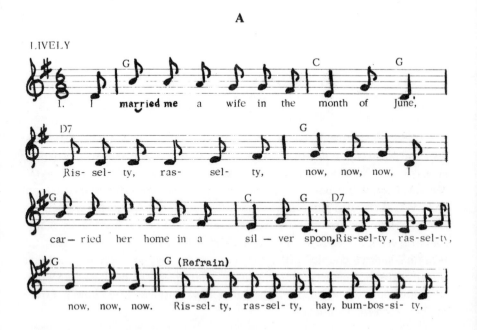

LIVELY

1. I married me a wife in the month of June,
Ris- sel- ty, ras- sel- ty, now, now, now, I
car— ried her home in a sil — ver spoon, Ris-sel-ty, ras-sel-ty,
now, now, now. Ris-sel- ty, ras-sel- ty, hay, bum-bos-si- ty,

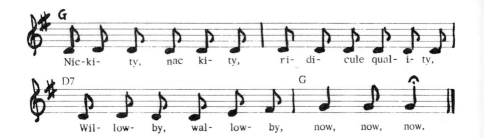

Nic-ki- ty, nac ki- ty, ri- di- cule qual- i- ty,

Wil- low- by, wal- low- by, now, now, now.

SCALE: Hexatonic (g a b d e f#).   MODE: Plagal.   RANGE: d'-b'
(Major 6th).   TONAL CENTER: G.   PHRASE STRUCTURE: A B A B
// C C B (2, 2, 2, 2, //, 2, 2, 2) or A A // B (4, 4, 6) barform.   MELODIC
RELATIONSHIP: The initial strophe of this nonsense song consists chiefly
of rapidly moving eighth-note rhythms in scalewise diatonic fashion, with a
refrain of patter-like character, and consisting almost wholly of the chant-like
repetition on the dominant tone D.
Cf. OFS III, p. 191, No. 439A, for general pitch levels and rhythmic pattern.

2. She combed her hair but once a year,
    Risselty rasselty now, now, now,
    With every rake she gave a tear,
    Risselty rasselty now, now, now.

    Refrain

3. She swept the floor but once a year,
    Risselty rasselty now, now, now,
    She swore the broom was far too dear,
    Risselty rasselty now, now, now.

    Refrain

4. She churned the butter in dad's old boot,
    Risselty rasselty now, now, now,
    And for a dasher she used her foot,
    Risselty rasselty now, now, now.

    Refrain

5. The butter came out a grizzley gray,
   Risselty rasselty now, now, now,
   The cheese took legs and ran away,
   Risselty rasselty now, now, now.

   Refrain

6. The saddle and bridle are on the shelf,
   Risselty rasselty now, now, now,
   If you want any more you can sing it yourself,
   Risselty rasselty now, now, now.

   Refrain

B

NICKETY NACKETY
(Child 277)

1. I married me a wife in the month of June,
   Nickety Nackety now now now,
   I escorted her home by the light of the moon,
   Nickety Nackety now now now.

   Refrain

   Nickety nackety nay down thackety
   Willity wallity rustico quality
   Nickety nackety now now now.

2. One day when I came in from the plow,
   Nickety nackety now now now
   Says, "Oh, my good wife, is my dinner ready now?"
   Nickety nackety now now now.

   Refrain:

3. There's a little piece of cornbread on the shelf,
   Nickety nackety now now now

If you want any more you can bake it yourself,
Nickety nackety now now now.

Refrain:

4. Oh, I went out behind the barn,
Nickety nackety now now now
And I cut me a hickory as long as my arm,
Nickety nackety now now now.

Refrain:

5. Then I went out to my sheep pen,
Nickety nackety now now now
And I grabbed me up an old sheep skin,
Nickety nackety now now now.

Refrain:

6. I laid that skin all around her back,
Nickety nackety now now now,
And with that stick I went whickety-whack
Nickety nackety now now now.

Refrain:

32. THE DEVIL'S SONG
(Child 278)

Child had only two texts of this humorous ballad, one English and one Scottish. He mentions others, one reworked by Robert Burns. He does not trace the ballad on the Continent, but he cites related folktales from the **Panchatantra** and from W. R. Ralston's **Russian Folktales,** p. 39. Other European folktales contain the ballad motifs, such as Types 810-814, **The Man Promised to the Devil;** and Type 1164, **The Evil Woman Thrown into the Pit.** The ballad has barely survived in Britain—three in England and one in Scotland (listed by Davis, MTBV, no. 40).

It has much more vigor and variation in America. Coffin lists about 70 references and sets up seven story types. It has been collected in Nova Scotia, Maine, Vermont, Pennsylvania, West Virginia (FSS, no: 30); Virginia (TBW, no. 66; MTBV, no. 40, 23 texts in all); North Carolina (SharpK, no. 40; NCF, II, IV, no. 45; BB, no. 60); Missouri (BSM, pp. 94-97, 2 texts); Ozarks, Oklahoma (BFSW, no. 53, one printed of 35); Texas, and Utah. Lawless lists 45 in print.

The ballad has not flourished in Kentucky. There is one text in BB, no. 60; one in Ritchie's **Singing Family** (pp. 143-144), and I have two. The present text, with its unusual cowboy refrain, was turned in without music by Mary Ellen Cobb in 1956, who says that she had it from Herbert Cobb, both of Knox County.

1. The old Devil come sneaking through the field,
    There is one in the family that I'm going to steal.
    It's neither your daughter, nor your oldest son,
    But it's the old woman for the crime she has done.

    REFRAIN:
    Come a Tie-y-yeppy, yeppy I yeppy aye,
    Come a Tie-y-yeppy yeppy aye.

2. The Devil come along, and put her in a sack,
    He looked like a peddler with a pack on his back;
    He took her home and throwed her down,
    And nine little devils come slipping around.

    REFRAIN

3. Nine little devils all tied up in chains,
    She up with a shovel, split out seven of their brains.
    One little devil peeped over the wall,
    Says, "Take her home, Daddy, she's going to kill us all."

    REFRAIN

4. Now you see what woman can do,
    They can out-do the devil,
    And their husband too.

    REFRAIN

33. SELLING THE COW
(Child 283)

Child had seven variants of this ballad, all broadsides and all from England. He describes it as "a specimen of its class." In it a farmer goes to pay his rent, is held up by a highwayman, but he throws his saddle over the hedge and escapes with the thief's horse and 600 pounds of gold and silver. Child summarizes other versions involving a girl going to sell corn, and a boy going to sell a cow ("The Yorkshire Bite"). Since Child designates these **in the class of** the "Crafty Farmer," some collectors include them as versions, others as related to or as secondary to no. 283. "The Crafty Farmer" has been found only twice in Britain since Child's time (in Scotland and in Devonshire: see NCF, II, 189); but "The Yorkshire Bite" has been found in Norfolk, Berkshire, and in Somerset (NCF, **ibid.**).

The ballad featuring the farmer has been found only in a single text in America (FSS, no. 31). The popular "Yorkshire Bite" has about fifteen references in Coffin. It has been collected in Newfoundland and in Nova Scotia. Three texts were recovered in Maine (BBM, pp. 406-413), and one in Vermont (a note in NGMS, p. 99, defends this 1769 version as older than Child's no. 283 of 1796). Three have been collected in North Carolina (NCF, II, IV, no. 20 and FSS, no. 30); West Virginia (FSMEU, pp. 149-152); Tennessee (FSSH); Michigan (BSSM, no. 157, one printed of three); Illinois (ASB, pp. 118-119); and Oklahoma.

This is the only text I am aware of from Kentucky. Most of the texts have refrains; the present one has a nonsense line very close to the NCF, B; "Like others, others to round tinty oh." It was sung for me in 1953 by Louise Bertrand, age about 65, from Pike County. She had learned it and a dozen such songs from her mother and from neighbors in her youth.

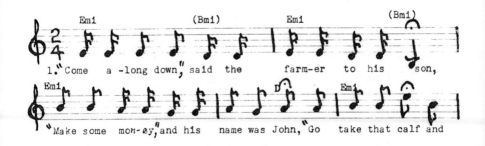

drive her to the fair, She's in good or-der and her I can spare, Lie

t'oth- er,_____ Rath-er ruther, ruther tum- a - ran-tannie-o.

SCALE: Pentatonic (e g a b d).   MODE: II; Plagal.   RANGE: b-e"
(Perfect 11th).   TONAL CENTER: E.   PHRASE STRUCTURE: A B C D
E F (2, 2, 2, 2, 2, 2) unusual structure. Possibly: A B C (4, 4, 4).   MELO-
DIC RELATIONSHIP: There are no tonal resemblances found in the numerous
variants of Child No. 283 examined. Note (again) the use of the fermata at the
cadences, for the purpose of either breath or memory.

2. He took that cow and he drove her in the ring,
    He didn't go far till he met with a man,

    . . . .
    He sold that cow for six times ten—
    Lie tother, rather ruther ruther tum-aran-tannie-O.

3. I'll fasten that money in my coatline, says he,
    Fear on the highway robbed on I'd be,
    Fine landlady all dressed so fine,
    Sewed that money in his coatline—
    Lie tother, rather, ruther ruther tum-a-ran-tannie-O.

4. The boy took a fright and he hurried right on.
    The highwayman mounted and he soon followed on,
    "Very well overtaken, very well," said he,
    "Very well overtaken on the main highway—"
    Lie tother, rather ruther ruther tum-a-ran-tannie-O.

5. They didn't go far until they struck a dark lane,
    He said, "Young lad, I'll tell you in plain,
    Your money I'll have without any strife,
    If you don't give it up, I'll end your sweet life—"
    Lie tother, rather ruther ruther tum-a-ran-tannie-O.

6. The boy jumped off and he quickly tore it out,
   In a high patch of weeds he strowed it all about,
   The robber jumped off and was picking up the strowed,
   The boy jumped on his horse and off he rode—
   Lie tother, rather ruther ruther tum-a-ran-tannie-O.

7. Didn't go far until he come to a door,
   Out come the old man kerthump on the floor,
   "What luck, what luck, sir," he cried with a curse,
   "Our old cow has turned into a horse—"
   Lie tother, rather ruther ruther tum-a-ran-tannie-O.

8. Took off his saddlepockets and begin to unfold,
   Found three thousand dollars in silver and gold,
   Two cases of pistols all loaded around,
   "Don't you think, old man, I've well sold your cow—?"
   Lie tother, rather ruther ruther tum-a-ran-tannie-O.

34. GOLDEN WILLOW TREE
(Child 286)

Child had three versions of the ballad for his entry. His A, from Pepys of 1682-85, names Sir Walter Raleigh in title and text, but Mr. Child is silent about the historical allusion. Some of the many variants of B and C appeared as stall-copies in Scotland. Variations in the narrative come mostly in the denouement. In A the ship-boy, refused his reward, sinks into the sea. In B he is thrown a rope and presumably he receives an estate as reward. In C he is refused the reward but is taken on board, dies soon after, and is buried in a cow-hide at sea. The ballad has been found since Child's time in tradition in England and occasionally in Scotland.

Coffin cites about 100 references to the ballad in North America. Although the American texts do not follow Child's A closely, they do rather often have its ending (Coffin's story Type A). It has been found in Newfoundland, New Brunswick, and Nova Scotia. In the United States it has been collected in Maine (BBM, pp. 339-347, 4 texts and a fragment); Vermont, Massachusetts, Pennsylvania, and in most states touching Appalachia—Virginia (TBV, no. 47, 6 and a fragment; MTBV, no. 43, one printed of 4); West Virginia (FSS, no. 32, 2 and a fragment; WVCS, no. 64; TBTWV, no. 15, 3); North Carolina (NCF, II, IV, no. 47, 6 texts and tunes, SharpK, no. 41, 3); Tennessee (ETFS, p. 37); Mississippi, Florida, and across the Midwest in Michigan, Indiana, Illinois, Wisconsin, Nebraska, Missouri (BSM, pp. 97-100, 3); the Ozarks, Oklahoma, and Utah. Lawless lists 88 in print.

Kentucky has yielded more texts of the ballad than has any other state. Three of the texts in the West Virginia collections came from Kentucky. There are six in SharpK (no. 41), and one or more in FSKM, E. M. Roberts's **The Great Meadow, KySyll.**, LT, BB, and I have three in my collection. The present version was turned in by Meta Back in 1961 from the singing of Jessie Gevedon, who learned it from her father in about 1910, all from Morgan County.

A

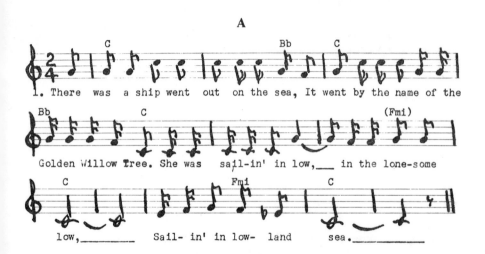

1. There was a ship went out on the sea, It went by the name of the Golden Willow Tree. She was sail-in' in low,___ in the lone-some low,_____ Sail-in' in low-land sea.___

SCALE: Tetratonic (c e♭ (e) f g) Inflected scale.   MODE: Authentic. RANGE: c' - c" (Perfect octave).   TONAL CENTER: C.   PHRASE STRUCTURE: A B C D (2, 2, 4, 3) unusual structure; possibly measures 7 and 8 result from undue prolongation on performer's part.   MELODIC RELATION-SHIP: See the following tune (variant B): "The Green Willow Tree", set to similar text. Observe in measure 9 the E-natural in ascending line, and the E-flat in descending, a practice of **musica ficta** that harkens back to medieval times. Cf. NCF, IV, No. 47A, on opening and closing phrases. Note the pre-dominant iterations of the tonic and dominant scale tones; also a touch of word painting - at least in stanza 1 - in measure 7, framing the word "low."

2. They had not sailed weeks more than two or three
   Till they espied the Turkish Revalee.
   She was sailing in low, in the lonesome low,
   Sailing in lowland sea.

3. I'll give you money and I'll give you fee,
   To my only daughter married you will be,
   If you'll sink her in low, in the lonesome low,
   If you'll sink her in lowland sea.

4. He turned upon his breast and away swam he,
   And he swam till he came to the Turkish Revalee,
   Sailing in low, in the lonesome low,
   Sailing in the lowland sea.

5. Some were playing cards and some were playing dice,
   And some were sitting around giving good advice,
   Sailing in low, in the lonesome low,
   Sailing in the lowland sea.

6. He had an instrument, he kept it for to use,
   And he made six holes, and the salt water gushed,
   Sailing in low, in the lonesome low,
   Sailing in the lowland sea.

7. Some with their hats and some with their caps,
   Trying to stop those salty water gaps,
   Sailing in low, in the lonesome low,
   Sailing in the lowland sea.

8. He turned on his breast and away swam he,
   And he swam till he came to the Golden Willow Tree,
   Sailing in low, in the lonesome low,
   Sailing in the lowland sea.

9. I'll not give you money and I'll not give you fee,
   Nor to my daughter married you will be,
   You sank her in the low, in the lonesome low,
   You sank her in the lowland sea.

10. If it wasn't for the love I have for your men,
    I'd serve you as I've served them,
    I'd sink you in low, in the lonesome low,
    I'd sink you in the lowland sea.

11. He turned on his breast and down sank he,
    He bid adieu to the Golden Willow Tree,
    Sailing in low, in the lonesome low,
    Sailing in the lowland sea.

B

MODERATELY

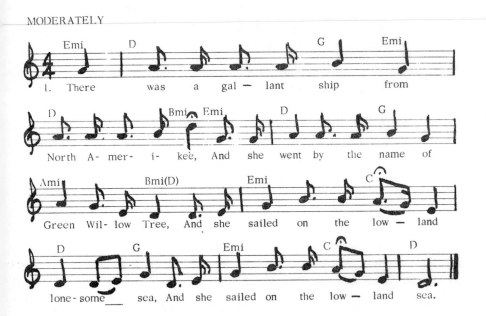

1. There was a gal — lant ship from North A- mer- i- kee, And she went by the name of Green Wil- low Tree, And she sailed on the low — land lone- some sea, And she sailed on the low — land sea.

SCALE: Pentatonic (g a b d e). MODE: III; Plagal. RANGE: d'-d"
(Perfect octave). TONAL CENTER: G; Circular tune. PHRASE STRUC-
TURE: A A^1 B B^1 (2, 2, 2, 2) or A B (4, 4). MELODIC RELATIONSHIP:
Cf. SharpK, I, 41C, "Golden Vanity," last two phrases. See "Golden Willow
Tree" in this collection for an entirely different setting. The fermatas in mea-
sures 4 and 6 can only be attributed to performance prerogative.

B. OTHER BRITISH BALLADS

35. O MOLLY DEAR
(Laws M 4)

This is a typical British import usually called "The Drowsy Sleeper," or "Awake, Awake," and has been collected many times in England. The early story is somewhat simple: A lover who has been fickle steals up to the constant girl's window and tries to make up. In some versions she refuses and he goes away with passion cooled. In elaborations of the story she calls him back, or lets him have his will, and then he leaves her in distress. In many texts in America he hears of a weapon in her father's hand. In the last stanzas of many texts the weapon is brought into use by the father. The lovers sometimes kill themselves with the weapon, a silver dagger. This Romeo and Juliet tragedy is also found in another ballad called "The Silver Dagger." See my no. 61 below.

The most complete notes and parallels are given by Belden (BSM, pp. 118-123). The most texts, ten in number, are given by SharpK, no. 57. Many other parallels are listed in NCF, II, IV, no. 71. This one was sung and tape recorded by Mildred Dupuy Webb, Greenup County, in 1959.

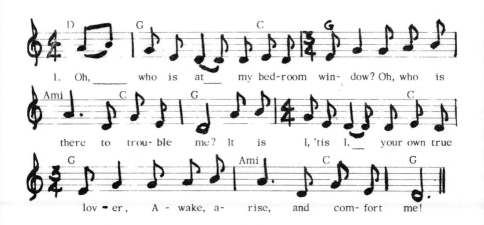

1. Oh,_____ who is at__ my bed-room win- dow? Oh, who is
there to trou- ble me? It is I, 'tis I,_ your own true
lov - er, A - wake, a- rise, and com- fort me!

SCALE: Pentatonic (g a b d e).   MODE: III; Plagal.   RANGE: d' - b'
(Major 6th).   TONAL CENTER: G; Circular tune.   PHRASE STRUC-
TURE: A B A B (2, 2, 2, 2), or A B (4, 4).   MELODIC RELATIONSHIP:
Cf. NCF, No. 71A, "The Drowsy Sleeper," where the first four measures show
similar melodic progressions. It is easy to imagine this tune being rendered in a
4/4 meter throughout; note consistency of metrical changes for both A and B.

2. O Molly dear, go ask your father
    If you my bride can ever be,
    And what he says come back and tell me,
    It's the very last time I'll trouble thee.

3. I dare not ask my father, Willie,
    For he lies on his bed of rest,
    And in his hand he holds a weapon
    To kill the one that I love best.

4. O Molly dear, go ask your mother
    If you my bride can ever be,
    And what she says come back and tell me,
    It's the very last time I'll trouble thee.

5. I dare not ask my mother, Willie,
    For she lies on her bed of rest,
    And in her hand she has a letter
    That often speaks of your request.

6. O Molly, Molly Melancholy,
    You've caused my poor heart to break,
    I've crossed the west lands of Kentucky,
    I've crossed the ocean for your sake.

36. THE GOOD SHIP CAME A-SAILING
(Laws N 8)

Upon the subject of disguises and tricks the broadside balladeers have
played almost endlessly but not too ingeniously. Professor Laws has sorted out

forty-three for the whole chapter, many of which are on the theme of girls disguising themselves and following their lovers to sea. The present piece is one of the shorter and less interesting ones. It has the often-used waist-fingers, cannon-ball and musket motifs. Its touching sentiment is in the seventh stanza: "If I should meet Mary. . ." Gardner and Chickering (BSSM, no. 61) name a very early broadside of this ballad, "The Undaunted Seaman. . . ," dated about 1690 and printed in **The Roxburge Ballads,** VII, 550. Belden (BSM, p. 178) gives two others of the 19th century: "The Youthful Damsel" and "Molly and William." Laws and Belden list the ballad in tradition in four shires of England.

In America it has had modest popularity. It has appeared in Nova Scotia (BSSNS, no. 35); in Virginia (SharpK, no. 121); North Carolina (NCF, II, IV, no. 99; JAF, 66:46); in Georgia (JAF, 44:99; FSSH, no. 42); and fragments in Iowa and the Bahamas.

Three texts have been reported from Kentucky: BKH, p. 106; FSMEU (p. 213, no. 99 (Laws N 7)); SharpK (no. 121C, tune). The present one was sung by James Hillman, Carter County, in 1959.

SCALE: Heptachordal (d e f# g a b c).   MODE: Mixolydian; Plagal.
RANGE: a - d" (Perfect 11th).   TONAL CENTER: D; note the emphasis
on the lowered 7th in measures 3 and 5.   PHRASE STRUCTURE: A B B A
(2, 2, 2, 2) Inverted reprisenbar.

2. There was a young farmer who lived with a neighbor by,
   Went to his best lover all with a broken sigh,
   Went to his best lover all for to let her know
   That he was bound to leave her far down some sea shore.

3. "Oh, stay at home, dear Willie, oh, stay at home," says she;
   "For sixteen weeks and better you know you've promised me,
   For sixteen weeks and better you know you promised me,
   Oh, stay at home, dear Willie, be kind and marry me."

4. "If I should stay at home, love, some other would take my place;
   Now, wouldn't that be a scandal, besides a great disgrace?
   When the captain calls for soldiers I for one must go,
   For I am bound to leave you far down some sea shore."

5. "My hair I'll cut off, men's clothing I'll put on,
   And go riding by your side, love, for to be your waiting one.
   I fear no men or danger, let them be ever so great,
   Like a true and faithful servant, upon you I will wait."

6. "You are little and slim around the waist, your fingers are too small,
   I fear you would not answer when upon you I would call,
   For the rifle balls doth whistle and the cannon balls doth fly,
   And the silver muskets on the ground where the dead and wounded lie.

7. "If I should meet my Mary upon the King's highway,
   Your riding by my side, love, what would my Mary say?"
   "Oh, Willie, oh, Willie, why couldn't I love her too?
   Why couldn't I step aside, love, while she would talk to you?"

8. "Oh, hold your tongue, my jewel, you have broken my tender heart,
   Now we'll get married before we ever part."
   So now these two are married and sailing o'er the main,
   May joy and peace go with them till they return again.

37. THE SILK MERCHANT'S DAUGHTER
(Laws N 10)

This is one of the typical broadsides of lovers' disguises and tricks. The girl falls in love with a porter in the household. The father forces him to flee; and the girl disguises herself and follows. Then on the sea, facing starvation, they draw lots to kill one. Her lover is the victim, she the one to kill him. It first appeared in thirty stanzas in 1794 titled "The Constant Lover," or "The Valiant Young Lady." Laws lists an English and a Scottish text.

In America it has appeared sporadically and in shortened form (seldom more than 16 stanzas): Newfoundland (BSSN, no. 15); it appears again in the Midwest (BSSM, no. 64; OFS, I, p. 222; BSI, no. 43); and in the South: West Virginia (FSS, no. 99 frag.); Virginia (SharpK, no. 4, FSV, p. 53); North Carolina (JAF, 28:160; NCF, II, no. 107, IV, no. 204; SharpK, no. 64); Mississippi (JAF 29:112; FSM, p. 148); and Florida (FSF, p. 395). Lawless lists 18 in print.

It has been found in Kentucky only twice to my knowledge, in SharpK, no. 64C, and in the KySyll. The present text was sung to Mrs. Ira Stacy and me by the preacher Verey Hamm of Rowan County in 1961. He had learned this and other folksongs and hymns from his father and his neighbors.

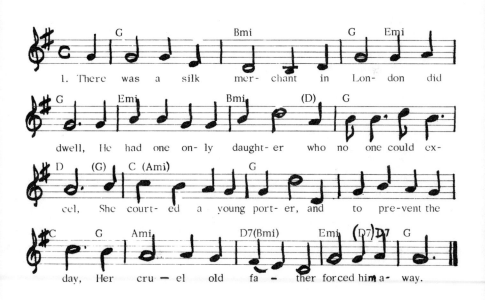

1. There was a silk mer-chant in Lon-don did dwell, He had one on-ly daught-er who no one could ex-cel, She court-ed a young port-er, and to pre-vent the day, Her cru-el old fa-ther forced him a-way.

SCALE: Heptachordal (g a b c d e f#).   MODE: Major; Plagal.   RANGE:
b' - d" (Minor 10th).   TONAL CENTER: G.   PHRASE STRUCTURE: A
B C D (4, 4, 4, 4).   MELODIC RELATIONSHIP: Cf. SharpK, I, No. 64,
phrases 1 and 2 closest; observe the "Scotch Snap" in measure 7.

2. First she lay madded and then she did mourn,
    Her dear loving porter would never more return,
    And then to follow him she quickly did conclude,
    She dressed herself in mandolee and after him pursued.

3. She sailed seas all over till she came to Bonville town,
    She walked into the city, she walked it up and down,
    At length she saw her porter standing on the street,
    She made it her business her truelove to meet.

4. Good morning, brother sailor, what ship do you belong?
    I came over on the Diamond, but now I'm going home.
    He said no more unto her but taking her on board,
    The captain inquired what she'd done with her sword.

5. According to the captain, this answer she gave,
    I fear that my sword my life it won't save.
    And while they all were sailing, at a distant length,
    The ship sprung a leak and to the bottom it went.

6. Provisions being scarce, death drawing nigh,
    Each one had to cast lots to see who would die;
    Cast lots, the captain shouted, and let us all see
    Among all the rest, who the murdered shall be.

7. Among all the rest this fair damsel was first,
    She had to die first to feed all the rest,
    But the saddest of misfortune that ever I did hear,
    Was this young lady to be murdered by her dear.

8. He called for a basin to catch her heart's blood,
    While leaning and trembling this fair damsel stood,
    Crying, Oh, my porter, my heart it doth bleed
    To think I'm here alone for poor hungry men to feed.

9. He called for a knife, the murder to do,
    Hold your hand, my loving porter, just for one word to two,
    I'm the silk merchant's daughter, from London I be,
    You see what I've come to by loving of thee.

10. She showed him a ring which between them was broke,
    This young man recognized it, in a moment he spoke,
    Crying, O my loving lady, my heart it doth burst,
    In hope of your long life, I will die first.

11. At that very moment they all heard a gun,
    Hold your hand, the captain shouted, we're near some ship or land,
    And in one half hour, or a little more,
    This ship of poor hungry men was safe upon the shore.

12. This couple they got married, this couple did agree.
    This couple they got married, this couple did agree,
    This couple they got married, he made her his wife,
    I'm sure that he loved her as dear as his life.

38. JOHN RILEY II
(Laws N 37)

The theme of the returning lover in disgusie proved so popular that the broadside composers used it again and again. Laws enters over a dozen on the one theme (ABBB, N 28-43). Some of the notes below for "The Soldier's Return" (N 42) overlap with the present ones, although "John Riley" is also a popular and distinct ballad in North America. Although the differences are minor, "John Riley I" has more specific details regarding the pretended death of Riley, and the lines have a different meter.

"John Riley II" has been found almost entirely in Appalachia. Aside from one text in Vermont (VFB), it has been collected in North Carolina (NCF, II, IV, no. 93; SharpK, no. 82, 4 texts); in Virginia (FSV, p. 49); in West Virginia (FSS, no. 95, "John Riley I"). It has been more popular perhaps in Kentucky than in any other state: SharpK, no. 82, 2 texts; Lomax, OSC, p. 168; LT, SFC, SCSM, DD, and I have six in my collection.

The present text was collected in 1957 by Charles Doll from the singing of Mrs. Elmar Mitchell, both of Whitley County. She had learned it from Molly Garland.

SCALE: Pentatonic (c d e g a).   MODE: III.   RANGE: c' - c" (Perfect octave).   TONAL CENTER: C.   PHRASE STRUCTURE: A B C D (2, 2, 2, 2).   MELODIC RELATIONSHIP: No analogous tune has been found by the editor.

2. I stepped up to her and I plainly asked her
    If she wouldn't be a poor sailor's wife.
    No, kind sir, I don't want to marry,
    I had rather live a single life.

3. Well, kind miss, what makes you differ,
    What makes you so far from all woman kind?
    You are young and a youthful damsel,
    You might marry or you might decline.

4. Well, kind sir, I'll tell you about it.
    I could have been married three years ago
    Unto a man named John Riley
    He is the cause of my overthrow.

5. He courted me both late and early,
   He courted me both night and day,
   Until he gained my heart's affection.
   Then he turned and sailed away.

6. Turn your back on Riley and forget him
   And go with me to a distant shore,
   We will sail over to Pennsylvania
   And bid our friends adieu for evermore.

7. I won't go with you to Pennsylvania,
   I won't go with you to a distant shore,
   My heart is for Riley and I can't forget him
   Although I may never see him any more.

8. He found out she loved him dearly,
   And he gave her kisses one, two, three,
   Saying this is the man whose name is Riley
   Who has been the cause of your misery.

9. If this is the man whose name is Riley,
   I'll go with you to a distant shore,
   We'll sail over to Pennsylvania
   And bid our friends adieu for evermore.

39. THE SOLDIER'S RETURN
(Laws N 42)

Ballads with a disguise theme began to appear in England in the late 18th century. The hero in these is generally a sailor who, on return, is concerned with identity. The later, somewhat shortened, texts in America often feature a soldier. Although he has usually been away for seven years, he names marriage in the first stanza. Laws lists two English broadsides, both in the Harvard collection. Belden (BSM, p. 148) lists many printings of it in Scotland, Ireland, Wales, and in six shires of England. Child admitted one version of this kind of story to his collection (no. 105).

In America it has had wide distribution: Nova Scotia, Massachusetts, West

Virginia (FSS, no. 92, WVCS, no. 18); Virginia (SharpK, no. 98; SCSM p. 260); Tennessee (ETWVMB, p. 64; FSSH, no. 59, ETSFF, p. 80); North Carolina (NCF, II, no. 92, one printed of eleven, IV, 15 tunes; SharpK, no. 98; FSSH, SCSM, p. 24); South Carolina, Georgia, Mississippi, and Texas. Lawless lists 60 in print.

Only three or four texts have been printed from Kentucky, although it is very popular wherever I have collected. One is in LT, p. 88; one in BHK, p. 77; JAF 22:67; TSCF, no. 14; and I have ten or so in my files. The present text was recorded from the singing of Mrs. Omeda Holbrook, Leslie County, in 1957.

SCALE: Hexatonic (g a b d e f#).   MODE: Plagal.   RANGE: d'-b" (Major 6th).   TONAL CENTER: G.   PHRASE STRUCTURE: A B A[1] C (2, 2, 2, 2) or A A[1] (4, 4).   MELODIC RELATIONSHIP: See "Pretty Little Miss" in this collection for a close variant. This particular version of the tune has not been found in the numerous collections examined:

2. Go way, go way, you handsome young soldier,
    You're not the man to marry me;
    I have a true lover in the army
    And he's far o'er the sea.

3. I have a true lover in the army,
   For seven long years he has been gone,
   And if he's gone for seven years longer,
   No other man shall marry me.

4. Perhaps he's on some ship and drowned,
   Perhaps he's on some battle field dead,
   Perhaps he's took some girl and married;
   Your loving boy you'll never see no more.

5. If he is on some ship and drowned,
   If he is on some battle field dead,
   If he has took some girl and married,
   I love that girl for loving him.

6. I am the man that you want to marry,
   I've just returned from o'er the sea.
   I could have married the King's only daughter
   But I have returned to marry thee.

40. BRAVE LIEUTENANT
(Laws 0 25)

The story narrated in this ballad has had a long and varied adventure. It once was told in Spain in the sixteenth century when conquistadors sailed the Spanish Main. It was treated in poetic form by Schiller in Germany, and by Hunt and Browning in England. In these treatments the proud lady usually gets slapped in the face with the recovered fan or glove.

The oldest ballad form is a broadside in **Percy Broadsides** of the eighteenth century. In it the point turns on the old saying: only the brave deserve the fair. The captain decides to return the fan or die. In the present text it is the other way round. Perhaps the reversal of roles in some versions is no more than a slip in transmission, but it has given a title "Bold/Brave Lieutenant" to some variants, including the present one. Other broadsides listed by Laws are from a Scottish Chapbook and from the English James Catnach. The ballad has some currency in English and Scottish tradition.

In America it has been collected in Nova Scotia, Vermont, Connecticut, Indiana, Ohio, and North Carolina (NCF, II, IV, no. 89). It has been somewhat popular in Kentucky. Hubert G. Shearin furnished a text for the article with G. L. Kittredge in **Modern Language Notes** (26: 113, 167); there is one in JAF, 49: 227; and the four in SharpK, no. 66, are from Kentucky.

The present text was recorded by Myrle Kinder in 1961 from the singing of Olieda Martin, both of Rowan County.

1. Down in Carlisle there lived a lady, A lady most beautiful and gay. She said she aimed to live a lady, And none on earth could her betray.

SCALE: Pentatonic (f g b^b c e^b).   MODE: IV, Plagal.   RANGE: c'-e^{b}" (Minor 10th).   TONAL CENTER: F.   PHRASE STRUCTURE: A B B^1 C (2, 2, 2, 2) or: A B^1 (4, 4).   MELODIC RELATIONSHIP: Cf. NCF IV, No. 89, for general relationship of tonal material; SharpK, I, No. 66B, "The Bold Lieutenant," similarities phrases 2 and 4.

2. He must be a man of honor,
    The bravest man on land or sea;
    Then there came two gallant lovers
    This fair young maiden for to see.

104

3. One of them was a brave lieutenant,
   A man of honor and a man of war,
   The other was a bold sea captain,
   Belonged to a ship called **Colonel Carr.**

4. Then she ordered a horse and carriage,
   A horse and carriage at her command,
   And then up rode these gallant lovers
   Until they came to a lions' den.

5. There they stopped and there they halted,
   And the young men stood gazing around,
   And for the space of a half an hour
   The girl lie speechless on the ground.

6. When at last she did recover,
   She threw her fan in the lions' den,
   Saying, Which of you to gain this lady
   Must return to me my fan again.

7. Then up spoke the brave lieutenant,
   He raised his voice most readily high,
   Saying, I am a man, a man of honor,
   I'll return to you your fan or die.

8. Down into the lions' den he wandered,
   The lions looked most fierce and grim,
   He ranged and ranged around among them
   And then retired out again.

9. When she saw her lover coming,
   And saw to him no harm was done,
   She threw herself all on his bosom,
   Saying, This is the prize that you have won.

10. Then up spoke the bold sea captain,
    He raised his voice most readiy high,
    Into this lonely woods I'll wander
    And conceal my body where none can spy.

41. THE BUTCHER BOY

(Laws P 24)

Although this English broadside is somewhat modern, it has become crossed with one or more similar stories, especially "There is an Alehouse in Yonder Town." Also its title varies from city to city including London, Jersey, Jefferson, and others. The crossing seems to account for the awkward change in point of view in the ballad—from first to third person.

Laws gives the synopsis and valuable data as usual. Of his three broadside references, one is a Philadelphia print, giving the setting as Jersey City. Perhaps a hundred different references are given in the headnotes in Laws, BSM, FSS, and NCF. It has been collected in Nova Scotia, Vermont, Massachusetts, New York, and in many Appalachian states: West Virginia (FSS, no. 145, 2 and a fragment); Virginia, North Carolina (NCF, II, IV, no. 81, 14 texts, not all printed, 3 tunes); Georgia, Florida; and in the Midwest: Missouri (BSM, p. 201, 8 and a valuable note), the Ozarks (OFS, I, 226, 5); Texas, and Wyoming. Lawless lists 108 in print.

Only two other texts seem to have been found in Kentucky—the Florida (FSF, p. 334) and one in **KySyll.** I recorded the present text in 1954 from the singing of Buell Kazee, who had learned it in his youth in Magoffin County. He recorded many songs for Brunswick in the 1920's.

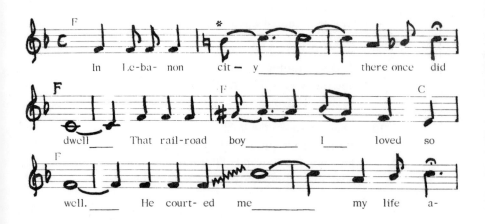

In Lebanon cit—y____ there once did dwell____ That rail-road boy____ I____ loved so well.____ He court-ed me____ my life a-

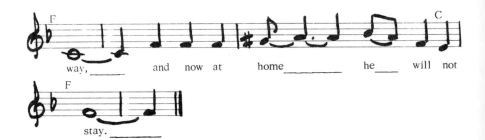

way,_____ and now at home_____ he____ will not

stay._____

SCALE: Hexatonic (f g# a b (b♭) c e) Inflected scale.   MODE: Plagal.
RANGE: c' - c" (Perfect octave).   TONAL CENTER: F.   PHRASE
STRUCTURE: A B A¹ B (4, 4, 4, 4) or A A¹ (8, 8).

* Note the appogiatura ornamentation in measures 1, 2, 5, 9 and 12, a bit reminiscent of the Scotch snap. The glissando in measure 8 was probably intended to equate with the effect in measure 1.

2.   There is a place in Lebanon town
     Where that railroad boy goes and sits down;
     He takes a strange girl on his knee
     And he tells to her what he won't tell me.

3.   She went upstairs to make her bed
     And not one word to her mother said;
     Her mother she went upstairs too,
     Said, Daughter, dear daughter, what troubles you?

4.   O mother, O mother, I cannot tell,
     That railroad boy I love so well,
     He's courted me my life away
     And now at home he will not stay.

5.   Her father he came in from work,
     Inquiring for his daughter she seemed so hurt;
     He went upstairs and the door he broke
     And found her hanging on a rope.

6.   He took he knife and cut her down
     And in her bosom these words he found;
     Go dig my grave both wide and deep
     Place a marble slab at my head and feet.

7. ....
....
And over my coffin place a snow white dove
To warn this world that I died for love.

42. PRETTY POLLY
(Laws P 36)

This story first appeared in England in 1750 as a garland or broadside titled "The Gosport Tragedy, or the Perjured Ship's Carpenter." It was composed by some ballad maker and seller, presumably using some actual happening. It had thirty-five quatrains.

The story though long-drawn-out is as follows: A ship's carpenter while on shore leave courts a young and beautiful mason's daughter. Though she pleads that she is too young and that her parents do not approve, she continues to listen to his vows—that he will go to heaven for her, or will anchor his ship and stay with her. She soon finds herself with child and then when he is to sail pleads for an honorable wedding. He sets a time and trysting place and leads her to a new-made grave on which he has dug most of the night. She pleads now for a life of disgrace, but he stabs her and buries her there.

His ship sets sail and soon the steward sees the ghost of a maiden with an infant in her arms. It is an omen of murder and disaster. The captain calls the crew together and threatens hanging if the murderer does not confess. Willie confessed killing Mary and he "Died raving distracted that same night."

Laws gives the title "The Cruel Ship's Carpenter" and a synopsis of the broadside at no. P 36, A, B. B shows how it has been modified and reduced from "The Gosport Tragedy" to "Pretty Polly." His notes and bibliography are succinct and up-to-date, but as he says, they are not intended to be exhaustive, especially for Britain. (Note that his numbering runs consecutively through NAB and ABBB from A to Q.)

The ballad has been collected in Newfoundland, Nova Scotia, and is widespread in Appalachia and the South. Representative texts with notes are as follows: FSS, no. 89 (3 texts); TBFMWV, no. 17 (2 texts) NCF (no. 264, 5 texts, IV, tunes to C, E, E(I)); SharpK, no. 49 (21 texts, 4 from North Carolina, 1 from Tennessee, 4 from Virginia, and 12 from Kentucky); FSF, p. 341; and OFS, II, no. 153 (3 texts). It has been quite popular in Kentucky, as these notes indicate:

The twelve in SharpK; one or more in SSSA, p. 53; FKH, p. 69; LT, p. 79; FSMEU (via W. Va.); JAF (20: 262; 40:276); and TSCF, no. 11. Lawless lists 69 in print. I have six texts in my collection. The present one was collected by Mrs. Myrle Kinder in 1961 from the singing of Olieda Martin and her husband, all from Rowan County.

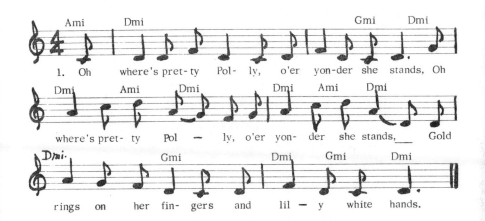

1. Oh where's pret-ty Pol- ly, o'er yon-der she stands, Oh
where's pret- ty Pol — ly, o'er yon- der she stands,___ Gold
rings on her fin- gers and lil — y white hands.

SCALE: Pentatonic (d f g a c).   MODE: II; Plagal.   RANGE: c' - d" (Major 9th).   TONAL CENTER: D.   PHRASE STRUCTURE: A B A[1] (2, 2, 2).   MELODIC RELATIONSHIP: Cf. NCF, IV, No. 64E (1) for general relationship; also SharpK, I, p. 49, "The Cruel Ship's Carpenter," version H, although in different meter compare first and final phrases for almost identical relationship; also, FSKH, p. 35, "The Gosport Tragedy," variant A.

2. O Polly, pretty Polly, come an' go along with me,
O Polly, pretty Polly, come an' go along with me,
Before we get married some pleasure to see.

3. I led her up the hollow and the wilderness so deep,
I led her up the hollow and the wilderness so deep,
Poor little Polly to mourn, cry, and weep.

4. O Willie, O Willie, I'm afraid of your ways,
O Willie, O Willie, I'm afraid of your ways,
I'm afraid you are leading my body astray.

109

5. O Polly, pretty Polly, you're guessing about right,
    O Polly, pretty Polly, you're guessing about right,
    For I dug on you grave the biggest part of last night.

6. We went on a few steps farther and what did we spy,
    We went on a few steps farther and what did we spy,
    A newly dug grave and a spade lying by.

7. She threw her arms around me, said spare my dear life,
    She threw her arms around me, said spare my dear life,
    Let me live a single girl if I can't be your wife.

8. O Polly, pretty Polly, that never can be,
    O Polly, pretty Polly, that never can be,
    For your bad reputation will follow after me.

9. I stabbed her to the heart and the heart blood did flow,
    I stabbed her to the heart and the heart blood did flow,
    Way down in the grave pretty Polly did go.

10. I threw the dirt over her and started for home,
    I threw the dirt over her and started for home,
    Left no one behind her but the little birds to moan.

11. A ship came a-sailing along the seaside,
    A ship came a-sailing along the seaside,
    And Willie mounted the ship for a ride.

12. He rode the ocean over his heart to content,
    He rode the ocean over his heart to content,
    The ship struck an iceberg and to the bottom it went.

13. O Polly, pretty Polly, she's now gone to rest,
    O Polly, pretty Polly, she's now gone to rest,
    O where's little Willie? In hell I guess.

43. ST. JAMES INFIRMARY
(Cf. Laws Q 26)

Although I had heard this blues song in Kentucky as early as the 1920's, I now find that it has not often come into the net of other collectors. There are two texts of a ballad in SharpK (no. 131) titled "St. James's Hospital." The story of the first text is simple: A father goes down to the hospital and finds his son dying. The remainder of A and all of B are variants of the "Streets of Laredo."

"The Streets of Laredo," the "Dying Cowboy," and perhaps other homiletic western pieces are really our American versions of the British broadside "The Unfortunate Rake," with a bad-girl relative called "The Young Girl Cut Down in Her Prime." Notes for these related pieces are best studied by Belden (BSM, pp. 392-398), Cox (FFS, no. 53), and indexed by Laws (ABBB, Q26, "Bad Girl's Lament," and NAB, B1, "Dying Cowboy"). See the 12 texts and one tune in NCF, II, IV, no. 263. Lawless lists 11 in print.

The present piece seems to be a Negro blues adaptation of the "Unfortunate Rake." It was sung by Orin Nelson for Sophia Keeney, Greenup County, in 1959.

*SCALE: Pentatonic (d f (f#) g a c) Inflected scale.   MODE: Irregular; Plagal.   RANGE: c' - d" (Major 9th).   TONAL CENTER: D. PHRASE STRUCTURE: A B A^1 C (2, 2, 2, 2) or A A^1 (4, 4).

* There are four occurrences of the F#, and excepting the ornamentation of F-natural in measure 6, two occurrences of the latter. If F-natural were considered the important scale step then the mode would be Pentatonic II. Note the "blues" element in final two phrases.

2. I went down to St. James Infirmary
    And I heard my baby moan,
    Stretched out on a long white table,
    So cold, blue, and alone.

111

3. I went down to St. James Infirmary,
    And I saw my baby there,
    Stretched out on a marble table,
    So cold, blue, and fair.

4. Sixteen coal black horses,
    All formed in a line,
    In the carriage she's a-ridin'.
    Goodby, sweetheart of mine.

5. When I die, pretty women, please bury me,
    Six more to sing a song,
    Got my pockets full of moonshine whiskey
    And I'll drink as the world rolls on.

44. BABES IN THE WOODS
(Laws Q 34)

This popular tragic story was first put into poetic form in England in the time of Shakespeare. He and other poets and dramatists in their poetry and plays refer to the belief that a robin will cover an unburied corpse. Later the story of the babes appears in the Pepys collection of about 1682, and in Thomas Percy's **Reliques** (II, 155-160). In these early variants the story is detailed and complex and comprises about twenty stanzas. A full summary of the narrative may be given as follows:

The parents of a boy of five years and a younger girl are on their deathbed. They reveal to the children's uncle a large sum of money that is for the boy when he reaches twenty-one and for the girl when she marries. When they ask the uncle to care for them he says, "I will as if they were my own children."

Later he plots a way to obtain the money—by murdering the babes. He hires two "ruffians" to take them, ostensibly to the city for schooling, but in reality to kill them. The two assassins quarrel over the rightness of the deed, and the more lenient ruffian kills the hard-hearted one. He then leaves the babes in the woods and never returns. The uncle does not prosper. His family die one by one and his stock and other property dwindle away. He dies in a debtor's prison. In the meantime the lenient ruffian falls afoul of the law for robbery and is to hang. He reveals the tragedy of the little babes and his part in it.

Laws in his notes gives the common title "The Children in the Wood" and lists several broadsides besides the ones given above, including **Roxburghe Ballads, II, 216, and** eleven English, Irish, and Scottish versions in the Harvard Library collection; and that it was registered in England in 1595.

Most texts in America are shorter than the twenty stanzas mentioned. None have been printed in Canada apparently. It has been found in Vermont, Michigan (BSSM, no. 141, longest text seen—19 stanzas); Indiana (BSI, no. 71); West Virginia (SharpK, no. 47, FSV, p. 38, TBMWV, p. 89, FSMEU, p. 216); Florida (FSF, p. 401); Missouri (BSM, p. 106); and NCF, II, no. 147. Lawless lists 25 in print.

Only one other text has been found in Kentucky: FSKM, p. 103. The present one was recorded by Mrs. Mildred D. Webb, Greenup County, in 1959.

SCALE: Heptachordal (c d e f g a b).   MODE: Major.   RANGE: d'-d" (Perfect octave).   TONAL CENTER: C.   PHRASE STRUCTURE: A B A^1 C (4, 4, 4, 4) or A A^1 (8, 8).   MELODIC RELATIONSHIP: This tune probably emanates from the late 19th century; possibly somewhat earlier.

2. And when it was night so sad was their plight,
    The moon went down, the stars gave no light,
    They set and sighed and they bitterly cried,
    The poor little babes they laid down and died.

3. And when they were dead, a robin so red
   Brought strawberry leaves and over them spread,
   And sang them a song the whole day long,
   The poor little babes, the poor little babes.

45. BILLY BOY

This is a rather old and widely known nursery song. It was current in England by 1787, as found in **Scots Musical Museum,** and it has appeared in nursery collections from then on. See Halliwell, **Popular Rhymes and Nursery Tales,** pp. 258-263. Almost any American collection or folklore journal contains a version. The items in the song vary from a few to a total of about twenty questions altogether (NCF, V, no. 121). Lawless lists 72 in print.

My version was sung by Mrs. Mary S. Nelson, Greenup County.

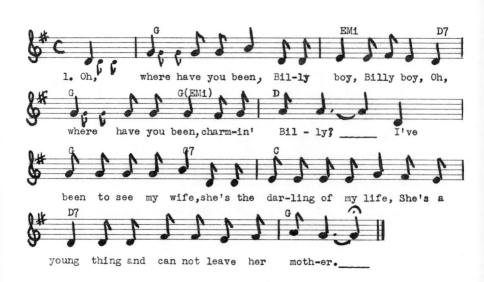

SCALE: Hexatonic (g a b d e f#). MODE: Plagal. RANGE: d'-b' (Major 6th). TONAL CENTER: G. PHRASE STRUCTURE: A B A[1] C (2, 2, 2, 2) or A A[1] (4, 4). MELODIC RELATIONSHIP: Cf. Bronson TTCB, No. 12, variant 13, closest of 29 variants.

2. Did she ask you to come in, Billy boy, Billy boy,
   Did she ask you to come in, charmin' Billy?
   She asked me to come in, with a dimple in her chin,
   She's a young thing and cannot leave her mother.

3. Is she fit to be a wife, Billy boy, Billy boy,
   Is she fit to be a wife, charmin' Billy?
   She's as fit to be a wife as a fork is to a knife,
   She's a young thing and cannot leave her mother.

4. Can she bake a cherry pie, Billy boy, Billy boy,
   Can she bake a cherry pie, charmin' Billy?
   She can bake a cherry pie quick as a cat can wink its eye,
   She's a young thing and cannot leave her mother.

5. Does she often go to church, Billy boy, Billy boy,
   Does she often go to church, charmin' Billy?
   Yes, she often goes to church with a bonnet white as birch,
   She's a young thing and cannot leave her mother.

6. How old is she, Billy boy, Billy boy,
   How old is she, charmin' Billy?
   She is six times seven, forty-eight and eleven,
   She's a young thing and cannot leave her mother.

46. FROGGIE WENT A-COURTIN

The most comprehensive notes available are in Opie and Opie **Nursery Rhymes,** no. 175. They trace it to its first mention in the English Stationers in 1580 and further say, "The earliest extant text is in Ravencroft's **Melismata** of 1611 where the tune 'The Marriage of the Frogge and the Mouse,' is made up of 13 verses, beginning:

It was the Froggie in the well,
Humble-dum, humble-dum,
And the merrie Mouse in the Mill,
Tweedle, tweedle, twino.

They reveal that "The Frogge's Courtship" and the nursery rhyme "The Frogge in the well" were once one song. They are so annotated in SharpK.

A history of the song is traced by Kittredge in JAF, 35(1923): 394. Full lists of parallels are in SharpK, nos. 220, 221, and 15, as well as in BSM, pp. 494-499, 7 texts, some titled "Kitty Alone." The most texts are found in NCF, III, no. 120 (27 versions, not all printed; one, "Kitchie Ki-Mi-O," in an appendix was adapted for a blackface minstrel a hundred years ago); V, 10 tunes, plus appendix items, making 37 instances of the song in the Brown collection. It is only modestly reported in Kentucky: LT, SharpK, FSSUS. Lawless list 182 in print.

The present item was sung by Orin Nelson for his wife Mary in Greenup County in 1959.

SCALE: Pentatonic (f g a c d). MODE: III; Plagal. RANGE: c'-d" (Major 9th). TONAL CENTER: F. PHRASE STRUCTURE: A B A^1 B^1 A^2 B^3 B (2, 2, 2, 2, 2, 2, 2,) or A A^1 A^2 (4, 4, 6). MELODIC RELATIONSHIP: Cf. NCF V, No. 120E, L, and EE, for tonal and rhythmic variants; SharpK, II, No. 220, versions E, F, and H; BFSS, No. 120, p. 251, beginning and end; ABFS, p. 310, "Frog went a-courtin'." See: "Crawdad Man" in this collection for almost identical tune.

116

2. He rode up to miss mousie's door, uh, huh,
   He rode up to miss mousie's door, uh, huh,
   He rode up to miss mousie's door,
   He knocked so hard he made it roar, uh, huh.

3. Miss mousie come down and let him in, uh, huh,
   Miss mousie come down and let him in, uh, huh,
   Miss mousie come down and let him in,
   The way they courted it was a sin, uh huh.

4. He took miss mousie upon his knee, uh huh,
   He took miss mousie upon his knee, uh huh,
   He took miss mousie upon his knee,
   And said Miss mousie won't you marry me? uh huh.

5. Uncle rat gave his consent, uh huh,
   Uncle rat gave his consent, uh huh,
   Uncle rat gave his consent,
   The weasel wrote the punishment, uh huh.

6. Where shall the wedding supper be, uh huh,
   Where shall the wedding supper be, uh huh,
   Where shall the wedding supper be?
   Way down yonder in a hollow tree, uh huh.

7. What shall the wedding supper be, uh huh,
   What shall the wedding supper be, uh huh,
   What shall the wedding supper be?
   Two green beans and a black eyed pea, uh huh.

8. Froggy went swimming across the lake, uh, huh,
   Froggy went swimming across the lake, uh, huh,
   Frogy went swimming across the lake,
   He got swallowed by a big black snake, uh huh.

C. AMERICAN BALLADS

47. WORLD WAR I SONG
(Laws A 15)

"Banjer" Bill Cornett of Knott County was the most outstanding banjo performer in the whole region and knew perhaps 300 folksongs. He sang in the trenches of World War I and then in the 1930's he gave the WPA collectors most of his songs, many of which have been issued by the Archive of American Folksong, Library of Congress. In 1960 three students of mine sought him out and recorded nine pieces, including "Barbara Allen" (above) and the present piece. Suddenly, Bill died of a heart attack while serving the state in congress at Frankfort. The joint houses held a memorial service featuring his banjo on a garlanded pedestal.

Mr. Cornett said on the tapes that this ballad related an experience of his in the World War I and was his own composition. This is only partially true. The first two stanzas are new; the others are adapted from "The Drummer Boy of Shiloh" (Laws A 15). For references see FSSH, no. 132; OFS, II, no. 239; NCF, II, no. 230 (2 texts and a fragment); FSMEU, p. 208. Mr. Erwin Silber (SCW, pp. 119-120, 140-142) names the author as William Shakespeare Hays of Louisville, Kentucky, prolific writer of 300 pieces, including "Little Old Log Cabin in the Lane."

The present piece was recorded by Catherin Nickles, Charles Patton, and Bulah Patrick, all of Knott County.

na- tive   land_____   To   fight   a   for — eign   foe.

SCALE: Tetratonic (e^b g b^b c).   MODE: Plagal.   RANGE: b^b - $e^{b''}$ (Perfect 11th).   TONAL CENTER: Eb.   PHRASE STRUCTURE: A B B^1 C (2, 2, 2, 2).   MELODIC RELATIONSHIP: Cf. NCF IV, No. 27 Al "Bonny Barbara Allan." This song, of relatively recent origin in the eastern hills of Kentucky, has the metric freedom and ad-lib style so peculiarly indigenous to the unsophisticated folk singer; yet, it is singularly charming in its unaffected simplicity. It was performed in an almost **Sprechstimme** fashion.

Note the use of the "Scotch snap" rhythm in the first three phrases.

2.   My mind goes back to those bloody days,
Of a friend I left behind,
There is no way that I can find,
That'll ease my worried mind.

3.   In the Argonne Forest and bloody ground,
Where the dead and dying lay,
Hermana was a friend of mine,
Who beat the drum that day.

4.   We gathered around this little Greek,
His drum was by his side,
He raised his hand and closed his eyes,
And prayed before he died:

5.   "Have mercy on our battlefield,
O Lord, our Heavenly Friend,
Have mercy on each sinful soul."
Each soldier cried Amen.

6.   As we gathered around our dying friend,
With hung down heads we cried,
And listened to the drummer boy,
Who prayed before he died.

7.   Well, angels at the throne of God,
Look down upon the brave,
Who fought and bled in the Argonne Forest,
Now slumbering in the grave.

48. DYING COWBOY
(Laws B 1)

This ballad is sometimes called "The Cowboy's Lament" or "The Streets of Laredo." It is a homiletic piece telling how the singer has done wrong and warning others. Its subject was once something else in the eastern states and was carried out west by young adventurous men and adapted to the barroom. The literary adventures of the song are fascinating to the folksong student, and may be stated as follows.

This was once an Irish homiletic ditty, sung in Cork around 1790. It was soon found in many shires of England titled "The Unfortunate Rake," unfolding the story of a dying soldier, now in the hospital. Quite frankly and bitterly he laments the treachery of a woman who gave him a disease and did not tell him in time, else he could have·got "salts and pills of white mercury," but now he says, "I'm cut down in the height of my prime." He requests an honorable burial and a military funeral: "Muffle your drums, play your pipes merrily and fire your guns right over my coffin" (Belden, BSM, pp. 392 - 393).

While still in England the second adaptation occurred. The sexes were reversed in order to warn the women. In "The Bad Girl's Lament" or "The Young Girl Cut Down in Her Prime" the scene is in St. James's Hospital. The girl rues her fall from the dance-hall to the ale-house to the poorhouse and death. She is begging her mother for a decent funeral: red roses for her coffin and as pallbearers six young sailors (Laws, ABBB, Q 26). A third and possibly simultuneous adaptation was the sailor's warning. In "The Sailor Cut Down in His Prime" a dying seaman in the hospital requests his father to hold up his aching head. The father promises soldier pallbearers, three young ladies with red roses, and perfume (SharpK, no. 131). See also NCF, II, IV, no. 263, for similar text and tune. Lawless lists 75 in print.

Texts of these many forms of the ballad have been found in America from Nova Scotia to Missouri. The last adaptation of course was to "The Cowboy's Lament" (see Barry, BFSSNE, 7:16-18). For Kentucky see FSMFU, pp. 180-209; BC, p. 419. My text, with first three stanzas missing, was sung by Mildred D. Webb, Greenup County, in 1959.

LIVELY

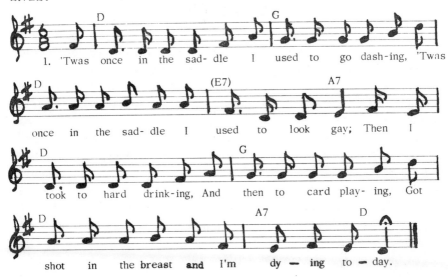

1. 'Twas once in the sad-dle I used to go dash-ing, 'Twas once in the sad-dle I used to look gay; Then I took to hard drink-ing, And then to card play-ing, Got shot in the breast and I'm dy — ing to — day.

SCALE: Hexachordal (d e f# g a b).   RANGE: d' - d'' (Perfect octave).
TONAL CENTER: D.   PHRASE STRUCTURE: A B A B¹ (2, 2, 2, 2) or
A A¹ (4, 4).   MELODIC RELATIONSHIP: For an almost identical tune
with slightly varied text Cf. NCF, IV, p. 296, No. 263, "The Unfortunate Rake."
Also, Cf. "The Cowboy Song" in this volume for same tune with different
metrical setting.

On close examination one can find a remarkable parody with "Believe me if all
those Endearing Young Charms."

2. Go bring to my bedside a bunch of young cowboys,
   And tell them the history of a comrade's sad fate,
   Tell each one another before they go further
   To stop the bold rambling before it's too late.

3. Go take this message to my gray-headed mother,
   Go break the news gently to sister so dear,
   But there is another far dearer than Mother
   Who'll weep when she knows I am dying out here.

4. Go beat the drums slowly, and play the fife lowly.
   Go play the death marches as you carry me along,
   To the graveyard they'll take me, throw the green sod o'er me,
   For I'm a gay cowboy and dying alone.

121

49. TRAIL TO MEXICO
(Cf. Laws M 1)

This is one of the typical British broadsides that have been brought to America and reworked as they journeyed across the land. A possible source of this song has been traced to a blackletter broadside of the 17th century in England titled "The Seaman's Complaint." In our country, versions of it have been found titled "Early in the Spring." Its story is of a Scottish seaman who goes to fight for his king, promising to marry his fair one when next they meet. After seven years he returns and her father says, "She has married for riches' sake." He curses money and girls that prove untrue. Though entreated to marry one kinder than she was, he will sail to America and cut his way where the bullets fly and sail on the sea until he dies. Texts and notes are found in Belden (BSM, p. 163), Cox (FSS, no. 111), and four texts in SharpK, no. 125, all from North Carolina. See also NCF, II, IV, no. 87.

By the early 1900's a cowboy version of the song began to be sung in the West titled "Trail to Mexico" (not to be confused with "Buffalo Skinners" or "Hills of Mexico," Laws, B10.) The nearest variant that I have seen is that of Sandburg's ASB, p. 285 which he heard in Fort Worth, Texas. The Lomaxes give a composite, including a refrain, also from Texas (CS, pp. 52-56).

The present text was collected by Betty Salisbury from the singing of Oscar McKinney, Floyd County, in 1961.

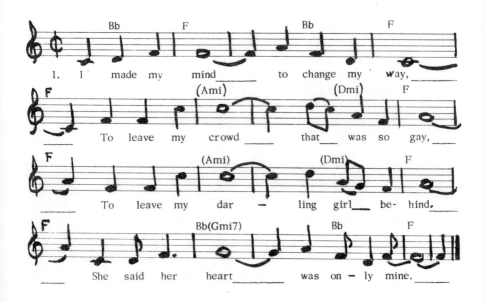

1. I made my mind to change my way,
To leave my crowd that was so gay,
To leave my dar — ling girl be- hind.
She said her heart was on — ly mine.

SCALE: Pentatonic (f g a c d).   MODE: III; Plagal.   RANGE: c'- d"
(Major 9th).   TONAL CENTER: F.   PHRASE STRUCTURE: A B B[1]
A[1] (4, 4, 4, 4) Inverted reprisenbar.   MELODIC RELATIONSHIP: The tune
is reminiscent of "Oh, bury me not on the Lone Prairie," especially in phrases
2 and 4. For another version of the same tune see OFS II, p. 84, No. 148A, "The
Rambling Boy."

2.   It was in the year of '83,
     When A. J. Stanton hired me,
     He said, "Ole boy, I want you to go,
     And follow my herd into Mexico."

3.   It was early in the year,
     I volunteered to drive those steers,
     I tell you boy it's a lonesome old go,
     As the herd rolled into Mexico.

4.   When I arrived in Mexico,
     I thought of the girl whom I loved so,
     I wrote a letter to my dear,
     Not one word in return did I hear.

5.   When I reached my own love's home,
     I mourned for the girl I thought my own,
     She'd wed a richer lover,
     Poor young feller, you'll have to seek another.

6.   O curse your gold and your silver, too,
     Curse the girl that won't prove true,
     I'll go back to the Rio Grande,
     And get me a job in a cowboy band.

7.   O buddy, O buddy, please stay at home,
     Don't leave forever on the roam,
     You'll find girls here more true than some,
     O please don't go where the bullets hum.

8.   I'll go back where the girls are true,
     False-hearted love I never knew,
     I'll go back where the bullets fly,
     And stay on the calf trail till I die.

50. THE BREAK AT JERRY'S ROCK
(Laws C 1)

This is the only evidence of this river-driving tragedy that I have seen from Kentucky. It came from a family of singers on the Ohio who have furnished me with at least a hundred songs. It is found abundantly in the Northeast from Nova Scotia (BSSNS, no. 153) to Maine; also in Pennsylvania, West Virginia, the Lake states, the Dakotas, and Oregon.

According to Barry's notes (BFSSNE, X, 18-20) my text is of the older Type I, because of the opening stanza with the rhyme be . . . me and the mention of finding only the head of the foreman Monroe. The facts related in this ballad have been difficult to authenticate. However, Mrs. Fannie Eckstorm (MM), who worked twenty years on this problem, came to the following conclusions.

The tragedy must have happened to a group of Canadian river drivers, working on the Seboois River in Maine during the Civil War. Though there was a Jerry's Rock on the East Branch of the Penobscot River, causing log jams and giving rise to tragedy and song, she believes that these Canadians probably did not know this but wrote their elegy from a similar incident at Grand Falls of the Seboois in the 1860's. The Jerry designation (only a few miles away) and the maiden (ending close to the rose-briar motif) were added by later singers. See Laws (NAB, pp. 63-65, 143) for summaries of the story and of the ballad. Lawless lists 29 texts in print.

The present version was sung by Orin Nelson for his wife Mary, both of Greenup County, in 1959.

bout some true-born shan-ty boys, so man-ful — ly and brave. It was
on a jam at Jer — ry's Rock where they met with a wa— t'ry grave.

SCALE: Pentatonic (d f g a c). MODE: II; Plagal. RANGE: c' - d"
(Major 9th). TONAL CENTER: D. PHRASE STRUCTURE: A B B¹ A¹
(2, 2, 2, 2) Inverted reprisenbar. MELODIC RELATIONSHIP: See "Lula
Vower" in this collection, first phrase only; also, **ibid.**, "California Joe" on opening and closing phrases. Cf. SharpK, II, No. 121, "William and Polly," on first
two phrases and general melodic contour.

2. It was on one Sunday morning
In the springtime of the year,
The logs were piled up mountain high,
We could not keep them clear;
But six of our brave shanty boys
Volunteered to go
To break the jam of Jerry's Rock
With the foreman Young Monroe.

3. They had not moved but a log or two
Till the boss he did say,
I'll have you boys be on your guard,
This jam will soon give way;
Scarely had these words been heard
Till the jam did break and go,
Carried off six of our brave shanty boys
And our foreman Young Monroe.

4. They roused up them poor shanty boys,
The sad news they did hear,
For to hunt for their lost comrades,
To their sad grief and woe,
All cut and mangled on the beach
Was the head of Young Monroe.

5. They taken him from the watery grave,
   Brushed back his raven hair,
   There's one sad form among them
   Whose cries rung the air;
   A lady from Sagnalt Town,
   Her sighs and cries
   They rung the air
   When her truelove he was drowned.

6. Miss Claire was a noble girl,
   Ike was her rightful friend,
   Her mother was a widow lady
   Lived near the Sagnalt Bend;
   About six weeks or better
   She was called to go;
   The last words she said to them
   Was to be buried by Young Monroe.

51. KENNY WAGNER
(Laws E 7)

Wagner, a bad man, presumably is still serving a life sentence in the Mississippi state pen. He murdered a sheriff in that state in the 1920's and fled to Tennessee. After breaking jail he was at large until caught and arrested by a woman sheriff in Texarkana. He was returned to Mississippi, tried, and sentenced to life for several murders.

A ballad in the third person titled "Kenny Wagner" has been collected in Mississippi, Alabama, and Arkansas. Another ballad in the first person (as the present text) has been recorded in many Southern states titled "Kenny Wagner's Surrender." Notes on the event and on the ballads may be found in ETSFF, p. 67 (3rd person version, p. 83), NCF, II, IV, no. 245, different tune to a different text.* It has been collected in Mississippi (FSM) and in Florida (FSF). My text was recorded by Mary Stuart Nelson, Greenup County, in 1959, as sung by her husband Orin.

* Tune is quite different, no similarity.

1. I'm sure you've heard my sto-ry From the Ken-ny Wag-ner song. It was down in Mis-sis-sip-pi, Where I took the road that's wrong.

SCALE: Hexachordal (e^b f g a^b b^b c). RANGE: $e^{b'}$ - c'' (Major 6th).
TONAL CENTER: E^b. PHRASE STRUCTURE: A A^1 A^2 B (2, 2, 2, 2) or A A^1 (4, 4).

2. I went from Mississippi
   To the state of Tennessee,
   They sent two men before me,
   For to take my liberty.

3. At first I started drinking
   And then I pulled my gun,
   And within a single moment
   The deadly work was done.

4. Young men, young men, take warning,
   Come take my last advice,
   Don't start the game of life wrong,
   You'll surely pay the price.

5. I rambled through the country
   But I never could find rest,
   Till I went to Texicana,
   Away out in the West.

6. The sheriff was a woman,
   She got the drop on me,
   I quit the game and surrendered,
   Gave up my liberty.

7. Young men, young men, take warning,
   Come take my last advice,
   Don't start the game of life wrong,
   You'll surely pay the price.

52. ROWAN COUNTY CREW
(Laws E 20)

In the 1920's a book came into our home called **Life Among the Hills and Mountains Of Kentucky** by W. R. Thomas, 1926. In it was a long poem called "The Rowan County Troubles." We read it aloud and one of my younger brothers memorized it. Our parents did not wholly approve of our excessive interest in the poem, and Mother would sometimes forbid us from going through it. She dreaded especially the last line.

Most American feuds but especially those in the border states and in Appalachia can be traced back to the great divide—the War between the States. After this war people knew crime, felt life cheapened, and saw that all people were not equal—that there could be injustice, lawlessness, and treachery.

Therefore the Rowan County troubles arose out of past war feelings, ties of blood, and the open ballot. Officers of the Confederate Army, and there were many in Appalachia who joined the Southern forces, returned to their mountain homes and for various reasons—hurt and pride mostly—they ran for office on the Democratic ticket against the strong victorious Republicans. Factionalism developed, voting became a key to loyalty, and sides were chosen.

From 1874 to 1884 factional bitterness increased in Rowan County. Sharp and shrewd campaigning raked the feelings of the county in choosing a High Sheriff. On election day in 1884, at the polling place in the courthouse of Morehead, the county seat, sharp words were passed, fists flew, pistols were fired. Solomon Bradley was killed, and Sheriff Day and John Martin were wounded, the latter in the forehead by a pistol butt.

Martin lived a mile east of the town. In a few months his wound was healed but the scar shone livid on his brow. Though no one knew for sure who hit John, he was of the fixed opinion that Floyd Tolliver made the throbbing scar. When he came into town in December in his wagon with his wife and two small sons, he ran into Tolliver and quarrelled about the row before. Pistols blazed. Tolliver fell dead. Martin was arrested and taken to jail.

To avoid trouble and mob action the authorities took Martin across two counties to the Winchester jail. The open murder and this caution by the judge (and his delaying the trial) aroused some hotheads to action. Five men appeared before the Winchester jailer with an order for the return of Martin to Morehead. The jailer, Martin, and his wife (in town) were uneasy and suspicious. However, the jailer felt bound to honor the order. They handcuffed the man and boarded the train. His wife, of course, bought a ticket and returned also.

At a small village called Farmers twelve miles from Morehead the train was stopped. Armed and masked men came aboard and shot the helpless Martin, who died in iron bands.

The feud was on now in earnest and lasted until 1888. State troops were called to the county on two occasions and were requested several more times. There were two pitched battles on the streets of Morehead. Of the 800 citizens of the town about half moved away before the troubles were put down (Thomas, BMMK, pp. 1-9; DD, pp. 148-150; James Watt Raine, **Land of Saddle Bags,** pp. 150-157).

The ballad of the Martin-Tolliver feud has only one form. Thomas gives the author as James W. Day of Rowan County. It is pretty well confined to Appalachia and the Ozarks (OFS, II, no. 169). This text was sung by Frances Ingram, Fleming County, to Mrs. Myrle Kinder, Rowan County, in 1961.

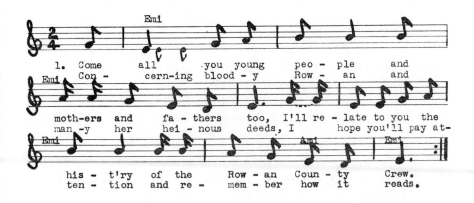

1. Come all .you young peo - ple and
Con - cern-ing blood - y Row - an and

moth-ers and fa - thers too, I'll re - late to you the
man -y her hei - nous deeds, I hope you'll pay at-

his - t'ry of the Row - an Coun - ty Crew.
ten - tion and re - mem - ber how it reads.

SCALE: Pentatonic (e g a b d).   MODE: II; Plagal.   RANGE: d'-b'
(Major 6th).   TONAL CENTER: E.   PHRASE STRUCTURE: A B A B
(2, 2, 2, 2) or A A (4, 4).   MELODIC RELATIONSHIP: Cf. SharpK, I, No.
6A "The Banks of Sweet Dundee," phrase 1, phrase 4 with our phrase 2. Our
tune most probably has discarded a B-phrase commonly found in other versions.

2. It was in the month of August, all on election day,
   John Martin he was wounded, some say by Johnny Day;
   Martin couldn't believe it, and he could not think it so,
   He thought it was Floyd Tolliver that shot the fatal blow.

3. They shot and killed Sol Bradley, a sober innocent man,
   To leave his wife and seven children to do the best they can;
   They wounded young Ed Sizemore, although his life was saved,
   He had learned to shun the grogshops by being so near the grave.

4. They shot and killed the deputy sheriff, Bumgardner was his name,
   They shot him from the bushes after taking deadly aim;
   The death of him was dreadful, may it never be forgot,
   His body was pierced and torn by thirty-three buckshot.

5. John Martin did recover, some months had come and passed,
   All in the town of Morehead those two men met at last;
   Tolliver and a friend or two about the streets did walk,
   He seemed to be uneasy, and no one wished to talk.

6. They stepped in Carrey's grocery, they stepped up to the bar,
   But little did he think he had met his fatal hour;
   The sting of death was near him, Martin rushed in at the door,
   A few words passed between them concerning the row before.

7. The people all got frightened and rushed out of the room,
   A ball from Martin's pistol laid Tolliver in his tomb;
   His friends were all gathered around him, his wife to weep and wail,
   John Martin was arrested and soon confined to jail.

8. He was put in jail at Rowan, there to remain a while,
   In the hands of law and justice waiting to stand his trial;
   The people talked of lynching him, at present though they failed,
   So Martin's friends removed him to the Winchester jail.

9. Some people forged an order, their names I do not know,
    The plans were soon agreed upon, for Martin they did go;
    Martin seemed discouraged, his life was in a dread,
    They've thought of a plan to kill me, to the jailer Martin said.

10. They put the handcuffs on him, his life was in distress,
    They hurried to the station, got on the night express;
    Along the line she lumbered, all at her usual speed,
    They weren't but two in number to commit this dreadful deed.

11. Martin was in the smoking car, accompanied by his wife,
    They did not want her present when they took her husband's life;
    When they arrived at Farmer, they had no time to lose,
    The men approached the engineer and told him not to move.

12. They stepped up to the prisoner with pistols in their hands,
    In death he soon was sinking, he died in iron bands,
    His wife she heard the horrid sound, she was in another car,
    She cried, "O Lord, they've killed him," when she heard the pistol fire.

13. The death of those two men have caused a great trouble in our land,
    Caused men to leave their families and take a parting hand,
    Reconciliation they never, never see.
    I wish that I could only see our land once more at peace.

14. I composed this as a warning, beware you young men,
    Your pistols will cause trouble, on this you can depend,
    All in the bottom of a whiskey glass a lurking devil dwells,
    It burns the breath of those that drink and sends their souls to hell.

53. THE JEALOUS LOVER
(Laws F 1)

This is a simple stark story of a lover stabbing his girl friend for no stated reason. Because no other details are given as to time and place, just the intriguing names of Edward and Ellie, this may be considered an improvement over its broadside form. This one and related murder ballads, such as "The Knoxville Girl" and "Pretty Polly" (Laws P 35 and 36 A and B, see 42 above) stem from Old World broadsides. For studies of the relationship of these and other ballads, see Phillips Barry, **American Speech,** III, 441-447; Laws, NAB, pp. 65-70, 184-188; and Wilgus, AFSS, pp. 288-290.

The present ballad is quite popular in America and has been found from Canada to Wyoming. Important notes and references are given in BSM, pp. 324-330 (18 texts, not all printed); NCF, II, no. 250, 23 texts, IV, 9 tunes to 5 titles; FSS, no. 38; OFS, II, no. 138 (10 texts, not all printed). Lawless lists 117 in print. It was collected in 1959 by Mrs. Sophia Keeney, age about 55, from the singing of Mrs. Violet Belford, both of Greenup County.

The following no. 54, "Pearl Bryan," is not the ballad of the girl whose head was never found. It is labeled F 1, The Jealous Lover (b) (Pearl Bryan II) by Laws. It was recorded by Mrs. Meta Back, age about 45, Morgan County, in 1960. She said of it: "I learned 'Pearl Bryan' from a little girl friend while I was going to school at Flat Woods when I was small."

SCALE: Heptachordal (e^b f g a^b b^b c d).   MODE: Major; Plagal.
RANGE: d' - c" (Minor 7th).   TONAL CENTER: E^b.   PHRASE STRU-
TURE: A B A B^1 (4, 4, 4, 4) or A A^1 (8, 8).   MELODIC RELATIONSHIP:
See "Pearl Bryan" (next tune) for a different setting of this ballad.

2. Come out, my lovely wonder,
   And cross the meadow gay,
   We'll walk and talk and ponder
   And name our wedding day.

3. Oh, Edward, they will miss me,
   I can no longer stay,
   The night grows dark and dreary
   And I can't retrace my way.

4. You'll trace your way no never
   In this wide world to roam,
   So bid your neighbors good-by,
   At least your friends at home.

5. Oh, out in the woods I have you,
   No one to hear your cry,
   You did not do as I bid you,
   Now, Ellie, you must die.

6. Down on her knees before him,
   She pleaded for her life,
   Into her snow white bosom,
   He plunged the fatal knife.

7. Oh, Edward, darling Edward,
   This was her dying breath,
   She threw her arms around him,
   Then closed her eyes in death.

8. The stranger come by in the morning,
   Found her lying on the sod,
   Where she may sleep and slumber
   And dream about her God.

54. PEARL BRYAN

1. Down, down in yon-der val-ley,
Where the flow-ers fade and bloom,
Our own Pearl Bryan is sleep-ing
In a cold and si-lent tomb.
She died not bro-ken heart-ed,
Nor by dis-ease she fell,
But in an in-stant part-ed
From her home she loved so well,

SCALE: Pentatonic (a^b b^b c e^b g).   MODE: Irregular; Plagal.   RANGE: e^b' - e^b'' (Perfect octave).   TONAL CENTER: A^b.   PHRASE STRUC-TURE: A B A B[1] // C C A B[1] (2, 2, 2, 2, // 2, 2, 2, 2; or A A[1] // B A (8, 8, 8, 8) Reprisenbar.   MELODIC RELATIONSHIP: See previous tune, "Jealous Lover."

2. One night when the moon shone brightly
   And the stars were shining too,
   Up to her cottage window
   Her dearest lover drew.
   Come, Darling, let us wander
   Through the valley deep and gay,
   Come, Darling, let us ponder
   Upon our wedding day.

3. Deep deep into the forest
   He led his love so dear,
   Said she, It's for you only
   That I would ramble here,
   For the night is cold and dreary
   And I'm afraid to stay,
   Besides, I'm tired and weary
   And I'll retrace my way.

4. Retrace your way no never,
   These woods you'll roam no more,
   No one, no power can save you,
   Pearl Bryan, you must die.
   What have I done, Scott Jackson,
   That you would take my life?
   You know I've always loved you
   And would have been your wife.

5. Farewell, my dear old parents,
   My face you'll see no more,
   Long long you'll wait my coming
   At your little cottage door.
   Farewell, my darling sister,
   Our peaceful happy home,
   Farewell, my dear old schoolmate,
   With you no more I'll roam.

6. While the birds were singing sweetly
   Their bright and glorious songs,
   They found Pearl Bryan's body
   On the cold and silent ground.

Come all you fair young ladies
Who choose to look this way,
Never put your trust in a young man,
For he will lead you astray.

55. OMIE WISE
(Laws F 4)

Though this narrative song is confused with an English love murder called
"The Oxford Girl," it is now clearly established as a separate North Carolina
murder, thanks to the researches of Belden, Hudson, and Schinhan, in NCF, II,
IV, no. 300 (8 texts, 2 tunes). From their documents the story runs as follows:

In 1808 in a sparsely settled community where new Salem now stands, there
lived a kind-hearted William Adams. He had taken in an orphan who grew into
a beautiful young woman and good house helper. Her name was Naomi Wise.

She was courted by a powerful young man, a bully from an aggressive
family from Polecat Creek, named Jonathan Lewis. Jonathan's mother, seeing
his attraction for Naomi, persuaded him to pay attention to his boss's daughter,
who was of a fine and wealthy family. Jonathan did not make much headway
with the rich girl and soon had his will of Naomi by promising to marry her. The
news of his promise and of Naomi's disgrace leaked out.

Jonathan arranged with Naomi to meet him at Adams' spring and take her
to be married. She brought her things and rode with him to Deep River. His
horse forded the stream to an island. Here he helped her down, tied her dress
over her head, and held her under the water until she drowned. Someone on the
river bank heard a scream in the dusk. Next morning when her body was found,
Jonathan came and stroked her hair—and denied the crime. From jail he
escaped for several years. He was traced to Kentucky and brought back for trial,
but was acquitted.

The ballad is found in many American collections, especially in Appalachia
and the South: In FSSH, 5 texts; BSM, 6 texts and references; OFS, 7; ETSFF,
p. 64. Laws (NAB, F4) gives a full listing of texts and recordings. Lawless lists 54
in print.

Kentucky has yielded only a modest number of versions: one of those in
BSM; a fragment in KFR, I (1955): 87; FSSUS, 209-210 (2 listed); and one in BS.
This ballad was sung in 1959 by Mrs. Elizabeth Elsbee, who had heard it from
Mrs. Trace Hamilton, both of Rowan County.

1. Come, lis – ten to my stc – ry of lit – tle O- mie Wise, And how she got de- lud- ed by John-ny Lew — is's lies. He told her he loved her, he told to her lies, He pro- mised to mar- ry her, to mar- ry O — mie Wise.

SCALE: Hexatonic (b^b c e^b f g a^b).   MODE: leans toward Mixolydian mode. Plagal.   RANGE: b^b - c" (Major 9th).   TONAL CENTER: B^b. PHRASE STRUCTURE: A B A B^1 (2, 2, 2, 2) or A A^1 (4, 4).   MELODIC RELATIONSHIP: Cf. NCF IV, No. 300A, almost identical except for different time signature and notational changes. For another version see "Tragic Romance" in this volume.

2.   He promised to meet her down by the old mill stream,
     He'd bring her some money, some other fine things;
     She ran like a fool to the cold water spring,
     But he brought her no money, no other fine things.

3.   He said, "Jump on behind me, we'll take a fair race,
     And when we get married, it'll be no disgrace."
     She jumped on behind him and away they did go,
     Down by John Adams' where the deep waters flow.

4.   They rode out in the waters and there they stopped to talk,
     She threw her arms around his neck, but there he pushed her off.
     Two little boys were fishing down by the river brink,
     They spied little Omie before she did sink.

5. They ran to the town and there they spread the news
   That Omie was drownded, poor Omie, Omie Wise.
   They went and got her out and they brought her to the bank,
   Her clothes were all wet, so they laid her on some plank.

6. They sent for John Lewis and brought him to the place,
   And set him right before her so he could view her face,
   "Right now I'll quit my rambling, I'll tell no more lies,
   Right now I'll confess that I drownded Omie Wise."

56. ROSE CONNOLEY
(Laws F 6)

This piece is more often called "Rose Connoley," or "Down in the Willow Garden," the victim's usual name, or the first line of the song, though it has some kinship to other murder ballads, especially "The Jealous Lover" and "The Knoxville Girl." It seems to be specific enough to be based on a separate crime. It was first mentioned in the 1911 **KySyll.** Mr. Cox (FSS, no. 91) reports two texts from West Virginia dated 1915 and 1917. It has appeared in scattered Appalachian collections since these dates. Alan Lomax declares it a West Virginia ballad (FSUSA, p. 302; FSNA, p. 261). See NCF, II, no. 67, 2, and IV, 2 other versions with tunes.

The present text was collected by Mary S. Stuart, Greenup County, in 1959 from the singing of her husband Orin.

1. Down in the wil - low gar - den, Where
me and my true love did meet, While

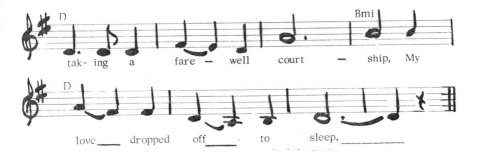

tak- ing a fare — well court — ship, My
love____ dropped off____ · to sleep._____

SCALE: Pentatonic (d e f# a b).   MODE: III; Plagal.   RANGE: a - d"
(Perfect 11th).   TONAL CENTER: D.   PHRASE STRUCTURE: A B C D
(4,4,4,4).   MELODIC RELATIONSHIP: NCF IV, No. 67 has three versions,
A, B, B[1], which are close in both tonal and rhythmical relationship; SFSEA, No.
129, phrase three.

2.   A knife in my coat pocket,
     But it wasn't for her to know,
     I murdered that fair young maiden
     Down under the banks so low.

3.   I taken her by her yellow hair
     And drug her over the ground,
     And threw her in the river
     That flowed to Knoxville town.

4.   For my father often told me
     That his money would set me free,
     If I would murder that fair young girl
     Whose name was Rose Connoley.

5.   Now my father sits in his cottage door
     With many a wishful eye,
     Looks upon the gallows
     Where his son soon has to die.

6.   My name is Patty McGreer,
     My name I don't deny,
     For the murder of a fair young girl
     On the scaffold I must die.

57. LULA VOWER
(Laws F 10)

This murder was committed in Floyd County, Kentucky, in 1917. Because the ballad has had limited distribution, a thorough study of the circumstances has not been made. Since I grew up in the territory (but can't recall ever hearing about this event), I can give general data, as follows.

John Coyer grew up at Auxier, a railroad stop and mining community on the Big Sandy River in Floyd County. He had courted Lula Viers before joining the Army in World War I. When he came back on a furlough and visited his girl friend, he evidently found himself inconvenienced—the girl was pregnant. How he got her to board the local train is unknown in detail, but they went up the river to the end of C & O line at Elkhorn City. There he drowned the girl, weighting the body with a piece of steel as the ballad says. The body washed a hundred miles down the Big Sandy into the Ohio, and was found below the mouth of Big Sandy at Ironton, Ohio.

The boy was brought back (or caught at) home and put in jail. The Army authorities came for him and evidently without much trouble gained his release and he went back into service. Apparently he never came back.

A text of the ballad close to those I have seen was recovered by Jean Thomas (BMMS, pp. 144-146). It is printed in full and discussed by Laws (NAB, pp. 66-70). I have two more texts in my collection and edited another for KFR, 1956, 60-62. The present variant was turned in to me by Nettie Cantrell in 1960 from the singing of her mother, Mrs. Clyde Cantrell, both of Morgan County.

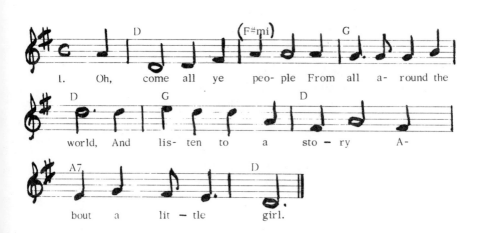

1. Oh, come all ye peo-ple From all a-round the world, And lis-ten to a sto—ry A-bout a lit—tle girl.

SCALE: Hexachordal (d e f# g a b).   RANGE: d' - e" (Major 9th).
TONAL CENTER: D.   PHRASE STRUCTURE: A A¹ B C (2, 2, 2, 2) or
A B (4, 4).   MELODIC RELATIONSHIP: Cf. "The Break at Jerry's Rock"
in this volume.

2. Her name was Lula Voyer,
   At Auxier she did well,
   A town in old Kentucky,
   A place you all know well.

3. She courted young Collier,
   Engaged to be his wife,
   Till he ruined her reputation,
   And stold her sweet little life.

4. Lula was persuaded
   To leave her dear old home,
   And board the morning train
   With John Collier to roam.

5. They went to Elkhorn City,
   Sixty-six miles away,
   And remained there at a hotel
   Until the close of day.

6. And then when darkness fell,
   They went out for a stroll,
   It was in December
   And the wind was blowing cold.

7. They stood there by the river,
   Cold waters running deep,
   Johnny said to Lula,
   "At the bottom you must sleep."

8. She threw her arms around him,
   "I pray you spare my life,
   And take me back to Mama
   If I cannot be your wife."

141

9. He tied her hands behind her,
   Before him she did kneel,
   And then he tied to her
   A piece of railroad steel.

10. He threw her in the water,
    Bubbles rising around,
    A bustle on the water,
    It was a sad and mournful sound.

11. John Collier joined the army,
    It was many months did pass,
    And in the Ohio River
    Her body was found at last.

12. They took her from the water
    And carried her up to town,
    The steel around her weighed
    Even thirty-six pounds.

13. They went for a printer,
    His name was Earl Dent,
    He printed in the paper,
    Around the world it went.

14. Her mother read the news,
    Sitting in her home,
    She quickly left her chair
    And rushed to the telephone.

15. She sent a message to Ironton,
    Saying, "I'll come and see
    The body of my own daughter,
    But surely it cannot be."

16. When she arrived at the place,
    She saw the clothes her daughter wore,
    And when she spied the corpse,
    Fell fainting on the floor.

17. They arrested young John Collier
    And sent him to county jail,
    None of his relation,
    Not one would go his bail.

18. They will send him to prison,
    Or lock him in a cell,
    Send him to the electric chair,
    And forward him on to Hell.

58. ELLEN SMITH
(Laws F 11)

This ballad is a short-lined version relating Peter DeGraff's side of the story of Ellen Smith's murder. A longer version in twelve stanzas is given by Belden and Hudson (NCF, II, no. 305). Their Number 306 in eight ballad stanzas is not very close in content to mine. The full circumstances of this murder are not detailed but some are given under no. 305 and by Ethel Richardson (AMS, p. 32). These facts are as follows:

In the 1890's near Winston-Salem, North Carolina, Peter DeGraff had been seeing Ellen Smith. Some texts say, presumably in his own words, that he loved the girl but would never have made her his wife. Ellen is suddenly found shot to death with a letter in her bosom written in Peter's handwriting.

He apparently disappeared and was known to have been in Roanoke, Virginia, and in New Mexico. He was brought back and tried in Forsyth County. He was sentenced to be executed for the crime, an appeal being denied by a higher court. While awaiting the death sentence he called for a guitar and composed a ballad voicing his surprise when he learned that Ellen had been killed.

Some texts of the ballad, as this present one, have the man confessing jealousy for committing the crime. One or more texts are in FSSH, FSKH, BKH, BS, FSM, WVF, 7:65. My version was sung with banjo accompaniment by Mary Wright, collected in 1959 by Mary S. Nelson, both of Greenup County.

1. Poor El-len Smith, Where was she found? Shot through the heart, ___ ly-ing cold on the ground.

SCALE: Pentatonic (f g a c d). MODE: III. Plagal. RANGE: c'-c" (Perfect octave). TONAL CENTER: F. PHRASE STRUCTURE: A B C D (2, 2, 2, 2). MELODIC RELATIONSHIP: Cf. NCF, IV, 305A, p. 326, for almost identical tunes. Simple and naive as our tune is, there seems to be a bit of drama in the descending lines of the first three phrases. Note the framing of the question in the antecedent phrase, and the straightforward answer in the consequent.

2. I asked her to marry me,
   Her answer was "No,"
   I shot her through the heart
   And she fell dead in the snow.

3. She fell to the ground
   With her hand on her breast,
   The sheriff and the blood hounds
   They gave me no rest.

4. They picked up their rifles,
   They hunted me down,
   They found me a-loafing
   Around near the town.

5. They took me to Richmond,
   A trial to stand,
   To live or to die
   As the law may demand.

6. The Jury found me guilty,
   The clerk wrote it down,
   They sentenced me to die
   Down in Frankfort town.

7. If I could go back home
   And stay when I go,
   Around poor Ellen's grave
   Pretty flowers I'd grow.

8. To all you good people
   This story I did tell,
   How I murdered poor Ellen
   'Cause I loved her too well.

59. SHUT UP IN THE MINES OF COAL CREEK
(Laws G 9)

Although there are only 5 texts of this song available, the facts of this mine disaster are already confused. George Korson (CDF pp. 275-277) gives the following basic facts: Eighty-four men and boys, out of a total payroll of eighty-nine, died in the Cross Mountain mine explosion at Briceville, Tennessee, on December 9, 1911. He quotes a United Mine Workers district president, William Turnblazer: "This ballad was composed and sung by Thomas Evans, who died a few years ago at Esserville, Virginia." Korson's first stanza begins "Fellow friends and miner boys," and the second stanza names the date as given above. The copy collected by Henry (SSSA, pp. 84-85) in Breathitt County, Kentucky, begins "Hello friends and miner boys." It gives the date above in the second stanza and runs to only seven stanzas in comparison with Korson's twelve. A text in KFR, 3 (1957), pp. 99-100, collected in Breathitt County, is a fairly close variant of Henry's seven stanzas; D. K. Wilgus cites a version in J. T. Adams's **Death in the Dark**, p. 96, which I have not seen. Green (OAM, pp. 85-86) cites the song as learned from Norman Gilford by Hedy West.

The number of those dead in the explosion is in dispute. Laws gives the number as 150, and so does stanza 3, line 1, in Korson's text, but his headnotes probably give the correct figure.

Two texts that I have collected in Harlan and Knox counties are variants of a distinctly different ballad in text and music from the three analyzed above. The Harlan County one sung by Dave Couch crosses from the mine disaster to stanzas from Child, no. 243. The present one was recorded by Annis Cottongim, Knox County, 1958, handed down from her sister-in-law's grandmother.

1. Shut up in the mines of Coal Creek, I know we're bound to die; But if we trust in Jesus, Our souls to heav'n will fly.

SCALE: Hexachordal (d e f# g a b).   RANGE: d' - d" (Perfect octave).
TONAL CENTER: D.   PHRASE STRUCTURE: A B B¹ C (4, 4, 4, 4).
MELODIC RELATIONSHIP: This tune is simple and naive, yet it embraces—
in miniature—a perfection of formal elements.

2. We're wearing our caps and lanterns,
    We're working bold and brave,
    About three o'clock this evening
    We are ready for our grave.

3. Farewell, little Annie my daughter,
    Farewell, my wife and child,
    Shut up in the mines of Coal Creek
    I know we're bound to die.

4. The birds are gladly singing,
    The sun is shining bright,
    But where we are this evening
    It's just as dark as night.

5. Shut up in the mines of Coal Creek,
    I know we're bound to die,
    But if we trust in Jesus
    Our souls to Heav'n will fly.

60. YOUNG CHARLOTTE
(Laws G 17)

This is one of the earliest and most widely known of native American
ballads. It first appeared in print by a known author in 1843. For this reason it
has retained its form and content, though it has traveled by oral and written
transmission over most of the country. Phillips Barry (JAFL, XIV, 156-68;
BFSSNE, 8:17; 12:26) pursued the quest of the ballad from 1912 to 1937 and
made an elaborate study of it and finally trailed it to the author and printed
original.

146

It was written by Seba Smith, a Maine-born New York reporter, who, under the pen name of Jack Downing, criticized Andy Jackson in the 1830's. In the New York **Observer** for February 8, 1940, appeared a story called "A Corpse Going to a Ball." The girl's name apparently was not given. Seba supplied some items, including the name, gave it the ballad form, and published his poem in **The Rover** for December 28, 1843. The rest has been performed by the ballad muse in America. The poem acquired an Irish air and was carried west by our pioneers before and after the Civil War. Belden in BSM, pp. 308, (4 texts, fragments) gives an excellent account of the ballad and of Barry's studies. See also NCF, II, IV, no. 209, 6 versions. One or more are in BSSM, BSI, FSNA, FSF, TFS. Lawless lists 66 in print.

In the many collections examined I do not find that this song has been discovered before in Kentucky. I have several complete texts attesting to its presence in many places in eastern Kentucky. The present variant was collected by Nell Adkins and Leota Sherman, Morgan County, in 1960.

SCALE: Pentatonic (e^b f g b^b c).   MODE: III; Plagal.   RANGE: b^b - e$^{b"}$ (Perfect 11th).   TONAL CENTER: Eb.   PHRASE STRUCTURE: A B C D (2, 2, 2, 2).   MELODIC RELATIONSHIP: Compare this tune with "Barbara Allen" in this volume; note almost identical melody in final four measures. Cf. NCF, IV, No. 209B, first phrase.

A singular characteristic of this melody is the movement in ascending and descending minor third intervals.

2. And yet on many a winter night
   Young swains were gathered there,
   For her father kept a social board,
   And she was very fair.

3. One New Year's Eve as the sun went down,
   Far looked her wistful eye,
   Out from the frosty pane
   As the merry sleighs dashed by.

4. At the village fifteen miles away
   Was to be a ball that night,
   And though the air was piercing cold,
   Her heart was warm and light.

5. How brightly beamed her laughing eye
   As a well-known voice she heard,
   And dashing up to the cottage door,
   Her lover's sleigh appeared.

6. "Oh, daughter dear," her mother cried,
   "This blanket around you fold,
   For it is a dreadful night abroad,
   You'll catch your death of cold."

7. "Oh, no, oh, no," young Charlotte cried,
   As she laughed like a Gypsy queen,
   "To ride in a blanket muffled up
   I never would be seen."

8. "My silken cloak is quite enough,
   You know it's lined throughout,
   And there's my silken scarf to twine
   My head and neck about."

9. Her bonnet and her gloves were on,
   She jumped into the sleigh,
   And swift they rode down the mountain side
   And over the valleys away.

10. They quickly sped through the frosty air,
    Five miles at length were passed,
    When Charles with few and shivering words
    The silence broke at last.

11. "Such a dreadful night I never saw,
My reins I scarce can hold."
Young Charlotte very faintly said,
"I am exceeding cold."

12. He cracked the whip, he urged his stead
Much faster than before,
And thus five other dreary miles
In silence were passed o'er.

13. Spoke Charles, "How fast the freezing ice
Is gathering on my brow."
Young Charlotte still more faintly said,
"I'm growing warmer now."

14. They reached the door and Charles sprang out,
And held his hand to her,
"Why sit you like a monument
That hath no power to stir?"

15. He called her once, he called her twice,
She answered not a word.
He asked her for her hand again,
But still she never stirred.

16. Then swiftly to the lighted hall
Her lifeless form he bore;
Young Charlotte's eyes were closed for aye,
Her voice was heard no more.

17. He wrung his hands, he tore his hair,
He kissed her marble brow,
And his thoughts flew back to where she said:
"I'm growing warmer now."

61. SINFUL TO FLIRT
(Laws G 19)

The first time I heard this ballad was from the singing of my older brother
Ted with guitar. He learned his stock of folksongs from neighbors, from radio

music books, and from phonograph records. This one was apparently in tradition since it has been collected over Appalachia and to some extent in the South.

It has been recorded in Virginia (FSSH, no. 72; FSV, pp. 94-95, 7 listed); North Carolina (FSSH, 2, NCF, II, no. 275, 7 texts, IV, 3 tunes); Tennessee (ETWVMB, pp. 90-91); Alabama (FSSH), Mississippi, and Texas. Two other texts have been collected in Kentucky (FSSH, and BTFLS, III, 93).

The present one was sung to me by Mary Ellen Hill in 1957 from the singing of her brother, both from Laurel County.

SCALE: Heptachordal (f g a b♭ c d e).   MODE: Major; Plagal.   RANGE: e' - d" (Minor 7th).   TONAL CENTER: F.   PHRASE STRUCTURE: A B C D (4, 4, 4, 4).   MELODIC RELATIONSHIP: Phrases A and B have elements in common; in fact, there is an almost consistent isorhythmic pattern to each of the four phrases.

2. How well I remember that night,
    He said he loved me far more than life.
    He kissed me and called me his own
    And asked me to become his sweet wife.

3. "Oh, Willie," I said with a sigh,
   "I'm sure I'll have say No,"
   He held my hand for awhile,
   Then whispered, "Farewell, I must go."

4. Next day down by the old mill
   They found poor Willie dead,
   Clutched close in his hand to his heart
   Was the rose he took from my head.

5. "Oh, Willie, my darling, come back,
   I will forever be true,
   Oh, Willie, my darling, come back,
   I love no other but you."

62. SILVER DAGGER
(Laws G 21)

Reference to this song has been made over the entry "O Molly Dear," since the last stanzas of that ballad have the Romeo and Juliet ending. Called often "Bedroom Window" or "Drowsy Sleeper," it has had rather wide broadside distribution in England. The Silver Dagger story could very easily have broken from that text. Regardless of origin, it now has an independent record in the American South and West. It began to appear from Kentucky in JAF, 20:267, and then in SharpK, no. 165, and FSS, no. 109, in the 1920's. The most important notes and parallels are given by Belden (BSM, pp. 118-126) as introduction to ten texts each of the "Bedroom Window," and "The Silver Dagger." For additional notes to the two see NCF, II, nos. 71, 72; IV, 2 tunes, varying titles. Cf. Laws ABBB, M 4 and 20 for more references to "The Drowsy Sleeper." Lawless lists 59 in print.

My text was recorded from Miss Annis Cottongim, Knox County, in 1958, from her mother, who had learned it thirty-five years earlier.

1. There was a young man who court- ed a
la - dy, He loved her as he loved his own
life; He of- ten vowed and de- clared unto her She would be his wed- ded wife.

SCALE: Pentatonic (f g a c d). MODE: III; Plagal. RANGE: c'-c" (Perfect octave). TONAL CENTER: F. PHRASE STRUCTURE: A B A¹ C (2, 2, 2, 2) or A A¹ (4, 4). MELODIC RELATIONSHIP: See in this collection "Some Have Fathers Gone to Glory," first two phrases similar; also, NCF, IV, No. 72D, first phrase.

2. When his parents came to know this,
    To break it up they both did try,
    Saying, "Son, O Son, don't be so foolish,
    She is too poor to be your bride."

3. When this young girl came to know this,
    She walked green fields and the meadow round,
    She ran till she came to broad, clear deep waters,
    At a pleasant place where she sat down.

4. When this young man came to know this,
    He walked green fields and the meadow round,
    He ran till he came to broad, clear deep waters,
    At a pleasant place where he sat down.

5. She picked up her silver dagger,
   And placed it through her snow white breast,
   There she reeled, and there she staggered,
   "Farewell, vain world, I'm going to rest."

6. This young man, being on the waters,
   He by chance heard her dying groans,
   He ran, he ran, till he ran distracted,
   "I am ruined at last, I'm left alone."

7. He picked up her bleeding body,
   And rolled her over in his arms,
   Saying, "There's no friend, no foe can save you,
   You must die with all your charms."

8. She turned her pale eyes upon him,
   Saying, "True love, true love, you've come too late,
   But be prepared to meet on Mount Zion,
   Where all our joys will be complete."

9. He picked up her bloody dagger,
   And placed it through his lily white breast,
   Saying, "Farewell, darling, now I join you,
   Farewell, vain world, I'm going to rest."

10. O parents, parents, please take warning,
    Don't ever try true love to part,
    If you do, you'll surely regret it,
    They'll take their own lives for each other's heart.

63. FLOYD COLLINS
(Laws G 22)

This song is a good example of the modern ballad muse at work: A man in trouble fighting for his life; rescue parties; newspaper reporters; radio and the phonograph adding to the popular media of communication. The whole nation aroused to a high pitch of compassion and concern.

The facts are well-known and may be stated briefly. The Collins family lived in Edmonson County, the cave region of south central Kentucky. In January 1925 Floyd and brothers discovered a narrow opening in the ground and explored into it and found long, narrow, and crooked caverns leading far underground. Floyd decided to go into it alone one morning. He was missing that night around the fireside. Next morning the men folk set out to hunt for him and in due course found him far down in a narrow passageway with his foot caught under a fallen rock. The alarm was given and rescue work went on around the clock for about three weeks. A shaft was sunk into the area and had reached the proper depth for digging horizontally to the spot when the young man yielded up his life. His casket may be seen today in the cave, now made safe from falling sandstone.

Green (OAM, pp. 124-126) says it was composed by Andrew Jenkins, and recorded by his family. A very few texts have been collected: BSSM (2 from Mich.), and four from Appalachia: NCF, II, no. 212, one and fragments; SSSA, 82-83; TFSB, 16 (1950), 29f; and BMMK, pp. 110-111. This text was sung for me by Mrs. Doris Breeding, Adair County, in 1958.

1. Oh, come all ye young peo-ple And lis-ten while I tell, The fate of Flo-yd Col-lins, The lad we all knew well. His face was fair and hand-some, His heart was true and brave; His bo-dy now lies sleep-ing In a lone-ly sand-stone grave.

SCALE: Heptachordal (e f# g# a b c# d#).   MODE: Major; Plagal.
RANGE: b - c#" (Major 9th).   TONAL CENTER: E.   PHRASE STRU—
CTURE: A B A C A^1 B C^1 D (2, 2, 2, 2, 2, 2, 2, 2) or A A^1 A^2 B (4, 4, 4, 4).
MELODIC RELATIONSHIP: Cf. OFS, III, p. 280 No. 513, "The Whole Hog or
None"; also, OFS, II, p. 220, No. 197A, first portion of tune. The above tune
has been used as a setting for numerous folksong texts. It came into widespread
popularity in 1925 following the death of Collins in a Kentucky cave tragedy,
making a handy setting for our ballad.

2.   O, mother, don't you worry,
     Dear father, don't be sad,
     I'll tell you all my troubles
     In an awful dream I had.
     I dreamed I was a prisoner,
     My life I could not save,
     I cried, "O must I perish
     In a lonely sandstone grave?"

3.   The rescue party labored,
     They worked both night and day,
     To move the mighty barrier
     That lay within the way,
     But on that fateful morning
     The sun rose in the sky,
     The workers were still busy
     To save him by and by.

4.   But O how sad the ending—
     His life they could not save,
     His body now lies sleeping
     In a lonely sandstone cave.
     Young people all take warning
     From Floyd Collins' fate,
     Make right with your maker
     Before it is too late.

*5.   It may not be in sandstone caves
      That we will find our tomb,
      But at the Bar of Justice
      We too must meet our doom.

*Sing to the final eight bars (with pickup) of music

64. ROVING GAMBLER
(Laws H 4)

This is another British import with hardly enough narrative to be called a ballad. Belden (BSM, p. 374) says that it is of probable Irish origin since it is found in many British collections. It usually features a journeyman and is often so titled, meaning one who has completed his apprenticeship and goes on daily wages or goes out to set up in business for himself. In the text given by Sandburg (ASB, p. 312) from Delany's **Songbok** the gamboling man finds himself cooled with a fan in the dwelling of a London girl.

In America the hero becomes a guerrilla man, a railroad man, a soldier boy, and especially a gambling man. Belden sees some connection between this story and the popular "Rebel Soldier" and "The Poor Stranger," which introduce "rye whiskey," and "poor stranger and far from my home" lines. See the full notes and parallels by Belden, with additions by Belden, Hudson, and Schinhan (NCF, III, V, no. 49), and Laws. It is found over the South (SSSA, OFS), Midwest (BSSM, BS), and West (TFS, ABSF, **Colorado Folksong Bulletin).** Lawless lists 25 in print. This text was given to me by Ruie Baker in 1961 from the singing of Sam Ritchie and Johnny Hall, all of Leslie County.

LUSTILY

1. I am a rov- ing gam- bler, I've gam- bled all a-
round, Wher - ev- er I meet with a deck of cards, I
lay my mon- ey down lay my mon- ey down,
lay my mon- ey down.

SCALE: Pentatonic (f g a c d).   MODE: III; Plagal.   RANGE: c' - c"
(Perfect octave).   TONAL CENTER: F.   PHRASE STRUCTURE: A B C
D A^1 C (2, 2, 2, 2, 2, 2) or A B A^1 (4, 4, 4).   MELODIC RELATIONSHIP:
Cf. NCF, IV, No. 42B (I) "Our Goodman" closest relationship; ABFS, p. 150, for
a closely identical tune by the same name; see, "I am a Little Scholar" in this
volume for identical tune.   This carefree song, with its familiar syncopation and
lilting gait, is doubtless of American folk origin.

2.   I've gambled down in Washington,
     Gambled down in Spain,
     I'm going down to Georgia
     To knock down my last game.
     Knock down my last game—
     Knock down my last game.

3.   I had not been in Washington
     Many more weeks than three,
     Till I fell in love with a purty little girl
     She fell in love with me—
     Fell in love with me
     Fell in love with me.

4.   She took me in her parlor,
     Cooled me with her fan,
     She whispered low in her mother's ear
     I love that gamblin man
     Love that gamblin man
     Love that gamblin man

5.   Daughter, dear daughter
     How could you treat me so
     To leave your dear old mother
     And with a gambler go—
     With a gambler go
     With a gambler go?

6. Mother, oh, dear mother,
   I'll tell you if I can,
   If you ever see me come back again,
   I'll be with that gamblin man—
   Be with that gamblin man
   Be with that gamblin man.

65. IF ONE WON'T ANOTHER WILL
(Laws H 12)

The theme of courting too slow, or of saying no and regretting it runs through earlier British collections. Belden in BSM, pp. 191-196, lists 4 in his headnotes, and Laws in ABBB, nos. 10, 11, and 12, analyzes 3 versions that have come from British broadsides to America, with the most common title "The Rejected Lover." His notes reveal that versions of the rejected lover have been collected thinly over America from Nova Scotia, Virginia, Minnesota, Kentucky and Missouri.

The present text may be distinguished from those above by the scornful rejection by the girl, by the stiff, formal exchange of letters, by the titles, and by the last proverbial line, "If one won't another will." This redaction of the ballad is largely confined to Appalachia. To Laws' note we add SharpK, no. 109 and TKMS, pages 94-96, titled "Gonesome Scenes of Winter." I have another close variant from Pike County. The present piece was sung by Orin Nelson in 1959 for Mrs. Sophie Keeney, both of Greenup County.

1. Drear-y seems the wea-ther, in-clined to frost and snow, Dark clouds 'round me hov-ered, the chil-ly wind did

blow. The lit- tle birds sang sweet- ly in
ev- 'ry bush and vine; My joy would be
dou- ble*d* if you were on — ly mine.

SCALE: Heptachordal (c d e f g a b).   MODE: Major; Plagal.   RANGE: b - e" (Perfect 11th).   TONAL CENTER: C.   PHRASE STRUCTURE: A B A B // C D A B (2, 2, 2, 2, // 2, 2, 2, 2) or: A A¹ B A (4, 4, 4, 4); Reprisenbar.   MELODIC RELATIONSHIP: A rather prosaic tune with 19th century overtones.

2. The night is swiftly passing, it's near the break of day,
   I'm waiting for your answer, kind miss what do you say?
   Kind sir, if I must answer, I'd choose a single life,
   For I never thought it suited for me to be your wife.

3. So take that for your answer, and for yourself provide,
   For I've found a new sweetheart, and you I've laid aside.
   It was about three weeks later this maiden's mind did change,
   She wrote to him a letter, said, sir, I am ashamed.

4. Kind sir, since you I've slighted, I cannot stand and mourn.
   Here is my heart, come take it and claim it evermore.
   He wrote to her an answer, and sent it back with speed,
   Said, once I loved you dearly, I loved you once indeed.

5. Kind miss, since I you slighted, I've looked some other way,
   Upon a fair young maiden more pleasing to me.
   Upon a fair young maiden where love can have its fill,
   This world is large and wide, if one won't another will.

66. JOHN HENRY
(Laws I 1)

Although this is a great American Negro ballad and purports to be based on a real person, the facts of John Henry's life are meager. There has been very little biography recorded—about a man by the name of Henry who worked on the Big Bend Tunnel on the C & O Railroad near Hinton, West Virginia, from 1870 to 1872. Indeed, fact-finders have found more details on another steel-driver, John Hardy, who worked on that job and later killed a man and was hanged in McDowell County in 1894. Both of these names began to be celebrated in work songs, hammer songs, and ballads many years later and in about the same year, 1909. Cox (FSS, no. 35, 9 texts) surveys the court records of John Hardy's trial and hanging in 1894, with little comment and no complete text on John Henry.

Guy B. Johnson (JHTD) made a study of the setting and of some thirty ballads. His conclusion was not too factual: "I prefer to believe that there was a Negro steel driver named John Henry at Big Bend Tunnel, that he competed with a steam drill, and that he probably died soon after the contest, perhaps from fever." See the summary of Laws (NAB, p. 246), citing 29 texts in Johnson, and 30 in Chappell, JHFS. For additional notes and texts see WVCS, no. 13; FSSH, no. 179; ETFS, p. 48; FSSUS, pp. 164, 211; BS, p. 407; NCF, II, 270, 8, IV, 8 tunes—4 different singers. Lawless lists 82 in print.

This version was sung in 1959 by Warren Wright to Mary S. Nelson, both of Greenup County.

A

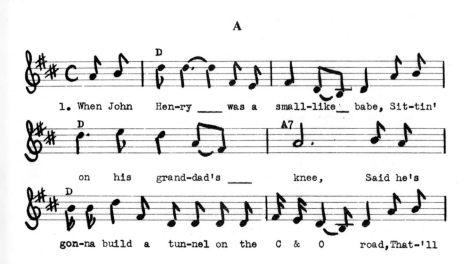

1. When John Hen-ry ___ was a small-like ___ babe, Sit-tin' on his grand-dad's ___ knee, Said he's gon-na build a tun-nel on the C & O road, That-'ll

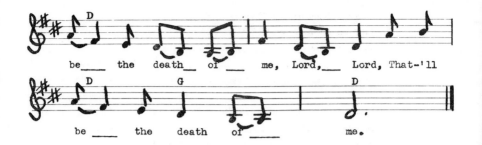

be___ the death___ of ___ me, Lord,___ Lord, That-'ll

be ___ the death of ___ me.

SCALE: Pentatonic (d e f# a b).   MODE: III; Plagal.   RANGE: a' - e"
(Perfect 12th).   TONAL CENTER: D.   PHRASE STRUCTURE: A B A^1
C C^1 (2, 2, 2, 2, 2) or A A^1 (4, 6).   MELODIC RELATIONSHIP: The
variants of this tune are legion. The two versions A and B in this collection seem
the more interesting of the several that we have recorded. The final phrase is
terminally incremented.

2. John Henry made a steel-drivin' man,
    Drove in a many a crew,
    Every time that hammer came down,
    You oughter seen that steel walkin' through, Lord, Lord,
    You oughter seen that steel walkin' through.

3. John Henry was driving in West Virginia,
    His friends all standing around,
    He looked up to the foreman and said,
    I'm gonna beat that steam drill down, Lord, Lord,
    I'm gonna beat that steam drill down.

4. John Henry set a drill in the top of the rock,
    Steam drill drivin' by his side,
    Steam drilled to the bottom in a minute and a quarter,
    Pitched down the hammer an' he cried, Lord, Lord,
    He pitched down the hammer an' he cried.

5. John Henry's folks they were mourning around,
    White folks they all seemed sad,
    When the foreman walked up with his head hangin' down,
    Our steel drivin' John Henry is dead, Lord, Lord,
    Said, our steel drivin' John Henry is dead.

6. John Henry had a dear little wife,
   Her name was Black Sally Ann,
   Went down to the steel drivin' crew,
   Said, You murdered my steel drivin' man, Lord, Lord,
   You murdered my steel drivin' man.

7. I've been in the east, I've been in the west,
   Been all over the land,
   But I never ran across the second man yet,
   Died with the hammer in his hand, Lord, Lord,
   Died with the hammer in his hand.

B

1. John __ Hen-ry was a lit-tle bit-ty boy, Sit-tin'
on his dad-dy's __ knee. And he picked up the ham-mer and the
lit-tle piece of steel. This ham-mer'll be the death __ of __
me, Lord, __ Lord, This ham-mer'll be the death __ of __ me.

SCALE: Pentatonic * (c d e♭ g a). MODE: Irregular; Plagal. RANGE:
g - e♭'' (Minor 13th). TONAL CENTER: C. PHRASE STRUCTURE:
A B C D D¹ (2, 2, 2, 2, 2) or: A B (4, 6). MELODIC RELATIONSHIP:
Cf. NCF IV, 270A and A (1) for relatively close variants; see "John Hardy" in
this collection, embracing ambiguous modal qualities. The final phrase is terminally incremented.

* This scale is identical with a Japanese "mixed" scale, called "Akebono." The
lowered third (D - flat) from tonic denotes a Negro influence.

2. John Henry had a little woman,
   And the dress she wore was blue,
   And the last words I heard that poor girl say,
   John, haven't I been true to you, Lord, Lord,
   John, haven't I been true to you?

3. John Henry had a little woman,
   And the dress she wore was red,
   She was comin' down the track, and she never look'd back,
   I'm goin' where my man fell dead, Lord, Lord,
   I'm goin' where my man fell dead.

4. John Henry said to the captain,
   When you go to town,
   Will you bring me back a nine pound hammer,
   To beat that old steam drill down, Lord, Lord,
   To beat that old steam drill down.

5. John Henry was standing on the right hand side,
   Steam drill standin' on the left,
   Before I let the steam drill beat me down,
   I'll hammer my fool self to death, Lord, Lord,
   I'll hammer my fool self to death.

6. John Henry said to the captain,
   A man ain't nothing but a man,
   Before I let the steam drill beat me down,
   I'll die with the hammer in my hand, Lord, Lord,
   Die with the hammer in my hand.

67. JOHN HARDY
(Laws I 2)

The biographical facts of John Hardy the Black steel-driver on the Big Bend
Tunnel are clear and grim, in contrast with those of the preceding steel-driver.
John Hardy murdered a man in the area and was hanged at Welch, West

Virginia, in 1894. J. H. Cox collected some data on him and presented it, along with nine ballads, in his FSS, no. 35. Although there is some confusion in the texts, they scarcely mention the name John Henry.

Versions of this ballad are pretty well confined to Appalachia: Four texts and notes in NCF, II, no. 244, 3 texts, IV, 3 tunes with one different singer. SharpK, no. 87; FSUSA, no. 85; OFS, II, no. 163 (3 texts); WVCS, no. 14; TSCF, no. 30. Lawless lists 47 in print.

The present variant was collected in 1959 by Mary S. Nelson from the singing of her husband Orin, both of Greenup County.

1. John___ Har- dy was a___ des-p'rate lit- tle man, And he car-ried two guns___ ev- 'ry day. He shot a man on the West Vir- gin-ia line, And you ought to seen John Har-dy get a- way,_____ And you ought to seen John Har-dy get a- way.

SCALE: Hexatonic (c d e (e^b) g a b^b) inflected scale.   MODE: Plagal; ambiguity of modal implications.*   RANGE: a - e^b" (Diminished 12th). TONAL CENTER: C.   PHRASE STRUCTURE: A B A^1 C C^1 (2, 2, 2, 2, 2) or: A A^1 (4, 6).   MELODIC RELATIONSHIP: Cf. NCF IV, 270A and A (I) for relatively close variants; see in this collection "John Henry" (A). The final phrase is terminally incremented.

* The lowered third and seventh (again) may be attributed to Negro influence.

2. John Hardy made it to that East Stone bridge,
   Where he thought he'd be free,
   But up stepped a man and took him by the arm,
   Saying, Johnny, come along with me,
   Saying, Johnny, come along with me.

3. Well, he sent for his mommy and his poppy too
   For to come and go his bail,
   But money won't go on a murder case,
   And they locked John Hardy up in jail,
   And they locked John Hardy up in jail.

4. John Hardy had a sweet little wife,
   And the dress she wore was red,
   She come down to that old jail house,
   Saying, Johnny, I wish I was dead,
   Saying, Johnny I wish I was dead.

5. I've been to the east and I've been to the west,
   I've been this wide world around,
   I've been to the river and I've been baptized,
   Now I'm standing on my hanging ground,
   Now I'm standing on my hanging ground.

68. FRANKIE DUPREE
(Laws E 24)

This is a murder ballad based on the exploits of a Black bandit and bad man. It is in a few collections of the South and Southeast (NCF, II, no. 247; FSV, p. 299; OSC, pp. 328-330; NWS, pp. 55-59). For a Black version see Laws I 11.

The biography of the man and his crimes may be summarized as follows: Frank Dupree grew up in Abbeville, South Carolina. He came on the scene in December 1921 in Atlanta, Georgia, where he had a gal Betty. In trying to appropriate a diamond for her in a jewelry store he shot a policeman down. Fleeing to Memphis and later to Chicago, where he was cornered, he killed a policeman and wounded several more. He was caught while getting his mail and sent to Atlanta for trial. He was executed for murder on September 1, 1922 (Morris, FSF, pp. 87-90). Lawless lists 6 in print.

The present text was sung by Fred Farrow near Demorest, Georgia, in 1954. He learned this in 1929 from Black banjo picker Ben Faggin of the same community.

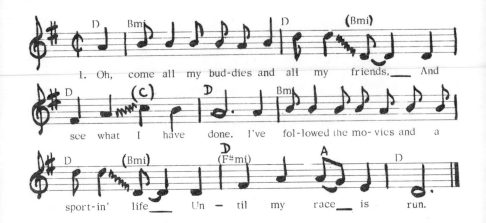

1. Oh, come all my bud-dies and all my friends,___ And see what I have done. I've fol-lowed the mo-vies and a sport-in' life___ Un — til my race___ is run.

SCALE: Heptachordal (d e f# g a b c). MODE: Mixolydian*. RANGE: d' - d" (Perfect octave). TONAL CENTER: D. PHRASE STRUCTURE: A B A B¹ (2, 2, 2, 2) or A A¹ (4, 4).

* Although the scale (itself) conforms to Mixolydian, the flatted seventh is doubtless due to the Negro blues idiom.

2. Well, I went to Atlanta with my sweetheart fair,
   And I walked in a jewelry store;
   I took a diamond while standing there—
   I'll never take no more.

3. Well, I took that diamond and I left that shop,
   And I walked out on the street;
   I pulled my pistol and I shot that cop
   And laid him dead at my feet.

4. I hired me a flivver to get away,
    But my get-away was too late;
    My sweetheart wouldn't leave that town
    And I couldn't flee away.

5. I was arrested and carried to trial,
    At last the judge did say,
    "Frankie Dupree is quite a child
    But he's thrown his life away."

6. Well, come on buddies and all my friends
    And listen unto me,
    Which way you live, live like men,
    Don't live like Frank Dupree.

69. STELLA KENNY
(Laws F 37)

Since this is a local story, the ballad seems to be confined to Kentucky: Jean Thomas, BTNMK (pp. 156-160), KFR, 1959, 131 and 1962, 116-124. There is a text in Williams, BS, p. 127. I have an article with text and tune in KFR, 1962, 116-124. The background of the story is as follows: In Fleming County in 1915 Robert Frazure's wife was having trouble with her fourth pregnancy. Robert, lame and somewhat frail, brought his sister's young, shy daughter Stella Kenny to his home to help his wife in the house and to help him with feeding and milking while he operated a general store.

In the spring some ten months later Stella's mother asked for her daughter to come home and help. Though the distance was over fifty miles to go into Carter County, Robert delayed and finally set out with her in his one-horse buggy, taking along a rope and a hatchet "to fight wild animals and robbers." Late that night in the woods near Olive Hill the people heard screams. A horse with empty buggy appeared on the streets. The people found Robert in the woods with scratches and bruises. He declared he had been attacked by robbers. Stella was found unconscious with many gashes in her head. Her parents were summoned only to see their seventeen-year-old daughter die without telling her side of the story.

Robert was tried three times before a jury convicted him of murder and sentenced him to life in prison. For the trial, an autopsy was performed on the girl, revealing a pregnancy of about four months. A doctor testified that he received a letter from one R. S. Frashure requesting medicine to cause miscarriage. Robert was released from the pen because he was suffering from tuberculosis.

This text was collected by Mrs. Alma Glore, Carter County, in 1961, from Mrs. Pearl Wilson, who stated that it was composed by Rassie Gee. The tune was recorded by Mrs. Charlene Potter.

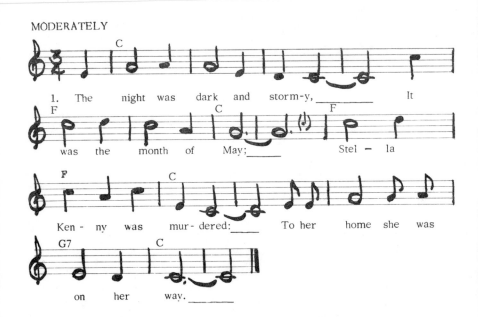

MODERATELY

1. The night was dark and storm-y, ___ It was the month of May; ___ Stel - la Ken - ny was mur - dered: ___ To her home she was on her way. ___

SCALE: Pentatonic (c d e g a). MODE: III. RANGE: c - d" (Major 9th). TONAL CENTER: C. PHRASE STRUCTURE: A B B¹ A (4, 4, 4, 4) or possibly A A¹ A² A³ (4, 4, 4, 4) Strophic form. Inverted reprisenbar. MELODIC RELATIONSHIP: Notice a trace of word painting in measure 11, with the sudden intervallic drop on the word "murdered," which, to some degree, is applicable to the other stanzas. A somewhat similar tune is to be observed in "The Blind and Helpless Child" of this volume.

2. From her Uncle Robert Frasure's
   Where she had been to stay
   And spent ten months with him
   Before this fatal day.

3. It was on one Sunday morning
   On the second day of May
   That they left Fleming County
   For her home they made their way.

4. It was on that rainy night
   While the rain and wind did sweep,
   That a horse and empty buggy
   Was found upon the street.

5. The officers they were summoned
   Each one his place did fill
   They found poor Stella murdered
   Upon the Garvin Hill.

6. She was carried to the City Hall
   Where she gave some awful sighs
   And the sight of her muddy clothes
   Would have brought tears to your eyes.

7. There was her dear old father
   Kneeling by her side,
   "With seven gashes in her head
   No wonder Stella died."

8. Robert Frasure had three children
   And a loving little wife,
   Who stayed beside him
   While he was tried for his life.

9. The jury found him guilty,
   And then they wrote it down
   The clerk announced his sentence
   A life in Frankfort town.

10. Now people, give attention
    And remember what I say
    That Mother will meet Stella
    In Heaven some sweet day.

11.   Now Stella has gone to heaven
       In that bright land so fair
       Where the Bible tells us
       There will be no murderers there.

70. TRAGIC ROMANCE

There are many songs of parting love and broken promises, but a close version to the present text I am unable to find. Perhaps this is because the story is localized in the Tennessee hills. The cause of this parting—boy seeing his girl in a man's arms and leaving her and learning too late that it was her brother with her—suggests a literary piece. And since the plot is openly revealed by the brother, there is obviously no theme of incest.

Perhaps this is a contrived story in imitation of other partings and has not had wide distribution. At least I have not found it in examined collections. This text was given to me by Miss Clara J. Dickinson, Greenup County, in 1959.

1. Nest-led in the heart of the Ten-ne-see hills,
Mid those peace-ful pine trees, the rock and the reel, There
stands my old home-stead of long, long a- go. It
brings back fond mem- 'ries of the one I love so.

SCALE: Heptachordal (f g a b^b c d e).　　MODE: MAJOR: Plagal.
RANGE: b^b - d" (Major 10th).　　TONAL CENTER: F.　　PHRASE
STRUCTURE: A B A B^1 (2, 2, 2, 2) or A A^1 (4, 4).　　MELODIC RELATION-
SHIP: See "Omie Wise" in this collection for an almost identical tune.

2.　I courted a maiden so sweet and so fair,
　　With rosy red cheeks and with chestnut brown hair,
　　She said that she loved me and said she'd be mine,
　　But I went away leaving her there behind.

3.　I saw her one night in the arms of a man,
　　A-hugging and kissing as true lovers can,
　　I went to my home with my heart filled with woe,
　　I packed my belongings determining to go.

*4.　For many long years this old world I did roam
　　With thought of my daring, my sweetheart, my own.

5.　While dining one night in a little country town,
　　A stranger walked in and by chance he sat down,
　　While talking of loved ones I happened to find
　　That his sister was that old sweetheart of mine.

6.　When he heard my story to me he then said,
　　"The girl you left there has a long time been dead.
　　She waited so long for the day that you'd return,
　　And just why you left her she never did learn.

7.　"I am the man that you saw that fatal night,
　　All locked in the arms of my sister so tight,
　　She loved you so truly but you broke her heart,
　　Poor stranger, from her you must ever more part."

*　Lines 3 and 4 missing.

71. I HEARD THE YANKEES YELL

In the limited collections I have examined this song does not appear. Since it reveals the fear and fright of a young soldier in the Confederate Army, one would not expect to find it in southern tradition. We have heard about the fierce Confederate Yell, but the Yankees must have had a curdling one, too.

It was sung in 1959 by a man of seventy-five years, Wash Nelson, recorded by Mary S. Nelson, both of Greenup County.

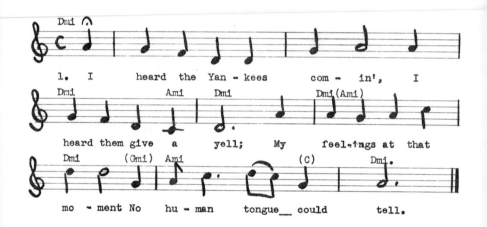

1. I heard the Yan-kees com-in', I heard them give a yell; My feel-ings at that mo-ment No hu-man tongue__ could tell.

SCALE: Pentatonic (d f g a c).   MODE: II. Plagal.   RANGE: c'-d" (Major 9th).   TONAL CENTER: D; Circular tune. It is significant to note that the frequency of temporal units on the tone A exactly approximates that on D.   PHRASE STRUCTURE: A A[1] B C (2, 2, 2, 2) or A B (4, 4).   MELODIC RELATIONSHIP: Cf. SFSEA, No. 98, "The Pilgrim," phrases 1 and 2; SharpK, II, 162B, "Sons of Liberty," compare beginning and end; our version, in both text and music, is apparently a contrafactum based on this very old Irish song.

Our tune, brief and naive as it is, was rendered in a very free ad-lib fashion, amidst a background of inarticulate strummings on the banjo.

For another interesting relationship see OFS, II, p. 272, No. 220, "The Battle of Shiloh's Hill."

2. I saw the smoke a-risin',
   It almost reached the sky,
   I said, "Lord have mercy on me,
   Is this my time to die?"

3. My captain he informed me,
   Perhaps he thought it all right,
   Before we reach the station,
   My boys, you'll have to fight.

4. At the age of sixteen
   I joined the jolly band.
   And marched from North Carolina
   Down to the Rio Grande.

5. I've crossed the Rocky Mountains
   And through the lonesome dell,
   Crossed the Rocky Mountain
   Where many a brave boy fell.

72. COWBOY SONG

There are several songs in the Lomax collection (CS) that have the same jigging rhythm as this song. A few in other collections have the same name, but none have any lines similar. Davis (FSV, p. 292) lists a cowpuncher song titled "Feet in the Stirrups" that may be a version of this one.

Mrs. Virginia Holmes of McCreary County turned in this piece in 1958 from the singing of school children.

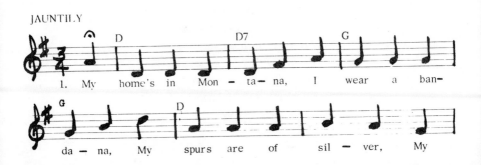

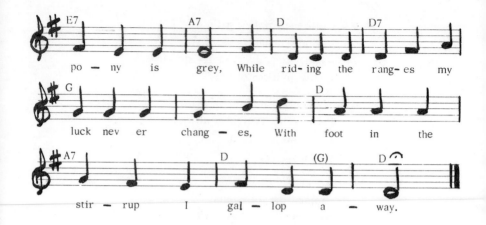

po — ny is grey, While rid- ing the rang- es my

luck nev er chang — es, With foot in the

stir — rup I gal — lop a — way.

SCALE: Hexachordal (d e f# g a b). MODE: Suggests major mode. RANGE: d' - d" (Perfect octave). TONAL CENTER: D. PHRASE STRUCTURE: A A[1] B C A A[1] B[1] C[1] (2, 2, 2, 2, 2, 2, 2, 2) or A B A B[1] (4, 4, 4, 4). MELODIC RELATIONSHIP: Cf. NCF, IV, No. 263, "The Unfortunate Rake" for an almost identical tune; also, FSSSNE, No. 7, II, "Lake Chemo," first four phrases almost identical; **Ibid:** see "The Cowboy's Lament." The tune is of Irish, or possibly earlier English origin. Note the correlation of the intervallic pattern with Morley's "Believe Me if All Those Endearing Young Charms."

2. When valleys are dusty
My pony is trusty,
He lopes through the blizzard,
The snow in his ears.
The cattle may scatter
But what does it matter—
My rope is a halter
For pig-headed steers.

3. When far from the ranges
I chop the pine branches
To heap on my campfire
When daylight is pale.
When I have partaken
Of beans and of bacon,
I whistle a merry
Old song of the trail.

73. LETTER FROM HOME

This western song seems to be in spirit and mood a traditional number. Its sentiment of a letter from a loving family back East is in the center of cowboy feeling (of the rather contrived kind admittedly). But I have been unable to see it in western and other collections, only a listing from Virginia (FSV, p. 290).

The text was collected by Mrs. Myrle Kinder in 1961 from the singing of Frances Ingram, both of Rowan County.

SCALE: Heptachordal (d e f# g a b c#).   MODE: Major; Plagal.   RANGE:
c#' - d" (Minor 9th).   TONAL CENTER: D.   PHRASE STRUCTURE:
A B A C // D B^1 A^1 C (4, 4, 4, 4 // 4, 4, 4, 4) or A A^1 B A^2 (8, 8, 8, 8) Reprisenbar.   MELODIC RELATIONSHIP: If this tune were set in 6/8 meter it would
make a pleasing, but innocuous, serenade.   A comparative analysis would indicate the second quarter note under "Jack" (final phrase) to be E.

*   At the close of stanza 3 the singer made a reprise of the first four lines of
stanza 2.   The tune is probably of 19th century origin.

2. "It's only a message from home, sweet home,
    From loved ones out on the farm:
    'From wife, from mother, from sister and brother,
    All praying to guide you from harm.
    Tonight the baby is whispering a prayer,
    To bless you wherever you roam,
    We'll welcome you, Jack, if you'll only come back,'
    Was the message from home, sweet home."

3. "So fare you well, my boys," said Jack,
    "I'm going to that land."
    And one by one each cowboy came
    And took him by the hand.
    One said, "If we had homes like you,
    We'd all be better men,
    But Jack, before you go, old pal,
    Please read that letter again."

    (Repeat first 4 lines of stanza 2)

74. CALIFORNIA JOE

This rather long story of western Indian massacre and the raising of the
foundling has a good theme and rough circumstantial detail to suggest
somewhat recent composition. When it came to my hand I felt that it might not

be in oral tradition. But now I find at least one clear version collected by the Lomaxes (CS, pp. 346-353). Though they do not date the source, they say: "Written by Captain Jack Crawford, Indian scout and hunter."

This copy was given to me by Ulysus C. Horne, Johnson County, in 1960 from the singing of a Mrs. Baker, who says that when a little girl she learned it from her grandmother.

SCALE: Pentatonic (d f g a c).   MODE: II; Plagal.   RANGE: c'-d" (Major 9th).   TONAL CENTER: D.   PHRASE STRUCTURE: A B A C (2, 2, 2, 2) or A A^1 (4, 4).   MELODIC RELATIONSHIP: The duplet in measure 3 was, in all probability, intended by Mrs. Baker to be sung as a quarter and eighth, as in measure 7.

2. Well once near old Fort Reno
    A trapper used to dwell,
    We called him Old Pat Reynolds,
    The scouts all knew him well.

3. One night the spring of '50
    We camped on Powder River;
    And we killed a calf of buffalo,
    And cooked a slice of liver.

4. While eating quite contented,
    We heard three shots or four,
    Put out the fire and listened
    And heard a dozen more.

177

5. We tied our horses quickly
   And waded up the stream,
   And there among the bushes
   I heard an awful scream.

6. And there among the bushes
   A little girl did lie;
   I picked her up and whispered,
   "I'll save you or I'll die."

7. This little maid was sixteen,
   And I was twenty-two;
   Says I, "I'll be your father,
   And love you just as true."

8. She nestled to my bosom,
   Her hazel eyes so bright,
   Looked up and made me happy,
   Though close pursued that night.

9. One year had passed with Maggie,
   We called her Hazel Eyes,
   And the youth was going to leave me,
   Was going to say good-bye.

10. Her uncle, Mad Jack Reynolds,
    Reported long since dead,
    Had come to claim my angel,
    "His brother's child," he said.

11. What could I say, we parted,
    Mad Jack was growing old,
    I gave to him a bank note
    And all I had in gold.

12. They rode away at sunrise,
    I went a mile or two;
    In parting she said, "May we meet again,
    And may God watch over you."

13. By a laughing dancing brook,
    A little cabin stood,
    As weary as long day scout,
    I spied it in the woods.

14. It was one grand panorama,
    The brook was plainly seen,
    Like a long, long thread of silver,
    All clothed in lovely green.

15. The pretty valley stretched beyond,
    The mountains towered above,
    And near those willow banks
    I heard the cooing of a dove.

16. While drinking from the grandeur,
    And resting in my saddle,
    I heard a gentle rippling,
    The sounding of a paddle.

17. I turned toward the eddy,
    A strange sight met my view,
    A maiden with a rifle
    In a little bark canoe.

18. She stood up in the center,
    With a rifle to her eye;
    I thought for just a moment
    My time had come to die.

19. But I raised my hat and told her,
    If it was all the same,
    To drop her little shooter,
    For I was not her game.

20. She dropped the deadly weapon
    And leaped from the canoe;
    Says she, "I beg your pardon,
    I thought you were a Sioux.

21. "Your broad rimmed hat and buckskin,
    Looked warrior-like and rough,
    And my bead was spoiled by sunlight,
    Or I'd have killed you sure enough."

22. We sat upon the mossy banks,
    Her eyes began to fill;
    The brook was rippling at our feet,
    And the dove was cooing still.

23. I smoothed her golden tresses,
    And her eyes looked up in mine;
    Though seemed in doubt she whispered,
    It was such a long long time.

24. Strong arms were thrown around me,
    "I'll save you or I'll die";
    I clasped her to my bosom,
    My long lost Hazel Eyes.

25. "The one who claimed me from you,
    My uncle good and true,
    Now sick in yonder cabin,
    Has talked so much of you.

26. "If Joe is living, darling,"
    He said to me last night,
    "He will care for little Maggie
    When God puts out my light."

27. We found the old man sleeping,
    "Hush, Maggie, and let him rest,"
    The sun was slowly sinking,
    In the far off glowing west.

28. Although we talked in whispers,
    He opened wide his eyes;
    "A dream, a dream," he murmured,
    "Alas, a dream of lies."

29. He says, "I dreamed I saw an angel,
    As pure as mountain snow;
    And near her at my bed side,
    Stood California Joe."

30. She drifted like a shadow,
    To where the old man lay,
    "You've had a dream, dear uncle,
    Another dream today.

31. "Now listen while I tell you,
    For I have news to cheer you;
    Hazel Eyes is happy,
    And Joe is truly here."

32. "For six long months of sickness
    She has trapped and nursed me too
    Good bless you, boy, I believe
    She is safe along with you."

33. "One year ago today, Joe,
    I see the mossy grave;
    We laid him 'neath the daisies,
    My uncle good and brave."

34. Where two hearts were reunited,
    While sitting at the stream,
    And two loves were closely kindled,
    In love's sweet happy dream.

75. CODE OF THE MOUNTAINS

This is a very apt and telling tale to come out of Appalachia. But I have been unable to find another collector of it in the volumes consulted. It reads like a poem of careful workmanship and probably could be found in some collections of poetry.

It was given to me by Mrs. Irene Howard, Greenup County, in 1959.

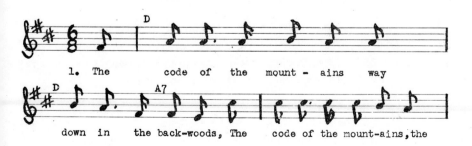

1. The code of the mountains way
down in the back-woods, The code of the mount-ains, the

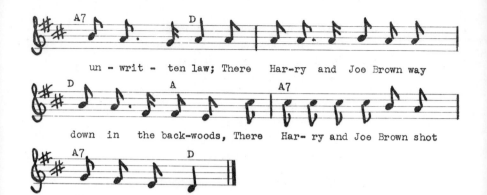

un - writ - ten law; There Har-ry and Joe Brown way down in the back-woods, There Har- ry and Joe Brown shot Char- lie Mc - Graw.

SCALE: Heptachordal (d e f# g a b c#).   MODE: Major.   RANGE: d' - c#" (Major 7th).   TONAL CENTER: D. Greatest tonal frequency on the dominant and the leading tone.   PHRASE STRUCTURE: A B A B[1] (2, 2, 2, 2) or: A B (4, 4).   MELODIC RELATIONSHIP: The basic rhythmic affection throughout is an isorhythmic pattern, with slight modification in B[1].

2. They caught him at daybreak way down in the backwoods,
    They caught him at daybreak down on his knees;
    He pleaded for mercy way down in the backwoods,
    He pleaded for mercy, they heard not his pleas.

3. Said Harry to Charlie way down in the backwoods,
    Said Harry to Charlie, "You thought you were shy,
    But the code of the mountains way down in the backwoods,
    The code of the mountains says that you must die."

4. He loaded his rifle way down in the backwoods,
    He loaded his rifle, Joe loaded his too,
    One shot at another way down in the backwoods,
    One shot at another and then it was through.

5. They buried poor Charlie way down in the backwoods,
    They buried poor Charlie without any prayer;
    The code of the mountains was down in the backwoods,
    The code of the mountains is the only law there.

6. Deep in the earth now way down in the backwoods
    Deep in the earth now lies Charlie McGraw;
    For the code of the mountains way down in the backwoods,
    The code of the mountains, the unwritten law.

76. THE DRUNKARD'S CHILD

In the collections of folksong at hand I cannot find a version similar to this one, although there are related songs with similar titles: NCF, III, V, no. 25, three texts and tunes; Earl J. Stout, FFI, nos. 97, 98, 4 texts; OFS, II, no. 309, five variants, etc. Of these several pieces concerning a child left alone and destitute by a drinking parent, the present song is somewhat different and perhaps more poetic.

It was sung by Roberta Bryant, Knox County, in 1957. She had heard it from Hazel Jackson, who had learned it in Bell County in about 1930.

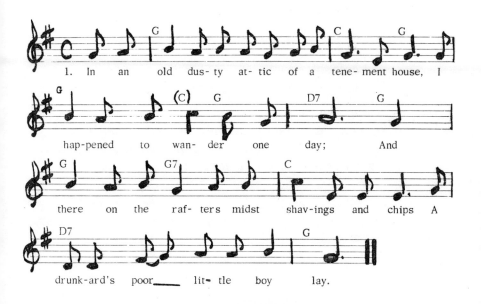

SCALE: Heptachordal (g a b c d e f#).   MODE: Major; Plagal.   RANGE: d' - c" (Minor 7th).   TONAL CENTER: G.   PHRASE STRUCTURE: A B A¹ C (2, 2, 2, 2), or: A A¹ (4, 4).   MELODIC RELATIONSHIP: The last four measures of our tune seem to paraphrase the closing section of "Red River Valley."

2. "Why are you lying up here in the cold;
    What makes you lie on this hard bed?"
    "My father's a drunkard and he beat me today—
    My darling old mother is dead.

3. "I'm hiding from Father and please sir don't tell,
   He beat me 'cause I would not steal,
   He said he would kill me the next time I failed,
   And I'm so afraid sir he will."

4. "I'm leaving you here, son," I sadly replied,
   "But I will be back right away."
   But when I returned to the attic I found
   That Jesus had been there that day.

5. The chips and the shavings were there as before,
   The little boy lay on his bed,
   With tears on his cheeks and his hands by his side,
   The poor little fellow was dead.

6. A picture of Mother lay close to his heart,
   A faint little note by his head,
   As I opened the paper my eyes filled with tears,
   For these were the words that I read:

7. "I'm riding with Jesus across the divide,
   With dear Mother forever I'll dwell,
   And thank you dear mister for your kindness to me—
   And now it's all right if you tell."

77. COWBOY JACK
(Laws B 24)

This song of separation and return to the grave of the broken-hearted girl has had some circulation in Appalachia. My brother Ted used to sing it with guitar in the 1930's, and I have another variant in TSFC, no. 22. Davis lists three texts in FSV, pp. 289-290. It is somewhat rare even in western collections. The Lomaxes (CS, pp. 230-231) have only one text and give one printed source, **Cowboy Sings,** by Kenneth S. Clark, New York, no date. See Laws for one other reference.

The present variant was sung in 1961 by Ruie Baker, who learned it from Mrs. Rose O'Dell, both of Leslie County.

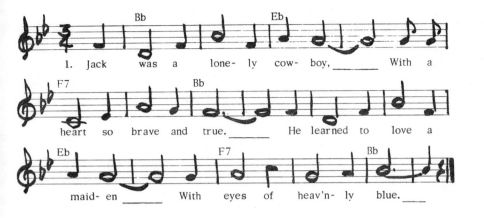

1. Jack was a lonely cowboy, _____ With a
heart so brave and true. _____ He learned to love a
maid- en _____ With eyes of heav'n- ly blue. _____

SCALE: Heptachordal (b♭ c d e♭ f g a).   MODE: Major; Plagal.   RANGE:
d' - c" (Minor 7th).   TONAL CENTER: B-flat.   PHRASE STRUCTURE:
A B A C (4, 4, 4, 4) or: A A¹ (8, 8).   MELODIC RELATIONSHIP: This tune
has been a common setting for numerous folk songs. It is probably of 19th
century origin, but the editor has been unable to trace it. Here again is to be observed an isorhythmic pattern of trochees throughout.

2. They learned to love each other,
   And named their wedding day,
   But a quarrel arose between them
   And Jackie rode away.

3. He joined a group of cowboys
   And tried to forget her name,
   Out on the lonely prairie
   She waited for him in vain.

4. One night when the work was over,
   Just at the close of day,
   Someone said, "Sing a song, Jack,
   It'll drive all cares away."

5. As Jack begin singing,
   His mind it wandered back,
   He sang of his blue-eyed maiden,
   Who was waiting for her dear Jack.

185

6. Jack left camp next morning,
   Breathing his sweetheart's name,
   Saying, "I'll go and ask forgiveness,
   For I know that I'm to blame."

7. When Jack rode into the prairie,
   He found a new made mound,
   His friends sadly told him
   They'd laid his truelove down.

8. They said when she was dying,
   She breathed her sweetheart's name,
   "Tell Jack I'll forgive him,
   But I know that he's to blame."

9. Your sweetheart waits for you, Jack,
   Your sweetheart waits for you,
   Out on the lonely prairie
   Where skies are always blue.

78. JUST FORTY YEARS AGO

This poem is obviously a piece to evoke nostalgia for romantic yesteryears. Sometime in its schoolday recitation it was given a simple melody. But as a folksong it has not lasted and now it hardly appears in the collections examined. The only texts found are from the Ozarks (OFS, IV, no. 869), and Oklahoma (BFSSW, no. 172). Randolph has some data on it. It seems to have been written in the 1840's and got wide distribution in the McGuffey **Fifth Reader** in 1879. See NCF, III, no. 335 (4 texts), V (2 tunes), for texts with the same title but with varying stories, and a reference to a song by William Willing.

The present text was sung by Olieda Martin, who heard it from her mother. Mrs. Merle Kinder recorded it in Rowan County in 1961.

1. I wan-dered to the vil-lage, Tom; I sat be-neath the tree Up-on the school-house play-ing ground, That shel-tered you and me. But none were there to greet me, Tom, And few were left to know Who played with us up-on the grass, Just for-ty years a-go.

SCALE: Pentatonic (f g a c d). MODE: III; Plagal. RANGE: c'-d''
(Major 9th). TONAL CENTER: F. PHRASE STRUCTURE: A B A¹
B¹ C D A¹ B¹ (2, 2, 2, 2, 2, 2, 2, 2) or A A¹ B A¹ (4, 4, 4, 4) reprisenbar.
MELODIC RELATIONSHIP: Cf. OFS IV, p. 394 "Forty Years Ago," remote
relationship. The rather odd punctuation of the tune with fermatas is interesting
and consistent in its application. At least in this instance it can hardly be assumed
that they serve as a vehicle of expediency – as in many cases – in which the
singer attempts to refresh his memory for the ensuing versicle. Note the cul-
mination points on the dominant degree in phrases C and D.

* Possibly intended to be sung F.

2. The grass was just as green, dear Tom,
    Barefoot boys at play
    Were sporting just as we did then,
    With spirits just as gay.
    But the master sleeps upon the hill,
    Which is cold and adorned with snow,
    Afforded us a sliding place
    Some forty years ago.

3. The old school house is altered some,
    Its benches are replaced
    With new ones very like the ones
    Our jack-knives had defaced.
    But the same old bricks are in the walls
    And the bell swings to and fro;
    Its music's just the same, dear Tom,
    As forty years ago.

4. The boys are playing the same old games
    Beneath that some old tree,
    I forgot the name just now,
    You played the same with me.
    On the same spot 'twas played with knives,
    By throwing so and so,
    The loser had a task to do
    There forty years ago.

5. The river's running just as still,
    But the willows on its side
    Are larger than they were, dear Tom,
    The stream appears less wide.
    The grapevine swing is ruined now
    Where once we played the fools
    And swung our sweethearts, pretty girls
    Just forty years ago.

6. The spring that bubbled 'neath the hill,
    Go by the spreading beech,
    Is very low, 'twas once so high
    That we could hardly reach.
    And kneeling down to take a drink,
    Dear Tom, I started so,
    To think how much that I have changed
    Since forty years ago.

7. Nearby that spring upon an elm
    You know I cut your name,
    Your sweetheart just beneath it, Tom,
    You did mine the same.
    Some heartless wretch has peeled the bark,
    'Twas dying sure but slow,
    Just as she died, whose name you cut
    There forty years ago.

8. My lips have long been dry, dear Tom,
    But tears came in my eyes,
    I thought of her I loved so well,
    Those early broken ties.
    I visited the old church yard,
    And took some flowers to strow
    Upon the graves of those we loved
    Just forty years ago.

9. Well, some within the church yard lay,
    Some sleep beneath the sea,
    But none are left of our old class
    Excepting you and me.
    And when our time shall come, dear Tom,
    And we are called to go,
    I hope we'll meet with those we loved
    Some forty years ago.

79. THE BLIND AND HELPLESS CHILD

Most editors declare that this piece is very successful with heart-strings. Randolph (OFS, IV, no.724) says that it was popular in the Ozarks in the 1880's. It has been widely diffused among the folk and occurs in most collections and journals, starting with JAF, 1916, 171. Belden has notes to five Missouri texts (BSM, pp. 275-276); Belden, Hudson, and Schinhan add more notes with their thirteen texts and three tunes from North Carolina (NCF, II, IV, no. 149). For other texts see FSV, p. 115; SSSA, pp. 128-129; SFQ, IV, 191; ETFS, pp. 5, 15, 61. Lawless lists 11 in print.

This version was recorded by Mrs. Sophia Stuart Keeney in 1959 from the singing of Mr. Orin Nelson, both of Greenup County.

1. They tell me, Poppy, that to-night You wed an-oth-er bride. _____ Will you clasp _her in your arms Where my dear moth-er died? __

SCALE: Hexachordal (d e f# g a b).   RANGE: d' - d" (Perfect octave).
TONAL CENTER: D.   PHRASE STRUCTURE: A B C D (2, 2, 2, 2).
MELODIC RELATIONSHIP: Cf. NCF, No. 149A, D, K; all three versions bear resemblance, and all in triple meter; Cf. "Stella Kenny" in this volume, for a similar tune.

2. They say her name is Mary, too,
   The name my mother wore,
   Say, Poppy, is she kind and true
   Like the one you wed before?

3. I heard her footsteps soft and low,
   Her voice so sweet and mild,
   And, Poppy, does she love me too.
   Your blind and helpless child?

4. Please, Poppy, do not bid me come,
   I could not meet her there,
   I could not meet her in the room
   Where my dear mother died.

5. Her picture's hanging on the wall,
    Her books are lying there,
    And there's her harp her fingers touched,
    And there's her vacant chair.

6. The chair by Mother's side I knelt
    To say my evening prayer,
    O Poppy, it would break my heart,
    I could not meet her there.

7. Now let me cry myself to sleep
    As I have often done,
    And softly to my chamber creep
    Where Mother and Dad did sleep.

8. And will she kindly press a kiss
    Upon my throbbing brow
    Just as my dear sweet mother did?
    Poppy, you're weepin' now.

9. Now let me kneel down by your side,
    And to my Savior pray,
    That God's right hand may guide you through
    Life's long and narrow way.

10. Her prayer was finished with a song,
    I'm weary now, she said;
    He took his blind child in his arms
    And laid her on her bed.

11. Just as he turned to leave the room
    A joyful cry was given,
    He turned and caught the last sweet smile,
    His blind child was in heaven.

12. He laid her by her mother's side,
    And placed a marble there,
    And there engraved in simple words,
    "There will be no blind ones there."

80. TWO LITTLE ORPHANS

The touching theme of this song is similar to others depicting children mistreated or neglected. There was a growing sentiment throughout the nineteenth century to idolize childhood and to write their stories. This song, obviously of recent composition, is well represented in collections. One or more texts are printed or listed in NCF, II, IV, no. 150 (4 texts, 12 tunes); FSV, pp. 114-115; BSSM, p. 483; SSA, pp. 126-127; ETWVMB, p. 32; BSSN, p. 483; ETFS, pp. 17-18.

The present text was recorded in 1959 by Mrs. Sophia Keeney from the singing of Violet Belford, both of Greenup County.

1. Two lit-tle child-ren, a girl and a boy,
Set by an old church door. The lit-tle girl's
feet were as brown as the curls, That fell on the dress that she
wore. The lit-tle boy's coat was rag-ged and
torn, And tears shown in each lit-tle eye, "Why
don't you run home to your mam-ma," I said, And
this was the maid-en's re - ply:

SCALE: Heptachordal (d e f# g a b c#).   MODE: Major; Plagal.
RANGE: c#'' - d'' (Minor 9th).   TONAL CENTER: D.   PHRASE
STRUCTURE: A B A C // D E D C (4, 4, 4, 4, // 4, 4, 4, 4) or A A¹ // B B¹
(8, 8, 8, 8).   MELODIC RELATIONSHIP: The tune is probably of 19th century origin, quaint and simple, with its preponderance of quarter-note values.

2.   Mama is in Heaven—they took her away,
      She was sent to her home warm and bright,
      She said they would come for her darlings some day,
      Perhaps they are coming tonight.
      We are too little to work, and we can't earn our bread,
      Jim's five years and I'm only seven,
      There's no one to help us since papa is gone,
      And our darling mama's in Heaven.

 * 3.   Papa was lost out to sea long ago,
      We waited all night on the shore,
      For he was a life-saving captain you know
      And he never came back any more.

4.   Then Mama took sick, angels took her away,
      She was sent to her home warm and bright,
      She said they would come for her darlings some day,
      Perhaps they are coming tonight.
      The sexton came early to ring the church bell,
      And found them beneath the snow white
      And angels made room the two orphans to dwell
      In heaven with their Mother that night.

      * Four lines missing.
        Sing these first four lines to the first section of music.

193

81. OLD LEE BLUES

This story of the old plug dog is not sung much in Appalachia since the collections at hand yield no other instances. It has a few characteristics of genuine folksong, though it probably was recently composed.

It was recorded with banjo accompaniment in 1954 by Fred Farrow, who learned it from an old Negro in his community near Demorest, Georgia.

SCALE: Pentatonic (e f# g# b c#).   MODE: III; Plagal.   RANGE: b - c#' (Major 9th).   TONAL CENTER: E.   PHRASE STRUCTURE: A B A C (2, 2, 2, 2) or: A A¹ (4, 4).   MELODIC RELATIONSHIP: Any association with the "Blues" idiom in this song is more applicable to the text than the tonal material. The tune has slight overtones of "The Girl I Left Behind Me."

2. Well, I took my dog to do some swappin',
    Thought I'd get ahead,
    About the time the trade come close,
    He took a runnin' fit.

3. I kept him tied about ten days,
    To see what he would do,
    But just as soon as he got loose,
    Took them runnin' blues.

194

4. Oh, people for miles around
   Were afraid of my old Lee,
   'Cause when he took a runnin' fit,
   That dog shore could speed.

5. 'Ell, I took him down into the woods
   And tied him to a log,
   I cocked my gun, shut my eyes,
   Said, "Fare you well, old dog."

6. I dug me a hole deep in the ground,
   Out under the yaller sky,
   I packed the dirt down on him good,
   Afraid he might get out.

7. Put a pineknot at the head of his grave,
   And on it placed some news:
   "Here lies the bones of dear old Lee,
   He died with the runnin' blues."

82. MAY I SLEEP IN YOUR BARN TONIGHT MISTER?

This lonesome song of grievance and loss seems to have no record before the twentieth century. The Texas version (PFLST, VI, pp. 124-125) adds more than the flight of wife and child with the stranger. In the husband's tramping he finds their trail and eventually learns how and where his loved ones have died and he falls on his knees and cries (NCF, III, no. 356, 3 texts and a portion from the Texas variant). See also ETWVMB, p. 117, and FSV, p. 77. The texts from the Ozarks (OFS, IV, no. 841) are close to this present number. Brother Ted sang a version in the 1930's, and I have four or five other variants from eastern Kentucky.

This version was sung by Orin Nelson for Sophia Keeney in Greenup County in 1959.

1. One___ night it was dark and was storm-ing,___ ___ When a - long came a tramp in the rain.___ ___ He was mak - ing his way to some sta-tion,___ For to catch___ a long dis-tance train. ___

SCALE: Heptachordal (f g a b♭ c d e). MODE: Major; Plagal. RANGE: c' - d" (Major 9th). TONAL CENTER: F. PHRASE STRUCTURE: A B C D (4, 4, 4, 4). MELODIC RELATIONSHIP: This tune closely parallels "Red River Valley." This process of adapting a new text in place of an old one is quite commonplace in folk music; the technique known as **contrafactum** goes as far back as Gregorian chant.

2. May I sleep in your barn tonight, Mister?
   It's so cold lying out on the ground,
   And that cold north wind it is whistlin'
   And I have no place to lie down.

3. I do not use tobacco or pipe, sir,
   Or carry any matches for a light,
   I will do you no harm, kind Mister
   If I sleep in your barn tonight.

4. It was three years ago this last summer,
   I shall never forget that sad day,
   When a stranger came out from the city
   And he said that he wanted to stay.

5. Now this stranger was tall, dark, and handsome,
   And he looked like a man who did well,
   Said he was stopping in the country,
   He wanted to stay for his health.

6. One night when I came from my workshop,
   I was whistling and singing with joy,
   I expected a kind-hearted welcome
   From my sweet loving wife and my boy.

7. But what did I find but a letter,
   It was placed in my room on a stand,
   And the moment my eye fell upon it,
   I picked it up in my hand.

8. Now this note said my wife and that stranger,
   They had left and taken my son,
   O I wonder if God up in heaven,
   Only knows what that stranger has done.

83. FATAL WEDDING

This is one of the composed popular songs of the late nineteenth century, put together by the author of a more popular song in Appalachia, "The Baggage Coach Ahead." He was Guss L. Davis writing for the music hall and theater trade, composing this piece in 1893, with words by W. H. Windom. According to Malone it was recorded in the 1920's by Vernon Dalhart and by Bradley Kincaid (CMUSA, pp. 58, 110).

Because of these recordings the piece has lasted longer than most sentimental songs. It has been collected in the Ozarks (OFS, IV, no. 766), in North Carolina (NCF, II, IV, no. 272), and in Virginia (FSV, p. 71, 6 texts listed). Factual information about it is well stated by Spaeth (REW, p. 172), and by Belden (BSM, pp. 141 - 143). This version was sung by a Church of God preacher, Vercy Hamm, with guitar, in Rowan County in 1961.

1. The wed-ding___ bells were ring-ing___ On a moon-lit win-ter's night, ___ The bride and groom were read-y, All with-in was gay and bright, ___ A wo-man___ and her ba-by came, And saw the lights a-glow, ___ She thought of how they shone for her___ just three short years___ a-go. ___

SCALE: Heptachordal (f g a b^b c d e). MODE: Major; Plagal. RANGE: c' - d'' (Major 9th). TONAL CENTER: F. PHRASE STRUCTURE: A B C D E F G D (4, 4, 4, 4, 4, 4, 4, 4) or A B C D (8, 8, 8, 8). MELODIC RELATIONSHIP: Beginning at measure 17 there are strong tonal resemblances to "Floyd Collins" in this collection.

2. She asked the gray-haired sexton
   To let her step inside,
   "I'm very tired, the baby's sick,
   So let me step inside."

"This wedding here," the sexton said,
"Is for the rich and grand,
With eager eyes and longing heart
Outside you'll have to stand."

3. She asked the sexton once again
   To let her step inside,
   "For baby's sake you may step in,"
   The gray-haired man replied,
   "If anyone knows the reason why
   This couple should not wed,
   Speak now or hold your peace forever,"
   Was what the preacher said.

4. "I must object," the woman said,
   with voice so meek and mild,
   "The groom is my husband, sir,
   And this our little child."
   "What proof have you?" the preacher said,
   "My infant," she replied.
   She held it up and knelt to pray,
   Then the little one died.

5. The parents of the bride then took
   This outcast by the arm.
   "We'll care for you through life," they said,
   "You saved our child from harm."
   The parents and the bride and outcast
   Swiftly drove away,
   The bridegroom died by his own hand
   Before the break of day.

6. No wedding feast was spread that night,
   Two graves were made next day,
   One for the little infant, and
   In the other the father lay.
   This story has been often told
   Round firesides warm and bright,
   The story of the poor outcast
   And the fatal wedding night.

7. While the wedding bells were ringing,
   While the bride and groom were there,
   Marching through the aisle together
   As the organ pealed an air,
   Telling tales of fond affection,
   Vowing never more to part,
   Just another fatal wedding,
   Just another broken heart.

84. FIRE TRAGEDY

Although the singer of this song said it was a true happening, he did not say when nor by whom the story was told in song. It is not found in any other collections and I assume that it was written by some eastern Kentucky bard. Although in regular meter and stanza, it has very few ballad idioms or commonplaces.

It was recorded by Wash Nelson for Mary S. Nelson, Greenup County, in 1959.

FREELY

1. Last Wednes-day night I spied a new light, shin-in' on yon — dows hill. Was moth-er up with a light, While ev — 'ry thing was still.

SCALE: Heptachordal (d e f# g a b c).   MODE: Mixolydian; Plagal.
RANGE: a - d'' (Perfect 11th).   TONAL CENTER: D.   PHRASE
STRUCTURE: A B C D (2, 2, 2, 2).   MELODIC RELATIONSHIP: This is
the only version of the song that the authors have found. It was performed in a
very free rubato manner and quasi narrative fashion, presenting some difficulties—
perhaps not altogether completely overcome—on the part of the transcriber. The
song moves with an unpredictable continuity, but possesses a quaint and ele-
mental character. This tune evidences a decidedly mixolydian mode, with strong
emphases on tonic "D" and dominant "A": It is not a circular tune. The harmonic suggestions are purely arbitrary.

2. These two little babes had gone to bed,
    While mother ached with pain,
    Said, "I'll go and get some linament
    But I'll soon return again."

3. She went down to a neighbor's house
    One hundred yards away,
    She did sit down to talk awhile,
    But did not mean to stay.

4. At last they heard a rumbling noise,
    Like thunder it did roar,
    They said it was amazing wonder,
    But they did not go to the door.

5. Then at last she started home again,
    Her house were in the flames,
    She screamed, "My darlin' babes, too late,
    And I'm the one to blame."

6. She bursted the door like thunder,
    The flames rolled overhead,
    She screamed, "My darlin' babes, too late,
    For now you both are dead."

7. And there they lay just face to face,
    Their arms 'round one another twined,
    Their flesh was burned to ashes,
    Their bones lay scorched on the ground.

85. THE LITTLE ROSEWOOD CASKET

This is a very sentimental piece with enough realistic detail to sound genuine to the singers and listeners of the late 1800's. The author is not known, but Belden (BSM, p. 220) has recorded a publisher with a copyright date of 1870. It is found in most collections from the Appalachians to Missouri and the Ozarks (OFS, IV, no. 763). In most of the texts the girl is simply abandoned with only tokens of a lover, such as love letters, ring, and locket. In some of the twenty-seven items from North Carolina (NCF, II, IV, no. 273) Belden and Hudson notice a distinct tone of jealousy, although they suppose it to have been added from "The Finished Letter." It has been collected in Illinois and Iowa, but more often in the South—Tennessee, Alabama, Arkansas, Texas. There is a Kentucky text in DD and I have about 15 in my archive. Lawless lists 47 in print.

The present text was given to me by Mrs. Elizabeth Elsbee from the singing of Mrs. George Evans, Rowan County, in 1959.

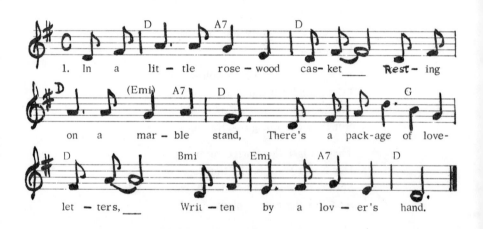

1. In a lit-tle rose-wood cas-ket Rest-ing on a mar-ble stand, There's a pack-age of love-let-ters, Writ-ten by a lov-er's hand.

SCALE: Hexachordal (d e f# g a b).   RANGE: d' - d" (Perfect octave).
TONAL CENTER: D.   PHRASE STRUCTURE: A A^1 A^2 B (2, 2, 2, 2) or: A A^1 (4, 4). A^2 is a transposition of material in A.   MELODIC RELATIONSHIP: Cf. NCF, IV, No. 273E and E (1). Also, OFS, IV, p. 270, No. 763 "The Little Rosewood Casket," almost identical tune. Note the emphasis of the dominant scale tone in the first three phrases.

2. Will you go and get them, sister,
   Read them o'er to me tonight,
   I have often tried but could not,
   For the tears would blind my sight.

3. Come up closer to me, sister,
   Let me lean upon your breast,
   For the tide of life is ebbing,
   And I soon will be at rest.

4. Read those letters he has written,
   He whose voice I've often heard,
   Read them over to me, sister,
   For I cherished every word.

5. I am resting now, my sister,
   Will you read those letters o'er,
   I will listen to the words of
   Him that I shall see no more.

6. And ere you shall have finished,
   Should I calmly fall asleep,
   Fall asleep in death to wake not,
   Dear sister, do not weep.

86. PRIS'NER AT THE BAR
(Cf. Child 209)

Mr. M. E. Henry collected a ballad "The Judge and the Jury" (FSSH, no. 32) in Tennessee and seeing that the story material was similar to that in Child no. 209, he sent it to Phillips Barry for comment. Mr. Barry replied to this effect:

". . . If there is a reminiscence of the Child ballad, it is hard to say, but there may be some, as 'George of Oxford' is fairly well known in the Southern Highlands. . . . I should publish it as an instance of deterioration in the process of ballad making. Child's 'Geordie' . . . is seen at once to be already on the downhill road; 'George of Oxford' and 'Charlie's Escape' are gaining speed on the decline, while 'The Judge and the Jury' is near the bottom of the hill."

It is not so much a deterioration of a ballad as a contrast in the use of similar material. The present melodrama could not possbily be a version of the Child ballad. The only other text I have seen and a close variant with the same title is in OFS, IV, no. 828. My text with tune was recorded by Mrs. Dorothy Major, Greenup County, in 1960.

MOVING

SCALE: Hexatonic (c d e g a b).   MODE: Plagal.   RANGE: b - d"
(Minor 10th).   TONAL CENTER: C.   PHRASE STRUCTURE: A B A
B C C^1 A B (4, 4, 4, 4, 4, 4, 4, 4) or: A A B A (8, 8, 8, 8) Reprisenbar.
MELODIC RELATIONSHIP: Cf. NCF, IV, No. 38 (1) phrase 2. Cf. Bronson
TTCB, III, p. 87, No. 28C, "The Jew's Daughter" — closest of 66 variants; also
OFS, IV, p. 348, No. 828, very close. Here encountered in our tune is the consistent pattern of **isorhythmic** trochees.

* Probably a lapse of memory on part of the singer, who should have sung:
"The boy accused of wrong."

204

2. A maiden fair with golden hair,
   Went swiftly through the crowd,
   The people gazed in wonder, but
   Spoke not one word aloud.
   Then turning to the judge's stand,
   One moment did she pause,
   And smiling through her tears she said,
   "Judge, let me plead the cause.

3. "O Judge, let your mind wander back
   To those long years gone by,
   And see your sweetheart and yourself,
   Just like this lad and I.
   If you have children of your own,
   Have mercy, I do pray,
   Remember, judge, you'll break my heart,
   If you send him away."

4. Then turning to the jury box,
   To make this simple plea,
   "The prisioner here in innocent,
   I know you'll set him free.
   Remember you were once a boy,
   Just like this fair young lad,
   If you convict him of this charge,
   You'll drive him to the bad.

5. "Next Sunday is our wedding day,
   The dreams of wondrous life,
   When at the altar he will make me
   His little loving wife.
   Unless you aim to blight our lives,
   Don't say that we must part,
   And don't forget your loving wife
   Was once your dear sweetheart."

6. The jury did not leave the room,
   For they had quick agreed,
   The foreman briefly signed a note
   And gave the judge to read.
   "Not guilty" were the only words
   The maiden heard them say,
   Her lover clasped her in his arms—
   Love always has its way.

87. GIVE MY LOVE TO NELL

This song, most often called "Jack and Joe" in the collections cited, is a somewhat recent piece, but its Enoch Arden theme has been appealing enough to bear repeating. Its earliest mention to my knowledge is in Kentucky (**KySyll**) in 1911. And except for one reference in New York, it is most often found in Appalachia and the South. There is a text in SSSA, p. 135, three in FSSH, no. 45 (one printed); Kincaid, **Favorite Old-Time Songs** p. 12; NCF, II, no. 274 (14 cited, 3 printed, IV, 3 tunes); OFS, IV, no. 813. Other references in headnotes cite the distribution of it by print and phonograph recordings in Tennessee, Florida, Illinois, Arkansas, and Wisconsin.

The present variant was sung by Orin Nelson in 1959 for Sophia Keeney, both of Greenup County.

206

SCALE: Hexatonic (g a b d e f#).   MODE: Plagal.   RANGE: d' - b' (Major 6th).   TONAL CENTER: G.   PHRASE STRUCTURE: A B A¹ C A B B¹ C (4, 4, 4, 4, 4, 4, 4, 4) or A B A C (8, 8, 8, 8).   MELODIC RELATIONSHIP: Cf. NCF, IV, No. 274B and D, for similarity in general melodic contour and basic rhythmic affection; close tonal identity in our phrases 7 and 8 with their phrase 4; also, **ibid**, 274K, very close overall relationship; **BMMK,** p. 13, "You're Sending me for Life, Judge", although in different meter, definitely an overall melodic relationship. Cf. OFS II, p. 101, No. 150-1 "The Noel Girl," almost identical except for initial interval. Note the **isorhythmic** pattern throughout.

2. "Give my love to Nellie, Jack,
    And kiss her once for me;
    The fairest girl in all the world,
    I know you'll say 'tis she.
    Treat her kindly, Jack, old pal,
    And tell her I am well;
    With parting words now don't forget,
    Just give my love to Nell."

3. In two short years Joe gained his wealth,
    Wealth to last for life,
    And then set sail across the foam,
    To make sweet Nell his wife.
    But when he learned one year ago,
    That Jack and Nell had wed,
    With sighs and threats he now regrets
    That he had ever said:

4. "Give my love to Nellie, Jack,
    And kiss her once for me;
    The fairest girl in all the world,
    I know you'll say 'tis she.
    Treat her kindly, Jack, old pal,
    And tell her I am well;
    With parting words now don't forget,
    To give my love to Nell."

PART II FOLK SONGS

A. LYRICAL AND LOVE SONGS

88. THE GYPSY'S WARNING
(and Answer)

Since this warning song has a copyright date (1864) and a long record in American music hall songsters, and the texts are nearly alike, we may assume that it has not been too much in oral circulation. The music was arranged by Henry A. Coard in Brooklyn in 1864. Although he gives no author of the words, Cox (FSS, no. 149, 1 text) lists 7 songsters containing the warning, no answers. Brewster reports a few texts of both warning and answer from Indiana (BSI, nos. 55 and 56). Randolph prints four variants from the Ozarks (OFS, IV, no. 743). See other texts in REW, p. 20; SSSA, p. 154; FSSUS, p. 220 (listed from West Virginia). Lawless lists 6 in print.

My text of the two parts was sung by Alma Glore, Carter County, in 1961. She says the song came down to her from her mother's people.

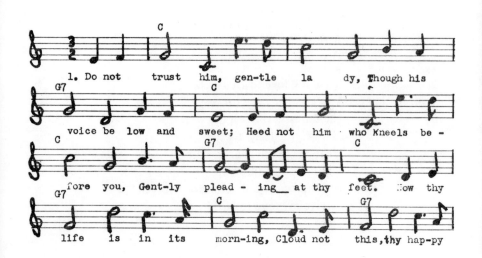

1. Do not trust him, gen-tle la dy, Though his
voice be low and sweet; Heed not him who kneels be -
fore you, Gent-ly plead - ing at thy feet. How thy
life is in its morn-ing, Cloud not this, thy hap-py

lot; Lis-ten to the Gyp-sy's warn- ing; Gen-tle
la - dy___ trust him not.

SCALE: Heptachordal (c d e f g a b).   MODE: Major.   RANGE: c' - e"
(Major 10th).   TONAL CENTER: C.   PHRASE STRUCTURE: A B A B¹
// C C¹ A B¹ (2, 2, 2, 2, // 2, 2, 2, 2) or A A¹ // B A¹ (4, 4, 4, 4) Reprisenbar.
MELODIC RELATIONSHIP: Cf. "No Sir" in this collection, phrase one; OFS,
No. 743A, p. 219, first four phrases almost identical.

A noteworthy characteristic of this tune is to be observed in the angularity of
melodic contour and wide intervallic skips, i.e., the major 10th ascending in measures 1, 5, and 13, and the descending minor 7th in measure 10.

2. Lady, once there lived a maiden,
    Pure and bright and like thee fair,
    Yet he wooed, he wooed and won her,
    Filled her tender heart with care.
    Then he heeded not her weeping,
    Nor cared he her life to save,
    Soon she perished, now she's sleeping
    In a cold and silent grave.

3. Keep your gift, I do not want it,
    Lady, I have prayed for this,
    For the hour that I might foil him,
    Rob him of expected bliss.
    Gentle lady, do not wonder
    At my words so cold and wild,
    Lady, in the green grave yonder
    Lies the Gypsy's only child.

His Answer

4. Lady, do not heed her warning,
    Trust me thou shalt find me true,
    Constant as the light of morning
    I will ever be to you.

Lady, I would not deceive thee,
Fill thy guileless heart with woe,
Trust me lady and believe me
Sorrow thou shalt never know.

89. LETTERS

This mildly satirical song of a broken engagement, also called "Charlie Brooks," has a literary and contrived form and content. It is not in very wide circulation and seems not to have been long in tradition. My informant was an old lady with a number of similar songs to contribute. She stated that she had learned this one in about 1890. Other texts that I have seen (OFS, IV, 735 and NCF, IV, 320) agree fairly closely with this one. There are four listed in FSV, p. 120.

The present piece was collected by Mrs. Gay F. Cottle in 1960 from the singing of Mrs. T. H. Easterling, both of Morgan County.

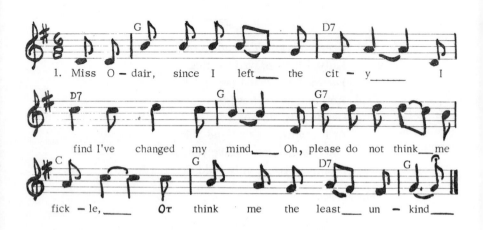

1. Miss O — dair, since I left___ the cit - y___ I find I've changed my mind,___ Oh, please do not think___ me fick — le,___ Or think me the least___ un - kind___

SCALE: Hexatonic (g a b c d f#).   MODE: Plagal.   RANGE: d' - d"
(Perfect octave).   TONAL CENTER: G.   PHRASE STRUCTURE: A B
A^1 C (2, 2, 2, 2) or: A A^1 (4, 4).   MELODIC RELATIONSHIP: Cf. NCF IV,
No. 320A, B, and C, for fairly close variants, OFS IV, No. 735A, p. 211 "Charlie
Brooks," phrases A and B.

Note scalar emphasis of mi, fa, sol, on initial tones of first three phrases.

2. For I find we were both mistaken,
    And that you'll never suit me—
    My heart is given to another.
    I hope, Miss Odair, you'll agree.

3. Please send me the ring that I gave you
    And the photo too if it's fair—
    Oh, please be so kind as to free me
    From this pit of pain, Nell Odair.

4. Send me the locket I gave you,
    Also my letters and books—
    Oh, please be so kind as to free me.
    Respectfully yours, Charlie Brooks.

5. Dear Charlie, I received your letter,
    The last one that you wrote me—
    I read it over and over,
    And of course, my friend, I'll agree.

6. For I'd rather that you would be happy
    With that pretty charming Miss Gray—
    Oh, Charlie, I heard all about it
    And thought it would end this way.

7. Here is your ring, dear Charlie,
    Don't give it to her I pray—
    Unless you tell her it was mine once,
    I've worn it a year today.

8. Only a year, dear Charlie,
    But a bright happy one to us both;
    You swore you would never forget me,
    But I find you untrue to your oath.

9. Here are your letters, dear Charlie,
    I burned mine when they came,
    I hope without reading them over
    You will at once consign yours to flame.

10. For you don't need them, dear Charlie,
    To remind you of words untrue,
    But since you requested them of me,
    I'll at once return them to you.

11. Here is your photo, dear Charlie,
    It is almost faded away,
    For I have kissed it so often,
    And this you may tell Miss Gray.

12. Now I will say good-bye to you,
    My letter is near its end,
    But remember that I am always,
    Forever and, ever your friend.

90. MAPLE ON THE HILL

I had heard this song as early as the 1930's in eastern Kentucky, but I was surprised to find that it had not been gathered into many collections of the last two decades. Perhaps it is a new and localized number. See NCF, V, no. 706, one tune and reference to JAF, 59, 452. Two texts of 1934 and 1936 are listed in Davis, FSV, p. 332. This version was given to me by Mary Stuart Nelson in 1959 from the singing of her husband Orin, both of Greenup County.

1. In a qui~et coun~try vil-lage stood a

ma- ple on the hill; There I sat with my Ja-

net- ta long a - go;___ And the stars were shin- ing

bright-ly we could hear the whip-poor - will, As we

vowed to love each oth - er ev - er - more.___

SCALE: Heptachordal (c d e f g a b).   MODE: Major; Plagal.   RANGE: a - a' (Perfect octave).   TONAL CENTER: C.   PHRASE STRUCTURE: A A[1] A B (4, 4, 4, 4) or A A[1] (8, 8).

* The performer completely elided the extra half-note on D. The tune, rather commonplace and cliche, has perhaps been superimposed on the text, in a sort of reverse **contrafactum** manner. The provenience of this tune (as is true of numerous others) doubtless lies in the realm of congregational hymnody of earlier days.

    2.   We would sing love songs together
         When the birds had gone to rest,
         And listen to the murmur of the rills,
         Then she threw her arms about me,
         Laid her head upon my breast
         As we sat beneath the maple on the hill.

    3.   We are growing old together
         And our steps are fading fast,
         As we listen to the murmer of the rill,
         Will you always love me darlin'
         As you did that starry night?
         I must leave you and the maple on the hill.

91. WEEPING WILLOW TREE

For thousands of years many flowers of the fields and trees and shrubs of the groves have been used as symbols and tokens of human emotions. The limp and dejected willow has been named a companion in sorrow and a shade for the grave. Thus it was in Shakespeare's time for Desdemona and Ophelia. It is likewise found in love laments and songs from Europe and Britain. The present song and related ones have gained popularity from stall and broadside printings in England and America as early as 1800 and have found their way across the states by oral tradition and in parlor songsters. In the 1920's they were further scattered by phonograph records.

Except for two texts without location (AMS, p. 56 and ASB, p. 314) and one in Charles Neely's TSSI, the song is more prevalent in the South. There are two in BSM, pp. 482-483 and three in OFS, no. 747 (also two phonograph listings); nine in North Carolina (ETWVMB, p. 65, and NCF, III, no. 267, 8, V, 2 tunes). For Kentucky there is one in BKH, p. 126, and I have about ten others. Lawless lists 21 in print.

The present text was contributed in 1957 by Elizabeth Robbins of Harlan County from the singing of her sister.

EASILY

1. My heart is sad and I am lone-ly, For the on-ly one I love is gone. Per-haps he's gone to see an-oth- er, And my poor heart is break- ing now.

SCALE: Hexachordal (e^b f g a^b b^b c). MODE: Plagal. RANGE: b^b - $e^{b''}$ (Perfect 11th). TONAL CENTER: E^b. PHRASE STRUCTURE: A B A C (2, 2, 2, 2) or: A A^1 (4, 4). MELODIC RELATIONSHIP: The authors have not found this tune among other versions examined. Simple as it is, there is a certain poignancy in the framing of "For the only one," and "my poor heart is breaking now."

Refrain—same music as for stanza:

Then bury me beneath the willow,
Beneath the weeping willow tree,
So he will know where I am sleeping,
Perhaps sometimes he'll think of me.

2. He told me that he loved none other,
But he had broken every vow,
I know he has gone to see another,
And my poor heart is breaking now.

Refrain

3. They told me that he did not love me,
But how could I believe it true,
Until an angel softly whispered:
He has proven untrue to you.

Refrain

4. Oh, place upon my brow a lily,
An emblem of the purest love,
And tell him that I died to love him,
But I could no longer win his love.

Refrain

92. PALE MOONLIGHT

This is a song of parting and the making of vows which are so often broken. It is not all here but by the other texts we know it has an Enoch Arden theme with a fateful ending. Randolph (OFS, IV, no. 803) has two fuller texts but no notes or parallels, only that his informant had heard it in about 1910. In the complete story the young man is away for one year and returns just too late. She is a new bride. He is found on the grass, a pistol by his side, and a note which reads: "I've loved you always. . ."

My piece was sung by Mrs. Mae Hart, Laurel County, in 1958.

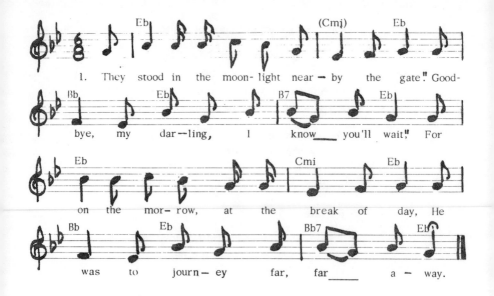

1. They stood in the moon-light near — by the gate." Good-
bye, my dar—ling, I know___ you'll wait." For
on the mor—row, at the break of day, He
was to journ—ey far, far___ a — way.

SCALE: Pentatonic (e^b f g b^b c).   MODE: III.   RANGE: $e^{b'}$ - c" (Major 6th).   TONAL CENTER: E^b.   PHRASE STRUCTURE: A B A^1 B $(2, 2, 2, 2)$ or: A A^1 $(4, 4)$.

Note the predominant iteration of G's and B-flats (3rd and 5th of tonic chord); also, the feminine ending on the third: G.

2. She ceased her weeping and smiled through her tears,
   Said, "I've been true love through these long years."
   He held her closer, his promised bride,
   And to her questions, these words replied:

3. I've loved you always, yes, I've been true,
   My heart shall ever be lonely for you,
   Believe me, my darling, far over the sea,
   Through life, through death, so faithful I'll be.

93. NO, SIR

This rather piquant song of love play, sometimes titled "My Father Was a Spanish Merchant," goes back to the 17th century and therefore originated in the time of Anglo-Spanish rivalry in the New World. It has been reported in various forms in England, including texts by Sharp in **One Hundred English Folk Songs,** and in his **A Selection of Collected Folk Songs** (Vol. 1). Reference was made above to a folktale that demanded No to all questions. Here the relation of song and tale is much closer. In folktale Type 853, and 853A, the Hero Catches the Princess with her Own Words, the hero so frames his questions that he entraps and seduces the girl. The tale is most popular in Scandinavia and in eastern Europe, but it is found in Ireland, England, and in America. There is a play-party game of it in Leah J. Wolford's **Play-Party in Indiana.**

The song itself has been fairly popular in America, especially in Appalachia and in the Midwest. Some editors arrange the stanzas to be sung by a boy and the refrain by a girl. There is a text in BSO, no. 48; one in OFS, III, no. 385; NCF, III, no. 14, 4 texts cited but only two printed, V, 2 tunes one by a different singer; TKMS, no. 17; BKH, p. 81. Lawless lists 12 in print.

The present text was recorded in 1958 by Mrs. Virginia Holmes from the singing of her mother, who had learned it in about 1900 in Barren County.

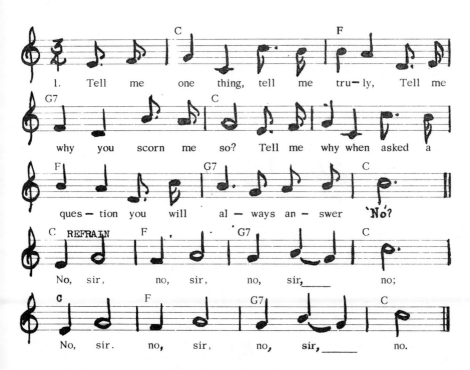

1. Tell me one thing, tell me tru-ly, Tell me why you scorn me so? Tell me why when asked a ques-tion you will al-ways an-swer "No?"

No, sir, no, sir, no, sir, no; No, sir, no, sir, no, sir, no.

SCALE: Heptachordal (c d e f g a b).   MODE: Major.   RANGE: c' - c"
(Perfect octave).   TONAL CENTER: C.   PHRASE STRUCTURE: A A^1
A B // C D C D (2, 2, 2, 2, // 2, 2, 2, 2, or A A^1 B B (4, 4, 4, 4).   MELODIC
RELATIONSHIP: Compare first strain of this tune with "The Gypsy's Warning"
in this collection; Cf. NCF, V, No. 14, three versions with melodic association
only in the refrain.

If, as Dr. Roberts states, the text "goes back to the 17th century," the music
most assuredly does not; however, the first two measures with up-beat appear in
the refrain of an old German student song.   A notable characteristic of this
melody is its angularity, embracing intervals of the 5th, 6th, 7th, and octave.

2.   My father was a Spanish merchant
     And before he went to sea,
     He told me to be sure and answer
     To all you said to me.

     Refrain

3.   If when walking in the garden,
     Plucking flowers all wet with dew,
     Will you be offended if I
     Have a walk and talk with you?

     Refrain

4.   If when walking in the garden,
     I should ask you to be mine,
     And should tell you that I love you,
     Would you then my heart decline?

     Refrain

94. MAN OF CONSTANT SORROW

In the late 1920's I can recall hearing this song for the first time. It was at
dusk on the rocky road past our house in eastern Kentucky. Mally Strugill, the
grown single son of our neighbor up the creek, went along the dark road, as he

often did, singing: "I am a man of constant sorrow . . ." His family ran the country store and owned the best talking machine and highest stack of records. People milled around the home seven days a week but especially on Sunday.

It is now surprising that this lonesome piece has not made its appearance in more collections. The only other listing is from Virginia (FSV, pp. 93). See SharpK, no. 167, for a very close first stanza in "In Old Virginny." That this song could have been adapted from a hymn, see my notes to "Wayfaring Pilgrim" and those of Schinhan to NCF, V, no. 771. My text, a bit garbled and short one or two stanzas, was recorded by Veneda D. Rose, Johnson County, Kentucky, in 1959. She says of it: "Buel Ward used to sing this for us twenty-five years ago. No party was complete without his solo."

SCALE: Hexachordal (g a b c d e).   MODE: Plagal.   RANGE: c' - c" (Perfect octave).   TONAL CENTER: ** G; Circular tune, Although there is an unusual emphasis on D, with a temporal frequency almost as much as G, there is little room for doubt that this is a circular tune.   PHRASE STRUCTURE: A B A B (2, 2, 2, 2) or: A A (4, 4).   MELODIC RELATIONSHIP: See "Wayfaring Pilgrim" in this collection for vague tonal relationship.

* If, in the final stanza, the tune is given a normal ending on G, the harmonizing instrument should play a G chord.

** The editor is aware that certain elements in this tune might be interpreted as indicating D as tonal center.

2. For six long years I've been in trouble,
   No pleasure here on earth I see,
   For in this world I'm bound to travel,
   I have no friends to help me now.

3. Tell my friends who've wondered about me,
   Why I'm wandering in the cold.
   I'm bound to ride that Northern Railroad,
   Perhaps I'll die upon the train.

4. Oh, you may bury me in some dark hollow,
   My friends, you'll never see me no more,
   Don't grieve for me while you're standing o'er me,
   While I am sleeping in my grave.

95. I'M NINE HUNDRED MILES FROM MY HOME

This song is usually sung farther south and mostly by Negroes, who generally call it "Reuben," "Old Reuben," and sometimes "The Railroader." It has many relations in white and Negro folksong, the oldest form possibly being the blues piece usually called "In the Pines" (FSUSA, no. 74, and one text in the present collection). It has not been very widely collected. One in Negro tradition (NWS, pp. 66) does not refer to the usual railroading, drinking or gambling, only to Reuben who had trouble all his life and is now dead. It has been collected in North Carolina (NCF, III, no. 236, 3, V, 3 tunes by 2 different singers); in Virginia (FSNA, no. 302); and in Missouri (FSSH, no. 163).

My text was collected by Mrs. Sophia Keeney from the singing of Mrs. Violet Balford in 1959, both of Greenup County.

train that I leave on, You can hear the whis-tle blow a hun-dred miles._____

SCALE: Tetratonic (e^b g a^b b^b).   RANGE: $e^{b'}$ - $b^{b'}$ (Perfect 5th).
TONAL CENTER: E^b.   PHRASE STRUCTURE: A B (4, 4); possibly A A^1 B (2, 2, 4) in which case it resembles Bar form.   MELODIC RELATIONSHIP: Cf. NCF, No. 236 (A), "Reuben's Train," which includes a four-measure refrain.

2. My baby said so,
   I will railroad no more,
   I will sidetrack my engine and go home.

3. If the train it runs right,
   I'll be home tomorrow night,
   Lord, I'm nine hundred miles from my home.

4. I will pawn you my watch,
   And I will pawn you my chain,
   And I will pawn you my gold diamond ring.

5. If that won't be enough,
   Get my baby out of jail,
   I'll pawn you my wagon and my team.

96. LITTLE BIRDIE

The song has many forms, but this one seems to be a deeply felt and aching lyric. This is not "Little Sparrow," and it is not "I Wish I Were Single Again." A possible evolution of this song might start with the one printed in REW, p. 26, from Ohio titled "A Married Woman's Lament," dated before 1850. A text with the REW title and with more lines that are parallel to the present one is in OFS, III, no. 366; other reports are BSO, no. 70; NCF, III, no. 28 (3 texts, V, tunes to A, C); SharpK, no. 86 (5 texts; C, D from Kentucky). The one listed in FSSUS, p. 226, no. 178, from Kentucky may be a version; FSNA, no. 84.

The piece was sung to Mrs. Ira Stacy and me by a banjo picking preacher Frank Riley, Rowan County, in 1961.

1. Lit–tle bird–ie, lit–tle bird–ie, What makes you act so queer? You've no cause for to wor–ry, Don't need no coat to wear.

SCALE: Pentatonic (f g a c d).   MODE: III; Plagal.   RANGE: c' - a' (Major 6th).   TONAL CENTER: F.   PHRASE STRUCTURE: A B A¹ B (2, 2, 2, 2) or: A A¹ (4, 4).   MELODIC RELATIONSHIP: Cf. OFS, IV, p. 122, No. 676A "The Dark Hollow"; also, for a comparable tune see "Single Girl" in this volume. One can observe, again, the singer's fancy in the use of fermatas, which seems to actually enhance the expressive content of the words.

Refrain — same music as for stanza

Little birdie, little birdie,
Come sing me one more song,
Have a short time for to stay here
And a long time to be gone.

2.   Married woman, married woman,
Come see what you've done,
You caused me for to love you,
Now your husband's done come.

Refrain

3. I'd rather be up some dark holler,
   Where the sun refuse to shine,
   For you to be some other man's woman,
   And never to call you mine.

Refrain

4. I'd rather be a sailor boy,
   A sailin' out on the sea,
   As to be a married man
   And live all alone.

Refrain

5. For a married man sees trouble,
   While a single man sees none,
   I'd rather be a single man
   And live all alone.

Refrain

97. LONESOME DOVE

This love lyric seems to echo lines from three or four other songs, and yet it has a unity and an inner tension of its own, blended of many elements by the lyric muse. For instance, it has stanzas from the text given above under Child no. 76, "The Lass of Roch Royal," but here however we have no shoe-my-foot lines. Its first two stanzas echo the words and feeling of "Lonesome Grove," a lyric of a man's desolation after the death of his wife and child by consumption. An early form of this song is printed by Jackson (SFSEA, no. 34) from the **Social Harp** of 1855, the text of which was supposedly composed by Wm. C. Davis. Most of his nine stanzas are found in the major collections, such as BSM, p. 486, SharpK, no. 147 (four tunes with fragments), and NCF, II, IV, no. 305. For other texts see OFS, no. 607; DD, p. 162; JAF, 25: 276 and 45: 83-85.

Stanzas 3, 4, and 5 here are close to stanzas in "Lonesome Road" (NCF, II, no. 292B), and echo Burns's "My Love is Like a Red Red Rose." Stanza 6 seems to be new material, here used to unify the lyric. The present text was sung by Warren and Mary Wright and recorded in 1959 by Mary S. Nelson, all of Greenup County.

MODERATELY

1. Oh, ___ don't you ___ see ___ that lone-some bird,
Fly-ing from pine to ___ pine? She's ___ mourn - in'
for ___ her own true love, Just like I ___ mourn for ___
mine.

SCALE: Heptachordal (d e f# g a b c#).   MODE: Major; Plagal.
RANGE: c#'-b' (Minor 7th).   TONAL CENTER: D.   PHRASE STRUC-
TURE: A B A¹ B¹ (3, 2, 3, 2) or: A A¹ (5, 5).

2. She sits alone in the lonesome pine
   And droops her little head,
   She's mourning for the one she loves,
   But the one she loves is dead.

3. Look down, look down that lonesome road,
   Hang your head and cry,
   But if you love me like I love you,
   We'll join our hands or die.

4. The crow is black, you know, my love,
   And never will turn white,
   Should ever I prove untrue to you,
   Bright days will turn to night.

5. Bright days will turn to night, my love,
   The elements will turn,
   Then fire will freeze, like us, my love,
   And the raging sea will burn.

224

6. Many a year may roll around,
   Before I call you mine,
   But I'll live alone, like the lonesome dove,
   And wait for that day to come.

7. So don't you see that lonesome dove,
   Flying from pine to pine,
   She's mourning for her own true love,
   Just like I mourn for mine.

98. SINGLE GIRL

There are two sides to the marriage tie, the man's regrets and the woman's woes. Songs have come down to us from England setting forth the trials and troubles of each side. It is now quite difficult to tell which partner complained first, perhaps both at about the same time.

By about the middle of the 19th century an English stall-print had appeared usually called "When I Was Single," relating a man's happiness with pockets full money. He then married and found the little wife to be the plague of his life. When she died he laughed till he cried. He married again and she was worse than the first (Belden, BSM, pp. 437-439, 3 texts; OFS, no. III; NCF, no. 19, 10 texts, V, 2 tunes). This piece has come to America and has spread over most of the land, assisted by the rowdy repartee of black-face minstrels (Sandburg, ASB, p. 47). Lawless lists 15 in print.

In England, in about 1850, appeared the first version of the woman's complaints. She used to be beautiful, had freedom and silks. Now she has rags and a baby on each knee. This song of the single girl has also spread to America and has been most often sung in Appalachia (SharpK, no. 86; five texts).

My piece was sung with the banjo in 1959 by Mrs. Mary Wright and collected by Mary S. Nelson, both of Greenup County.

225

SCALE: Hexatonic (f g a c d e).   MODE: Plagal.   RANGE: c' - a' (major 6th).   TONAL CENTER: F.   PHRASE STRUCTURE: A A¹ (4, 3). The singer's rendition of this song would allow for other possibilities of metrical barring. There is definite evidence of erosion.   MELODIC RELATIONSHIP: See "Little Birdie" in this collection for a comparable tune.

2.   Married girl, married girl,
     Has trouble all her life,
     Oh, trouble all her life.

3.   When I was a single girl,
     I saw a happy time,
     Oh, I saw a happy time.

4.   But how I am a married girl,
     Have trouble all the time,
     Oh, have trouble all the time.

5.   Single girl, single girl,
     She goes just where she please,
     Oh, she goes just where she please.

6.   Married girl, married girl,
     Baby on her knees,
     Oh, a baby on her knees.

7.   When I was a single girl,
     I dressed in silks so fine,
     Oh, I dressed in silks so fine.

8.   Now I am a married girl,
     And I wear rags all the time,
     Oh, I wear rags all the time.

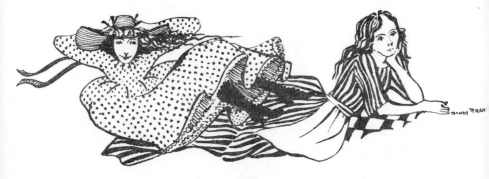

226

99. THE HOOT OWL SONG

This song is worn enough in the groove of the love lament tradition to be fairly old. The reference to the nightingale, although it also features the hoot owl and the whippoorwill, suggests kinship with British lyrics. The only trouble is I have never seen the song before and cannot find it in collections, unless the one listed by Davis (FSV, pp. 100) titled "When you Hear the Whippoorwill Calling" is a version.

This text was collected by Mrs. Mary S. Nelson from Mrs. Mary Wright, who sang it with her banjo in Greenup County in 1959. She said it had been handed down from her great-grandmother.

SCALE: Heptachordal (b^b c d e^b f g a). MODE: Major. RANGE: b^b - d" (Major 10th). TONAL CENTER: B^b. PHRASE STRUCTURE: A B A^1 C (2, 2, 2, 2) or: A A^1 (4, 4). MELODIC RELATIONSHIP: A predominant harmonic type motive, with angularity of melodic contour.

Folk singers frequently employ the **fermata** in the most unpredictable places (see measure 4); possibly in this instance the singer was refreshing her memory for the ensuing line of text.

2. When the fog is on the deep blue river,
   And the mist is on the mountain high,
   And the nightingale sings in the twilight,
   There let me slumber when I die.

3. I'm goin' down to the deep blue river,
   Down where the cool sweet waters flow,
   Goin' to lay me down and sleep forever,
   There let me slumber when I die.

3. I'm goin' down to the deep blue river,
   Down where the cool sweet waters flow,
   Goin' to lay me down and sleep forever,
   There where the snow-white lilies blow.

4. I don't see why I love you, darlin'
   It's plain you never cared for me,
   But still my mind is on you, darlin',
   It makes no difference where you be.

5. When you hear the whippoorwill callin',
   It's time to plant corn, it's time to plant corn,
   And when you wake and hear sweet music,
   It's the nightingale at the break of morn.

100. IF YOU WERE MY TRUE LOVE

This piece is firmly in the tradition of love lyrics, but it is not close to any stanzas that I have seen. It is distantly related to the other sympathetic bird laments, such as "Lonesome Dove" (see above) and "The Turtle-Dove" (NCF, III, no. 249), but no lines are close.

The song was recorded by Bertram Draughn in 1961 from the singing of Mildred Creighton, both of Perry County.

1. If you were my true love, And I were your beau, I'd go to some big cit-y, Tell the whole-wide world so.

SCALE: Hexachordal (e f# g# a b c#). RANGE: b - c" (Major 9th).
TONAL CENTER: E. PHRASE STRUCTURE: A B B¹ C (2, 2, 2, 2).
MELODIC RELATIONSHIP: The tune seems inconspicuous except for the **echappee-like** treatment and downward skip on "some big city," and the framing of the penultimate measure: "whole-wide world."

2. But you're not my true love,
And I'm not your beau,
I'll go to some still waterfall
And hang my head low.

3. Hang my head low, love
And hang my head low,
And listen to the little birds
As the hours come and go.

4. And each little singing bird,
With its head on its side,
Will twitter to its little mate,
And my heart-break confide.

5. Oh, what shall I do, dear,
When I've shed all my tears,
Oh, what shall I do, dear,
Through the long weary years?

6. For spring time will pass, dear,
And summer will too,
And white-headed winter
Will know I love you.

101. THE WAGONER'S LAD

This is a favorite folk lyric, found in abundance in Appalachia and sparsely elsewhere. It has almost enough narrative to be a ballad, except that the feeling is predominant, especially in those texts borrowing from "Old Smoky," and "The False-Hearted Lover." A composite of the story may be constructed, as follows: A wagoneer (Willy) is leaving Nancy's home in North Carolina (or on New River) for Georgia, or to join the army. He says her parents don't like him because he is poor, or is a drinker, and he does not want to marry her for her gold. Nancy bewails his going and tries to dissuade him because of night travel or bad weather. When he persists in going she says that she then will court whom she pleases, or that she would go with him but Mama has treated her kindly. In a few versions she decides to throw her belongings on the wagon and elope with him.

Versions of the song have been printed in SharpK (no. 117, 6 texts from NC, KY, Tenn, and Va.); in NCF (III, no. 250, 3 full texts and 3 fragments, V, 8 tunes); in SCSM (pp. 272-282, 8 and a fragment from NC and VA); in FSSH (no. 90, 2 texts from NC and GA); in FSS (no. 146, 1 text, sung by a lad in about 1870); and in FSV (pp. 83-85, 19 texts listed, including "Old Smoky," and "Kitty Wagner"). See KMFS, pp. 69-74 ("Old Smoky" stanzas 3, 5, 6) for lines that are similar. Lawless lists 41 in print.

The present text was sung in 1954 by Buell Kazee, with banjo. He had learned it and many other songs from his people in Magoffin County and had recorded this one in the 1920's for Brunswick.

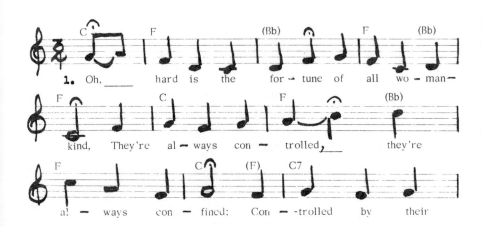

F — pa — rents un — til they are wives, Then

slaves to their hus — bands the rest of their lives.

SCALE: Pentatonic (f g a c d).   MODE: III; Plagal.   RANGE: c' - d"
(Major 9th).   TONAL CENTER: F; Circular tune.   PHRASE STRUC-
TURE: A B B A (4, 4, 4, 4) Inverted reprisenbar.   MELODIC RELATION-
SHIP: Cf. NCF, V, No. 250A, p. 157-158, "Young Girls, Take Warning," last
two phrases very close; **Ibid.** 250G has identical melody.

Observe the use of fermatas, on the initial anacrusis and at regular two-measure
intervals throughout; in this instance it might appear that the singer had some
breath problems.

2. I am a poor girl, my fortune is sad,
    I've always been courted by the wagoner's lad,
    He courted me daily, by night and by day,
    And now he is loaded and going away.

3. Your parents don't like me because I am poor,
    They say I'm not worthy of entering their door,
    I work for my living, my money's my own,
    And if they don't like me they can leave me alone.

4. Your wagon needs greasing, your whip is to mend,
    Come sit here by me as long as you can.
    My wagon is greasy, my whip's in my hand,
    So fare you well, darling, no longer to stand.

5. Your horses are hungry, go feed them some hay
    Then sit down here by me as long as you stay.
    My horses ain't hungry, they won't eat your hay,
    So fare you well, darling, I'll feed on the way.

102. FAIR AND TENDER MAIDENS

This love lament is sometimes called "Come All You Fair and Tender Ladies" (SharpK, no. 118, 18 texts) because of the opening line, or "Little Sparrow" (BSM, p. 477) because the lamenter wishes she were a little sparrow to fly to her lover's breast.

These few lyric stanzas are all we have of what might once have been a Scottish ballad or two. In his headnote to ten versions of "Jamie Douglas" (no. 204), Child details the marriage in 1670 and the divorce in 1681 of James and his wife, who was apparently slandered by their chamberlain. Child's earliest text of no. 204 was from 1776 in patchwork condition.

In the meantime Child discovered an earlier (1727) version of a related ballad called "Waly, Waly, Gin Love Be Bonny" (IV, 93). It is mostly a love lament with lines about love being bonny when it is new

But when 'tis auld, it waxeth cauld,

And fades away like morning dew.

Stanzas containing these and other lines have come to America and persist in tradition.

In addition to the references given above, there are others in Appalachia: FSS, no. 140; FSSH, no. 79; NCF, II, nos. 141 and 162, III, V, no. 254 (3 tunes); FSSUS, pp. 72, 227; WVCS, no. 21; BFSSW, no. 95. Lawless lists 46 in print. The present short text was sung in 1961 by Oscar McKinney, recorded by Betty Salisbury, both of Floyd County.

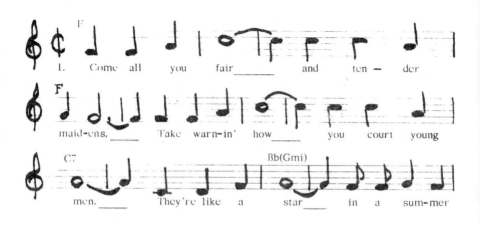

1. Come all you fair and ten-der maid-ens, Take warn-in' how you court young men. They're like a star in a sum-mer

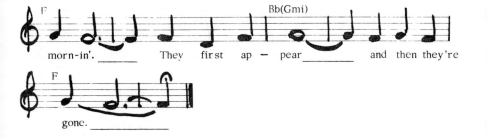

morn-in'. _____ They first ap — pear _____ and then they're gone. _____

SCALE: Pentatonic (f g a c d).   MODE: III. Plagal.   RANGE: c' - c" (Perfect octave).   TONAL CENTER: F.   PHRASE STRUCTURE: A A¹ B B¹ (4, 4, 4, 4) or: A B (8, 8).   MELODIC RELATIONSHIP: Cf. SharpK, II, No. 18; of the eighteen versions see K, M, and N for close parallels; BMMK, p. 141, "Come all ye Fair and Pretty Damsels," closely related material. Phrases A and B (above) show common relationships.

Note the **appoggiatura** treatment at the beginning of lines 2, 4, and 5.

2. They'll tell you all some lovin' story,
   They'll make you think that they love you well,
   And away they'll go to court some other,
   Leave you there in grief to dwell.

3. I wish I was on some tall mountain,
   Where the ivory rocks are black as ink,
   I'd write a letter to my false true lover,
   Whose cheeks are like the mornin' dew.

4. Oh, love is handsome, love is charmin',
   And love is pretty while it's new,
   Love grows old and love grows colder,
   And fades away like mornin' dew.

103. PRETTY LITTLE PINK

This delicate love lament does not have enough narrative to stabilize it in tradition. As a result I find it only in scattered collections in America. Sometimes the boy seems to be jilted and bids the girl farewell, as in Randolph's OFS, no. 756. Carl Sandburg has two fragments from Illinois and Kentucky (ASB, p. 166). He says they were used by marching soldiers in the Mexican War. Henry has two texts from the Southern Highlands (FSSH, no. 80), in one of which the boy names his hanging day. In my text the boy also wails his goodnight confession of love because he knows he is going to be slain, what for, we do not know.

For other shorter texts see NCF, III, no. 78 ("Coffee Grows on a White Oak Tree", 9 versions, not all printed, and V, tunes for D and G). Lawless lists 7 in print. The song was sung and tape recorded in 1957 by Doris Breeding, Adair County, learned from her mother.

MODERATELY

My pretty little Pink, so fare you well, You slight-ed me, but I wish you well; If you on earth no more I see, I could-n't treat you like you have me.

SCALE: Pentatonic (c d e g a).   MODE: III; Plagal.   RANGE: g - e"
(Major 13th).   TONAL CENTER: C.   PHRASE STRUCTURE: A B
B A[1] (2, 2, 2, 2) Inverted reprisenbar.   MELODIC RELATIONSHIP:
A noteworthy feature of this tune is the almost continuous reiteration of the
harmonic motive, with its inversions throughtout the tonic chord. Cf. FSKH,
p. 30, "Butcher Boy," first phrase; NCF, V, No. 13(c) in different meter, but
scale tones of our piece are traceable throughout.

2. The fairest face and the neatest hands,
   The fairest face and the neatest hands,
   The fairest face and the neatest hands,
   I love the ground where on she stands.

3. I would build my house on some mountain top,
   I would build my house on some mountain top,
   I would build my house on some mountain top,
   Where the sun it failed to shine.

4. I will love you till the day I die,
   I will love you till the day I die,
   I will love you till the day I die,
   To think of you it makes me cry.

5. The winter had broke and the leaves turned green,
   The winter had broke and the leaves turned green,
   The winter had broke and the leaves turned green,
   And me, a poor boy, is going to be slain.

6. Come, my little Pink, come and see me die,
   Come, my true love, come and see me die,
   Come, my dearest dear, come and see me die,
   I will meet sweet Jesus in the sky.

7. And when you pass on by my grave,
   So when you pass on by my grave,
   And when you pass on by my grave,
   You can view the green grass which over me waves.

104. IN THE PINE

This item is a typical American love lyric and as usual it exchanges stanzas with others, such as "The Lonesome Road" (ASB, p. 322), and with "The Longest Train" (FSNA, no. 290). These composites are found in scattered collections, especially in Appalachia and the South. See SharpK, no. 203, NCF, III, no. 283, V, tunes for other versions, and Gordon, FSA, pp. 83-84.

The present piece was recorded in 1961 by Sophia Keeney from the singing of Negro Bill Williams, both of Greenup County.

LILTING

1. In the pine, in the pine, where the sun nev-er shines,___ And I shiv-er when the cold winds blow.___ Oh, ___ dar-ling, my dar-ling, don't tell me no lies, ___ Where___ did you___ stay last___ night?___

REFRAIN

In the pine, in the pine, where the sun nev-er shines,___ And I shiv-er when the cold winds___ blow.____

SCALE: Pentachordal (d e f# g a).   MODE: Plagal.   RANGE: a - a' (Perfect octave).   TONAL CENTER: D.   PHRASE STRUCTURE: A B A B[1] // A[1] B[1] (4, 4, 4, 4, // 4, 4), or overall A A[1] // A[2] (8, 8, 8).   MELODIC RELATIONSHIP: There can be little doubt that both words and music are compatible with an American provenience. The entire tune is built on a theme of eight measures, used twice for the stanza, and again in almost exact repetition for the Refrain. NCF V No. 283 is melodically related.

2. Oh, the longest train I ever saw,
    Was on the Dixie line,
    The engine passed at eight o'clock,
    And the cab went by at nine.

    Refrain

236

105. DARK HOLLOW BLUES

This is a poignant love lament, relating as it does the regretful story of a stranger who goes to another state and is smitten almost at first sight. The parents will not let them get serious and he has to leave without learning her name. It is memorable to me because I recall it as about the first sad song I ever heard (and partially learned) in eastern Kentucky in about 1920. A young man often stopped at our house to sing and play the organ, and the pangs of loneliness linger over the words—

Born and raised in Old Virginny,
North Carolina I did go,
Got struck on a purty little woman,
But her name I did not know—

The song seems to be totally confined to Appalachia. There is one text with no references in NCF, III, no., 279, no tune; four in SharpK, no. 167, titled "In Old Virginny," from North Carolina, Kentucky, and Virginia; seven are listed in FSV, p. 59-60; and one from Kentucky in SFC, pp. 134-135. Lawless lists 2 in print. It was recorded by Buell Kazee in the 1920's. Compare "Little Birdie" above for likeness, especially stanza 3.

The present piece was recorded in 1959 by Mary S. Nelson from the singing of her husband Orin, both of Greenup County.

SCALE: Pentatonic (d e f# a b).   MODE: III; Plagal.   RANGE: a - d"
(Perfect 11th).   TONAL CENTER: D.   PHRASE STRUCTURE: A B B¹
C (4, 4, 4, 4).   MELODIC RELATIONSHIP: Any association with the
"Blues" is more in the words than in the tonal material of this tune.

2. Her hair was brown and curly,
    And her cheeks were rosy red,
    On her breast she wore a white lily,
    O the tears that I have shed.

3. When I'm asleep I dream about you,
    When I wake I have no rest,
    Every moment seems like an hour,
    O the pains go through my breast.

4. I'd rather be in some dark hollow
    Where the sun don't never shine,
    As for you to be some other man's darling,
    When you ain't no longer mine.

5. Poppy said I must marry,
    Mommy said it'll never do,
    But, little girl, if you are willing,
    I will run away with you.

6. I'd rather be in some dark hollow
    Where the sun don't never shine
    As for you to be some other man's darling,
    When you ain't no longer mine.

106. SWEET FERN

A more frequently used title for this piece is "Sweet Bird." I wonder as do Belden and Hudson how the fern got into the piece and what it means. See their versions with both titles (NCF, III, V, no. 295, 7 texts and 2 tunes). This is a rather wistful song of longing and yearning. Spring has come, the birds have returned to the woodlands. The girl's love for her sweetheart far away is renewed and she longs for his return.

The popularity of the piece seems to be restricted to Southern Appalachia. I have heard it often in Kentucky and have several other texts. Aside from the North Carolina texts, a Virginia (FSV, p. 103) and **KySyll.** listing, it does not appear in other collections examined. This text was given to me by Veneda D. Rose, Johnson County, in 1959.

1. Spring-time is com-ing, sweet lone-some bird, Your

e—cho in the wood-lands I hear.____ Down

in the mea-dow so lone-some your sing-ing While the

moon-light is shin—ing so clear.____ I

know he's a—way in a far dis—tant land. In a

land that's o—ver the sea.___ Oh, go a—way sing-ing your

sweet lit-tle song, And tell him to come back to me.

(Refrain) Sweet fern, sweet fern, Oh tell me is my dar-ling still

true? Sweet fern, sweet fern, I'll

be just as hap-py as you.

SCALE: Heptachordal (d e f# g a b c#).   MODE: Major; Plagal.
RANGE: c#' - c#" (Perfect octave).   TONAL CENTER: D.   PHRASE
STRUCTURE: A A^1 B A^2 // C C^1 (4, 4, 4, 4 // 4, 4). Reprisenbar plus strophe.
MELODIC RELATIONSHIP: Cf. NCF, V, No. 295A and B, for two comparable
tonal settings. The rather sophisticated modulation to the dominant in phrase
B is evidence that this tune has not been long in tradition.

2. Oh, tell me, sweet fern, is he thinking of me,
    Of the promise he made long ago?
    He said when he returned from far over the sea—
    Oh, why do the years roll so slow?
    I know he's away in a far distant land,
    In a land that's over the sea,
    Oh, go away singing your sweet little song,
    And tell him to come back to me.

    Refrain

3. Upon my finger he placed a gold ring,
    On the day he was leaving his home.
    I promised I'd be his own little girl,
    And Love him wherever he roamed.

I know he's away in a far distant land,
In a land that's over the sea,
Go fly to him singing your sweet little song,
And tell him to come back to me.

Refrain

107. NEW RIVER TRAIN

This song was sung a great deal in eastern Kentucky in the 1920's and 1930's, especially by young men in order to emphasize the number a girl could love. (By cumulation I have heard the number go up to twelve.) Now I am taken by surprise to find that the song has very little distribution over the country. There is a close version in the North Carolina material (NCF, III, V, no. 103), with a list of recordings in the American Folk Song Archive from Connecticut, Virginia, and Ohio. Davis lists two texts from Virginia (FSV, p. 249).

At times I have had a notion that this river could be the New River in West Virginia along whose winding channel runs the C & O railroad through the Big Bend Tunnel. But there is little other evidence to connect the song with West Virginia. The present text was sung by Helen Pope, Harlan County, in 1958.

1. I'm leav—ing on that New Riv—er train, I'm leaving on that New Riv—er train, The same old train that brought me here, Now it's go—in' to car—ry me a — way.

SCALE: Hexachordal (d e f# g a b).   RANGE: d' - b' (Major 6th).
TONAL CENTER: D.   PHRASE STRUCTURE: A A[1] B C (2, 2, 2, 2) or A B (4, 4).   MELODIC RELATIONSHIP: The harmonic pattern of this tune would precisely fit "Oh, When the Saints go Marching In," and doubtless many others. In NCF, V, No. 103 ("New River Train") the first phrase is close and the last 4 measures are practically identical.

241

2. Oh, darling, you can't love but one,
   Oh, darling, you can't love but one,
   You can't love but one and have any fun,
   Oh, darling, you can't love but one.

3. Oh, darling, you can't love two,
   Oh, darling, you can't love two,
   You can't love two and your little heart be true,
   Oh, darling, you can't love two.

4. Oh, darling, you can't love three,
   Oh, darling, you can't love three,
   You can't love three and still love me,
   Oh, darling, you can't love three.

5. So I'm leaving on that New River train,
   Yes, I'm leaving on that New River train,
   The same old train that brought me here,
   Now it's going to carry me away.

B. HYMNS AND HOMILETIC SONGS

108. OUR LORD HAS RISEN

This Easter hymn is a distinct version from those in the limited collections at hand. One from early America by Jackson (SFSEA, no. 47) titled "Weeping Mary" begins with the line: When weeping Mary came to seek her loving Lord and Savior— It deals with the same event, but its meter and text are different. This one may not have had a long period in tradition, because it is not well-known and the text does not seem to have been worn by oral tradition.

It was recorded from the singing of Miss Willie Steele, Menifee County, in 1959. She learned it from her father who in turn had heard it sung by a blind man in Knott County in about 1910.

1. Oh, Mar-y she came the Lord Je-sus to seek, At the dawn of the morn on the first of the week, With spic-es and oint-ment and__ rich-est per-fumes, To em-balm__ our Lord where He lay in the tomb.

SCALE: Pentatonic (d e f# a b).   MODE: III.   RANGE: d' - e" (Major 9th).   * TONAL CENTER: D.   PHRASE STRUCTURE: A B C D (2, 2, 2, 2).

* The temporal frequency of the dominant tone A is in ratio of 2 to 1 with the tonic D. Noteworthy in measures 4 and 5 is the melodic movement of successive intervals of perfect 5ths upward.

2. And as she approacheth, the earth it did quake,
   And likewise the keeper did tremble and shake,
   An angel descended and rolled back the stone
   From the door of the tomb and he sat there upon.

3. His face was like lightning, his raiment like snow,
   Said He to the woman, "Fear not for I know,
   I know you seek Jesus who was crucified,
   But, lo, He is risen as He prophesied.

4. "Your Lord He has risen as to you He said,
   'Why seek ye the living in the tomb of the dead?'
   He arose and departed, O, be not afraid,
   Come see the place where He laid.

5. "Go tell His disciples He arose from the dead,
   Now don't you remember the words that He said?
   He arose and departed, your Lord you may see,
   He goeth before you into Galilee."

6. And when His disciples this word they did hear,
   At the place appointed they all did appear,
   There Jesus met with them their causes to relieve,
   But some of them doubted while others believed.

7. There Jesus said to them, "All power is mine,
   It was given Me from My Father Divine.
   Go, teach all the nations in every land,
   Baptizing them freely as I do command."

8. And when He had told them all things they should do,
   He arose from the earth and straight upward He flew.
   There stood an amazing and astonished crowd,
   Lost sight of our Lord as He entered a cloud.

9. And while they stood gazing in wonder amazed
   'Twas a man in white raiment said, "Why do you gaze?
   The very same Jesus who was taken away
   Will come in like manner as He went away."

109. WAYFARING PILGRIM

This old hymn of earthly trials and tribulations has had a revival in Appalachia in recent years, although it has been sung in our churches for the past hundred years. George Pullen Jackson (SFSEA, no. 40) has traced it to its first appearance in a white spiritual songbook, the **Sacred Harp** of 1844, where he finds a source for the text and tune. John G. McCurry, the compiler, entered it and gave it an air he had learned in Georgia when he was eight years old. Dr. Jackson lists related tunes in eight or ten ballads, including "In Old Virginny" (Sharp, no. 167). See Schinhan's valuable musical notes to the hymn in NCF, V, no. 771, and his additional references.

Jackson also relates the texts of the hymn to folk materials, especially SharpK, no. 167C, beginning "I am a man of constant sorrow." A song in the present collection, "Dark Hollow Blues," begins with the same line.

This variant of the old hymn was sung by Shelby Johnson for Mrs. Myrle Kinder, Rowan County, in 1961.

SCALE: Heptachordal (e^b f g a^b b^b c (d^b) d). Inflected scale. MODE: Major; Plagal. RANGE: b^b - e^b" (Perfect 11th). TONAL CENTER: E^b. PHRASE STRUCTURE: A B A^1 B^1 // C D A B^1 (2, 2, 2, 2, // 2, 2, 2, 2) or A A^1 // B A^1 (8, 8, // 8, 8) Reprisenbar. MELODIC RELATIONSHIP: Cf. NCF, IV (C), p. 246 for almost identical tune in Pentatonic mode II; Also Cf. NCF, V, No. 771, embracing same melodic contour, but with an implication of minor harmonies in contrast to ours in major mode; WSSU Ch. 19, version a-2, p. 251; SharpK, II, No, 167C, p. 233, for general melodic contour, but in different mode; **Ibid**, No. 40, p. 70, for a different modal setting, with analogous melodic contour.

The intrusion of D-flat in measure 11 is obviously the influence of the Negro idiom; the D-flat taken in the context of the over-all scale pattern would indicate Mixolydian mode. The character of the tune seems to evolve from its melodic skips (from tonic to dominant), and its consistent lingering on scale-steps 1, 4, and 5.

* Pitch uncertain; probably intended for B-flat.

2. I know dark clouds will gather o'er me,
    I know my pathway's rough and steep,
    But golden fields I have before me
    Where weary eyes no more shall weep.
    I'm goin' there to see my mother,
    She said she'd meet me when I come,
    I'm just a-goin' over Jordan,
    I'm just a-goin' over home.

3. I want to sing salvation's story
    In concert with the blood bought band,
    I want to wear a crown of glory
    When I get home to that good land.
    I'm going there to see my classmates,
    They've passed before me one by one,
    I'm just a-goin' over Jordan,
    I'm just a-goin' over home.

4. I'll soon be free from every trial,
    This form will rest beneath the sod,
    I'll drop the cross of self-denial,
    And enter in my home with God.
    I'm goin' there to see my savior,
    Who shed for me His precious blood,
    I'm just a-goin' over Jordan,
    I'm just a-goin- over home.

110. DARK IS THE DESERT

This old sturdy hymn was collected and turned in to me by Mrs. Myrle Kinder, Rowan County, Kentucky, in 1961, from the singing of Rev. Luther Bradley of the Rowan County Primitive Baptist Church. He said of it: "This hymn was brought to Kentucky in 1784. A minister leading a pioneering band composed it one night on the way." This evidence has the ring of truth although I am unable to verify it. The hymn suggests an individual apocalypse on the frontier. I have been unable to find anything close to it in the hymn collections examined.

1. Dark and thorn-y is the des - ert, Through which pil - grims make their way, But be - yond this veil of sor - row, Lies realms of end - less day. Dear young sol - diers do not mur - mur At the trou - bles on the way, Meet the toils and fight with cour - age, Nev - er faint, but watch and pray.

SCALE: Pentatonic (f g a c d).   MODE: III; Plagal.   RANGE: c' - d" (Major 9th).   TONAL CENTER: F.   PHRASE STRUCTURE: A B A^1 B^1 // C C^1 A^1 B^2 (2, 2, 2, 2, //, 2, 2, 2, 2) or A A^1 // B A^2 (4, 4, 4, 4). Reprisenbar.

247

2. He whose thunder shakes creation,
   He that bids the planets roll,
   He that rides upon the tempest,
   And whose scepter sways the whole:
   Jesus, Jesus will defend you,
   Trust in Him and Him alone,
   He has shed His blood to save you,
   And will bring you to His throne.

3. There are flowers and fields of pleasure,
   And the hills of endless rest,
   Joy and peace and love shall ever
   Reign and triumph in your breast.
   There's ten thousand flaming Seraphs,
   Flying across the heavenly plain,
   There they sing the immortal praises,
   Glory, glory is their theme.

4. Sitting in heavenly hosts enraptured,
   Gazing on these shining bands,
   Wandering at their costly garments,
   And the laurels in their hands;
   There upon the golden pavement,
   See the ransomed march along,
   While the splendid courts of glory
   Sweetly echo with their song.

5. Here I see the under shepherds,
   And the flock they feed below,
   Here with joy they dwell together,
   Jesus is their shepherd now;
   Will you help the helping spirit,
   Welcome to the blissful plain?
   Glory, Laud, there and salvation,
   Reign, sweet Jesus, ever reign.

111. SHIP THAT'S SAILING BY

This is one of the numerous hymns with traditional patterns for oral singing. They have the allegory of the ship sailing over dividing waters. Also they are incremental and cumulative—allowing for repetition by adding family members. A related piece is "Old Ship of Zion."

Versions of these hymns have been collected in North Carolina (NCF, III, no. 625, 3 texts titled "Ship of Zion" and "She'll Be Comin' Around the Mountain," V, 5 tunes, 2 by different singers); in Virginia (FSV, p. 306); and in the Ozarks (OFS, IV, no. 659).

The present text was sung by Orin Nelson in 1959 for Sophia Keeney, both of Greenup County.

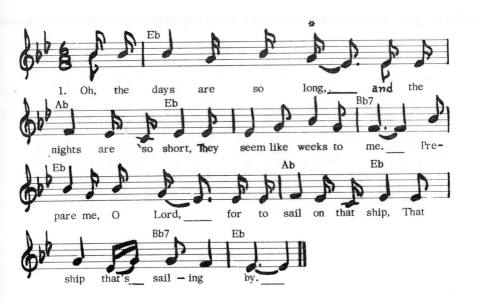

SCALE: Pentatonic (e^b f g b^b c).   MODE: III; Plagal.   RANGE: c' - b$^{b'}$ (Minor 7th).   TONAL CENTER: E^b.   PHRASE STRUCTURE: A B A C (2, 2, 2, 2) or A A^1 (4, 4).

* Perhaps the single noteworthy aspect of this plebeian tune is the "Scotch Snap" treatment in measures 1, 5, (and 6).

2. I once had a mother, but now I have none,
   She's gone to her home on high,
   Prepare me, O Lord, for to sail on that ship,
   That ship that's sailing by.

3. I once had a father, but now I have none,
   He's gone to his home on high,
   He's gone up yonder for to sail on that ship,
   That ship that's sailing by.

4. I once had a brother, etc.

112. JACOB THE PILGRIM

Mrs. Iva Stacy made contacts in the rural areas of Rowan County in 1961 for her collection project in my folklore class. When she had located several singers, I took a tape recorder and journeyed with her over most of the county. In a little remote valley one afternoon we stopped to see some ladies active in the Holiness Church. We found Mrs. Alice Gregory at the home of Mrs. Stella Hamm. They wanted to sing songs from several paperback hymnals, but I prevailed on them to sing folk hymns they knew in oral tradition. Mrs. Hamm brought out a sheaf of loose paper "ballets" and from them sang several numbers, including the present text.

I have been unable to find anything close in the collections examined, although this is a well-known dramatic event in the Bible. See related texts, titled "Jacob's Ladder," etc., in NCF, III, V, no. 536.

SLOWLY

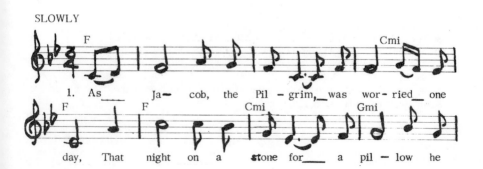

1. As Ja— cob, the Pil - grim, was wor - ried one day, That night on a stone for a pil — low he

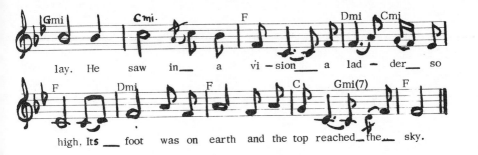

lay. He saw in_ a vi-sion_ a lad—der_ so high, Its _ foot was on earth and the top reached_the_ sky.

SCALE: Heptachordal (f g a b♭ c d e♭). MODE: Mixolydian. Plagal. RANGE: c' - c" (Perfect octave). TONAL CENTER: F. PHRASE STRUCTURE: A B A¹ C (4, 4, 4, 4) or A A¹ (8, 8). MELODIC RELATIONSHIP: The pure Mixolydian character of this tune shows an interesting use of tonal material, and it is not to be associated with any Negro influence. Like the previous song, the "Scotch snap" rhythm in measures 2, 6, 10, and 15 lends a distinct character.

Refrain: (same music as for stanza)

Hallelujah to Jesus Who died on the tree,
To raise up His ladder of mercy for me.
Press upward, press upward your prize to enview,
A crown of bright glory is waiting for you.

2. This heavenly ladder is strong and well made,
It's lasted for ages and not yet decayed,
Some people may venture by faith to go up,
The angels will help them from bottom to top.

Refrain

113. I'LL BID YOU FAREWELL

Although there are dozens of farewell hymns in the many collections at hand, especially in G. P. Jackson's volumes, I have not discovered a version close to the present text. It is a typical revival number, with the personal note in the last stanza where the itinerant man of God sings:

"After warning poor sinners, away we must ride—"
The literary quality of the hymn indicates that it has not been long in oral tradition.

This folk hymn was sung to Mrs. Iva Stacy and me by Anna Lewis, Rowan County, in 1961. She had often sung it in the United Baptist Church.

SCALE: Hexachordal (f g a b♭ c d).   MODE: Plagal.   RANGE: c'- d" (Major 9th).   TONAL CENTER: F; with strong emphasis on C. Circular tune.   PHRASE STRUCTURE: A B C D C¹ D E F (2, 2, 2, 2, 2, 2, 2, 2) or A B B¹ C (4, 4, 4, 4, 4).   MELODIC RELATIONSHIP: Cf. ABFS, p. 160, "Polly Williams," phrase 5 with our variant (a), and our phrase 1 with their phrase 3; our phrase 3 with their phrase 4.

Regardless of the singer's association of this song with the church, the tune, like so many others, undoubtedly had its roots in secular folksong.

2. My brethern and sistern all joined in a band,
   Who feel love and friendship, come give me your hand,
   The time is fast coming when we must all part,
   In the name of my Jesus here's my hand and my heart.

3. Once more, my dear brethern, I bid you farewell,
   Come follow the Savior Who saved you from Hell,
   On the top of Mount Calvary He was nailed to the wood,
   From the spear and the nail heads came water and blood.

4. The work is now finished that He came to do,
   The way of salvation is open for you;
   The way is now open that leads unto the good,
   And you may walk in it, 'tis marked with blood.

5. Perhaps there are mourners that come here today,
   Who feel great desire that Christians should pray;
   We'll pray for you mourners that make yourselves known,
   Relying that Jesus will answer His own.

6. If you shall prove faithful to your blessed Lord,
   Then honor and favor shall be your reward;
   The song of salvation we'll then sing aloud
   When Jesus and angels shall come in the cloud.

7. He will call you His ransomed, the price of his blood,
   Joint heirs of salvation and heirs of your God;
   When we all meet together on Canaan's bright shore,
   Where are weeping and sorrow and partings no more.

8. Poor mourners desponding, with hearts almost broke,
   Who feel a desire to Jesus now look;
   Your Savior stands ready with arms opened free,
   Poor shelterless doves there for refuge may flee.

9. After warning poor sinners, away we must ride,
   We trust in all dangers the Lord will provide;
   If I see you no more while life doth remain,
   At the great Resurrection I'll meet you again.

114. THE OLD CROSS ROAD

This song and the following two, although apparently in folk hymn tradition, have been difficult to establish in collections examined. There are songs in the G. P. Jackson volumes on the same subjects but do not seem to be versions of the present hymns. This one was sung to me by Miss Clara J. Dickison, Greenup County, in 1959, from her family.

The following cumulative hymn "Some Have Fathers Gone to Glory" was collected by Mrs. Mary S. Nelson in 1959 from the singing of Mrs. Carl Woods, Floyd County.

And the following hymn "I'm so Glad Today I'm Ready" was sung by Miss Clara J. Dickison in 1961.

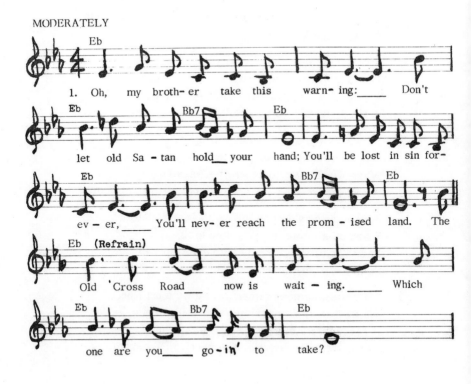

MODERATELY

1. Oh, my broth-er take this warn-ing: Don't let old Sa-tan hold your hand; You'll be lost in sin for-ev-er, You'll nev-er reach the prom-ised land. The Old Cross Road now is wait-ing. Which one are you go-in' to take?

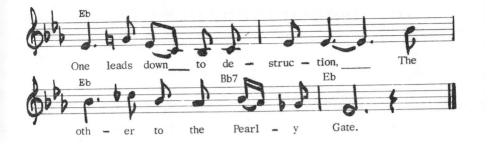

One leads down___ to de - struc - tion, ___ The
oth - er to the Pearl - y Gate.

SCALE: Hexatonic (e♭ g♭ (g) a♭ b♭ c d♭) Inflected scale.   MODE: Leans
toward Dorian with G♭; Mixolydian with G natural.   RANGE: b♭ - d♭"
(Minor 10th).   TONAL CENTER: E♭.   PHRASE STRUCTURE: A B A
B // C B A¹ B (2, 2, 2, 2, // 2, 2, 2, 2) or A A // B A¹ (4, 4, 4, 4) Reprisenbar.
MELODIC RELATIONSHIP: The tune evidences obvious Negro influences;
note the lowered 3rd and 7th scale tones; also, instability of 3rd degree: G, G♭.

2. One road leads up to Heaven,
    The other goes down below;
    Jesus our Savior will protect you,
    He'll guide you by the Old Cross Road.

    Refrain

3. Soon your life will be over,
    You'll have to face the Old Cross Road;
    Will you be ready then, my Brother,
    To shun the one goes down below?

    Refrain

4. Soon my life will be over,
    And my race on earth is run;
    But I have got one thing waiting,
    A crown that outshines the sun.

    Refrain

115. SOME HAVE FATHERS GONE TO GLORY

MODERATELY

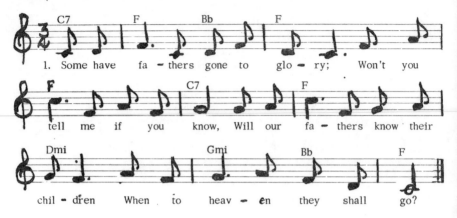

1. Some have fa - thers gone to glo - ry; Won't you tell me if you know, Will our fa - thers know their chil - dren When to heav - en they shall go?

SCALE: Pentatonic (f g a c d).   MODE: III; Plagal.   RANGE: c'- c"
(Perfect octave).   TONAL CENTER: F. Circular tune.   PHRASE
STRUCTURE: A B B¹ C (2, 2, 2, 2).   MELODIC RELATIONSHIP: See "A
Mother Went out on a Party" in this collection, phrases 1 and 2; also, first two
phrases of "Silver Dagger." Cf. ABFS p. 672, "The Other Shore" for a different
musical setting; the usual procedure in such songs is to include (in subsequent
stanzas) mother, father, brother, sister, neighbor, etc.

2. They'll be watching from some window,
   While we roam some distant shore,
   They will know that we are coming,
   And will meet us at the door.

3. Some have mothers gone to glory;
   Won't you tell me if you know,
   Will our mothers know their children,
   When to heaven they shall go?

4. They'll be watching from some window,
   While we roam some distant shore,
   They will know that we are coming,
   And will meet us at the door.

5. Some have brothers gone to glory;
   Won't you tell me if you know,
   Will our brothers know their children,
   When to heaven they shall go?

6. They'll be watching from some window,
   While we roam some distant shore,
   They will know that we are coming,
   And will meet us at the door.

7. Some have sisters gone to glory,
   Won't you tell me if you know,
   Will our sisters know their children,
   When to glory they shall go!

8. They'll be watching from some window,
   While we roam some distant shore,
   They will know that we are coming,
   And will meet us at the door.

116. I'M SO GLAD TODAY I'M READY

SLOWLY

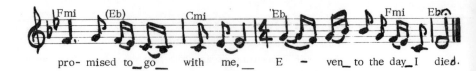

pro- mised to_ go_ with me,_ E - ven_ to the day_ I died.

SCALE: Pentatonic (e^b f g b^b c).   MODE: III; Plagal.   RANGE: b^b - c"
(Major 9th).   TONAL CENTER: E^b.   PHRASE STRUCTURE: A B A^1
B^1 (3, 2, 3, 2) or: A A^1 (5, 5). Phrases 1 and 3 probably shortened by the singer;
might normally be 4, 2, 4, 2 structure.   MELODIC RELATIONSHIP: The
tune shows an interesting use of Pentatonic material. Measures 4, 7, and 9
embrace a bit of melodic ornamentation that is somewhat idiomatic of the
spiritual song.

2. Then bury me in the little graveyard,
    Place my Bible by my side,
    Tell all the people standing around me,
    How I loved before I died.

3. Tell my mother I'd like to see her,
    And I'd like to shake her hand,
    Tell her that I'll meet her yonder,
    Over in that Promised Land.

4. Tell my old gray-haired daddy,
    Who has worked so hard for me,
    That I'm coming home to see him,
    And the One Who died for me.

117. SEVEN BLESSINGS OF MARY

In medieval England we first find poems on the five blessings or joys of
Mary. Later these poems become the great carols of the Church. From the
French we seem to have received versions of Noels with seven joys. And from
more recent times in England and in America the number has increased to a

maximum of twelve, presumably to match a companion popular carol "The Twelve Apostles."

"Seven Blessings" is more rare in American collections than the Apostles carol. Davis lists six texts in FSV, pp. 297-298. For earlier notes, those by Cox in FSS, no. 135, are fairly complete for the Old Country, plus JAF, 5, 535 and 32, 501 (the Cox text). The most recent notes and comments are given in NCF, II, IV, no. 51 (one text and tune). The only text that I have seen with seven blessings and therefore almost identical with the present carol is in FSNA, no. 123, recorded in the South. Lawless lists 12 in print. My variant was sung in 1961 by Mildred Creighton and recorded by Mr. Bertram Draughn, both of Floyd County.

MOVING

SCALE: Hexachordal (d e f# g a b).   MODE: Plagal.   RANGE: a - d"
(Perfect 11th).   TONAL CENTER: D.   PHRASE STRUCTURE: A B C
B D E F A^1 F (2, 2, 2, 2, 2, 2, 2, 2, 2) or A B C A^1 (4, 4, 6, 4).   MELODIC
RELATIONSHIP: The initial B and C phrases have elements in common. Cf.
NCF, **IV**, p. 51 for fragmentary melodic similarity. The six-measure C phrase
shows internal incrementation.

* First beat on D was executed by singer as a quarter-note, with elision of the
two syllables: Fa-ther.

2. The very next blessing that Mary had was the blessing of two,
    To think that her son, Jesus, could read the Bible through,
    Could read the Bible through; come all ye in the wilderness,
    Glory be to the Father and the Son and the Holy Ghost throughout
    eternity.

4. The very next blessing that Mary had was the blessing of four,
    To think that her son, Jesus, could make the rich to poor,
    Could make the rich to poor; come all ye in the wilderness,
    Glory be to the Father and the Son and the Holy Ghost throughout
    eternity.

5. The very next blessing that Mary had was the blessing of five,
    To think that her son, Jesus, could make the dead to live,
    Could make the dead to live; come all ye in the wilderness,
    Glory be to the father and the Son and the Holy Ghost throughout eternity.

6. The very next blessing that Mary had was the blessing of six,
    To think that her son, Jesus, could make to well the sick,
    Could make to well the sick; come all ye in the wilderness,
    Glory be to the Father and the Son and the Holy Ghost throughout
    eternity.

7. The very next blessing that Mary had was the blessing of seven,
    To think that her son, Jesus, had died and gone to heaven,
    Had died and gone to heaven; come all ye in the wilderness,
    Glory be to the Father and the Son and the Holy Ghost throughout
    eternity.

118. I AM A LITTLE SCHOLAR

The naive little boy, obviously going to a religious or parochial school, reminds the listener of "Little Hugh of Lincoln," although there is no further comparison between it and the much older ballad (Child no. 155). I cannot find any other evidence of it in tradition, unless 'The Little Schoolboy" listed by Davis (FSV, pp. 302) from Virginia is a variant.

My text was given to me by Mrs. Catherine Nickles from the singing of James Nickles of Knott County in 1959.

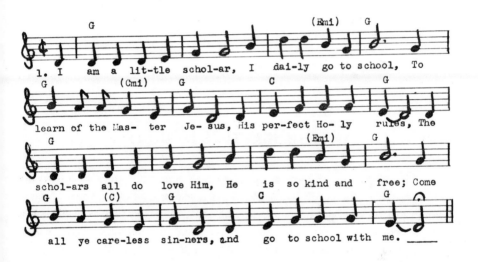

SCALE: Pentatonic (g a b d e).   MODE: III; Plagal.   RANGE: d'- d" (Perfect octave).   TONAL CENTER: G. Circular tune.   PHRASE STRUCTURE: A B A B (4, 4, 4, 4) or: A A (8, 8).   MELODIC RELATIONSHIP: See "Roving Gambler" in this volume for an almost identical tune, with slight modifications; Cf. MTBV, No. 38, version 38 AA, p. 102, "Our Goodman," first four phrases (down to the refrain) almost the same as ours; NCF IV. No. 42B1 has very close relationship.

Note the **appoggiatura**-like treatment at the imperfect plagal cadences of the B phrases.

2. I am a little Christian, the Lord hath made me so,
   All over a new creature, what wonders can He do;
   I love the things I hated, I hate the things I loved,
   My Master is preparing me to reign with Him above.

3. I am a little preacher, I preach the Gospel free,
   Whate'er my Master gives me I give it all away;
   And when my heart is empty, I go to Master's store,
   He smiles in love upon me and gives me all the more.

4. I am a little poet, I wrote this little song,
   And ofttimes it doth cheer me when I am all alone;
   And if there is another who would wish to learn the same,
   I pray the Lord to set their souls all in a heavenly flame.

119. THE SKEPTIC'S DAUGHTER

This long literary homily has scarcely been in tradition since most texts are close variants. Randolph (OFS, IV, no. 601, one printed of two) cites variants found in two songbooks, one as early as 1894, and states that he heard it at a brusharbor church service near Springdale, Arkansas. And well it might be used in camp meetings since its theme is conversion from skepticism. Another close variant with tune is given by Schinhan in NCF, IV, no. 328.

Although I have three or four other texts, I have never heard it sung all the way through. My informant, Mrs. Anna Lewis, was stout and sickly and sang only the first stanza and recited the remainder from a long printed sheet. I was assisted in finding her in 1961 by her neighbor, Mrs. Ivy Stacy, both of Rowan County.

MODERATELY

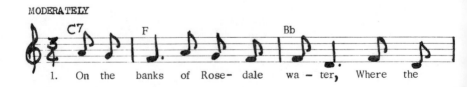

1. On the banks of Rose-dale wa-ter, Where the

bloom-ing flow- ers smile; Lived a rich and love- ly

daugh- ter, A rich skep- tic's on- ly child. Crowned with

know- ledge, health and beau- ty, Learned in all the clas - sic

lore, And for vir - tue, love, and du- ty, She was

queen of Rose- dale shore.

SCALE: Pentatonic (f g a c d). MODE: III; Plagal. RANGE: c'- d"
(Major 9th). TONAL CENTER: F. PHRASE STRUCTURE: A B A B[1]
C C[1] A[1] B[1] (2, 2, 2, 2, 2, 2, 2, 2) or: A A[1] B A[1] (Reprisenbar). MELODIC
RELATIONSHIP: Cf. OFS IV, p. 613, "Little Willie," phrase B.

2. Famed for genius, sense, and wisdom,
   She became her parents' pride;
   When she gained the skeptic's system,
   She was almost deified.
   Far and wide they saw her power
   Over all disputants rise,
   And her genius seemed to tower
   Like a goodness in their eyes.

3. A large meeting was progressing
   Near her father's flowery grove,
   Where poor sinners were professing
   All the bliss of Christian love.

"Father, let me show the Bible
To this poor illiterate clan,
That it's nothing but a libel
On the character of Man."

4. "Go, my daughter, you are able
To destroy their Sabbath theme;
Go and prove their Book a fable
And their doctrine all a dream."
Dressed in all her pride and glory,
She went forth to join the throng,
Where she heard the Gospel story,
Both in sermon and in song.

5. Soon a thrill of deep conviction
Seized upon her guilty soul,
Filled her heart with an affliction
That her mind could not control;
Calmly rose she without falter,
All her follies bade farewell
And came in before the altar
Where in humble prayer she fell.

6. Casting all her cares on heaven,
Every prayer went to the throne,
Till her sins were all forgiven
And the Savior was her own;
Then she hastened to her father
To inform him of God's love
And to tell her aged mother
There's a better world above.

7. "Well, my daughter, it's reported
You have joined that ignorant horde,
To their doctrine been converted,
All against your father's word."
"Oh, dear father, show me favor,
I've not joined that ignorant horde,
But have joined the blessed Savior,
Who is Christ the righteous Lord!"

8. "Well, my daughter, your behavior
   Seals your doom without delay,
   You must either leave your Savior
   Or your father's house today."
   "Oh, dear father, I will love you
   Though you drive me from your door,
   None on earth I'll place before,
   But I'll love the Savior more."

9. "Then begone from me forever,
   I will see your face no more,
   All your kindred ties you sever
   When you leave your father's door."
   "Only let me have your favor
   And I'll be your willing slave,
   But I cannot yield my Savior,
   No, I'd rather choose the grave."

10. "There's your likeness, clothes and purses,
    Take them and at once depart,
    For your prayers seem more like curses
    On my wounded broken heart."
    "Good-by, father, will you greet me
    Where the happy millions dwell?
    Here's my hand, oh, will you meet me
    Where we'll no more say farewell?

11. "My dear mother, I have often
    Thought of riches, pride and birth,
    But I'm now an outcast orphan
    With no home or friends on earth.
    Though my father and my mother
    Drive me homeless from their door,
    I've a friend more dear than brother
    Who will keep me evermore."

12. Leaving mansions, fields, and fountains
    From the scene she turned away,
    Up the wild and rocky mountains
    Where her path in twilight lay.
    To the bright and distant halo
    Slowly journeyed she along,
    While her voice in lovely echo
    Filled the valley with her song.

13. Rose the evening mild and gentle,
In sweet zephers fanned the moor,
And the night had spread her mantle
As the skeptic left the door.
"Oh, dear Mary, come and listen
To the lovely sound I hear,
Oh, come quickly—how my system
Feels a weight I cannot bear."

14. The wife came on the veranda
Where she heard the notes abroad,
"Oh, my husband, it's Amanda
In sweet converse with her God.
Hear it through the starry region,
How the heavenly anthems rise,
Oh, dear husband, her religion
Is the doctrine of the skies."

15. But her words were scarcely spoken,
Ere she sank in anguish wild,
And the father's heart was broken
As he sped toward the child.
Up the mountain dark and lonesome,
Guided by her lovely song,
Clasped his daughter to his bosom,
"Oh, my child, forgive this wrong.

16. "Oh, come back and save your father,
'Tis your prayers that let him live,
Come, my child, embrace your mother,
And our wretched hearts forgive."
"Yes, my father, I'll go with you,
And we'll join the heavenly theme,
Singing glory hallelujah
To the Savior's glorious name."

17. Shouting glory to her Savior,
She returned in heavenly love,
Where her parents soon found favor
In the joys of heaven above.
They with all their sins forgiven
Went rejoicing on their way
To their home high up in heaven,
To the realms of endless day.

120. DRUNKARD'S DREAM

The best informants on this temperance dream piece trace it back to England of the 1850's, titled "The Husband's Dream." Following the usual pattern of American migration, it is now found sparingly on the East Coast and in abundance in Appalachia, the Midwest, and in the Ozarks. Essential information and references are given by Cox (FSS, no. 129), Randolph (OFS, II, no. 307), Belden (BSM, p. 469), and by Belden, Hudson, and Schinhan (NCF, III, V, no. 22, 5 texts, one printed, 2 tunes; no. 23, same title is related). Lawless lists 12 in print.

The present version was sung by Mrs. Louisa Harris of Bell County, in 1957. She had lived in the Ozarks where she had learned it and a few other songs.

SCALE: Pentatonic (e g a b c).   MODE: II.   RANGE: e' - e" (Perfect octave).   TONAL CENTER: E.   PHRASE STRUCTURE: A B A^1 B^1 (2, 2, 2, 2,) or: A A^1 (4, 4).   MELODIC RELATIONSHIP: Cf. NCF V, No. 22D, "The Drunkard's Dream," for an almost identical tune in phrases 1, 2, and 3.

2.   Your wife and children, are they well?
     You once did treat them strange,
     But are you kinder to them now
     What's made this happy change?

3. It was a warning dream I dreamed
   That heaven sent to me,
   To keep me from a drunkard's curse,
   From woe and misery.

4. My poor wife in sickness lay
   And sunken were her eyes,
   I starved my children night and day
   And heard their wailing cries.

5. I'd laugh and sing the drunkard's curse,
   With mirth the earth would ring,
   And like a brute I fell asleep,
   And dreamed this fateful dream.

6. Oh, I dreamed I staggered home,
   Oh, what a silent gloom,
   My wife not there, where could she be?
   And strangers in the room.

7. I heard them say, poor thing, she's dead,
   She has lived a wretched life,
   For grief and sorrow has broke her heart,
   She's been that drunkard's wife.

8. My little children standing around
   And unto their father said,
   Oh, Father, Father, wake her up,
   The people say she's dead.

9. I stood one moment in a maze,
   And hastened to where she lay,
   I dreamed I kissed her violet lips,
   And they were as cold as clay.

10. Oh, Father, Father, wake her up,
    The people say she's dead,
    When I waked my married dear
    Was kneeling by my bed.

11. Oh, Mary, speak to me,
    I'll never, never cause you pain,
    I'll never grieve your lovin' heart,
    I'll never drink again.

121. NO DRUNKARD

In the collections at hand I cannot find a very close parallel to this song. There are, however, many songs relating a girl's preference for and aversions to a marriage partner. SharpK (no. 272) has two texts in which the girl prefers the soldier and sailor. The one text of Randolph (OFS, II, no. 493) rejects the blacksmith, sheriff, preacher, and gambler for the railroader. The girl in Belden's two texts (BSM, pp. 262-263) rejects those too rich, too poor, too old, too young, etc. And almost every kind of man and boy is rejected in the North Carolina collection of about 20 variants (NCF, III, no. 173, 19 entered but not all printed, V, 5 tunes).

The woman in the present text concentrates on the woes of life with the drunkard, in contrast to a Romeo who will love and protect her here below and will be with her in the next world. It was collected by Mrs. Doris Breeding in 1958 from the singing of her mother, Mrs. C. R. Moss, both of Adair County.

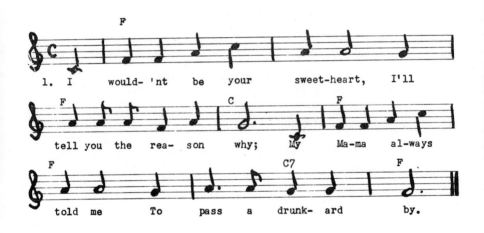

1. I would-'nt be your sweet-heart, I'll
tell you the rea- son why; My Ma-ma al-ways
told me To pass a drunk- ard by.

SCALE: Tetratonic (f g a c).   MODE: Plagal.   RANGE: c' - c'' (Perfect octave).   TONAL CENTER: F.   PHRASE STRUCTURE: A B A C (2, 2, 2, 2); or A A^1 (4, 4).   MELODIC RELATIONSHIP: Cf. NCF V, No. 17H, measures 1 to 4.

2. She says it is too dangerous,
    For a girl as young as I
    To fall in love with a handsome young man
    Who has a drunkard's eye.

3. A blue-eyed man I much admire,
   Though the black-eyed man I will win,
   The poor pitiful red-eyed man
   Is a man that is very thin.

4. This I have said for many a year,
   I will say it all my life,
   I never, no, never
   Will be a drunkard's wife.

5. When to the altar I am led,
   I hope to feel and know
   I married a man to love and protect me
   Wherever I may go.

6. Together we may live,
   Together we may die,
   And when we leave this earthly home,
   I will go to the One on high.

7. To that beautiful home in Heaven,
   Where God in peace has said,
   Never a drunkard in that Holy Land
   Can hope to be led.

122. A MOTHER WENT OUT ON A PARTY

No other collection examined has a close version of the present song. The refrain line "Please, mama, please stay home with me" relates it to similar sentimental pieces in tradition; in fact, Eddy Arnold recorded a song with this title in the 1940's.

It was recorded from Shirley Wilson, Knox County, in 1957.

1. A moth-er went out on a par-ty, She left at

home her ba - by son. He cried and begged her not to

leave him, But she would not give___up her fun.

SCALE: Pentatonic (g a b d e).   MODE: III; Plagal.   RANGE: d' - d"
(Perfect octave).   TONAL CENTER: G.   PHRASE STRUCTURE: A B A
B¹ (2, 2, 2, 2) or: A A¹ (4, 4).   MELODIC RELATIONSHIP: See "Some
have Fathers Gone to Glory" in this volume for similar tune.

2. She leased and laughed and did some drinking,
   The world for her was full of glee,
   But now and then these words would haunt her,
   "Please, Mama, please stay home with me."

3. But soon she joined the merry makers,
   The world for her was full of glee,
   But now and then these words would haunt her,
   "Please, Mama, please stay home with me."

4. She left the party fellin' dizzy,
   With many a drink upon her breath,
   She hurried home and found her baby
   In rage and pain and near in death.

5. The doctor came and looked on sadly,
   The case was hopeless he could see,
   The baby died these words a-pleading,
   "Please, Mama, please stay home with me."

123. BOYS IN BLUE

Although this piece dramatizes a Union Soldier boy returning in his coffin, it does not seem to have come out of the 1860's. In fact it is very much like a composed sentimental number from the stage of the 1890's. It is not well known in tradition. I have discovered, aside from about four texts in eastern Kentucky, a single version from the Ozarks (OFS, IV, no. 696) titled "The Express Office." Mr. Randolph has the word of a singer as having heard the song in about 1900. My piece was sung by Mrs. Ann Jones of Bell County in 1957.

SCALE: Heptachordal (f g a b^b c d e). MODE: Major; Plagal. RANGE: c' - c'' (Perfect octave). TONAL CENTER: F. PHRASE STRUCTURE: A B C D A B C D^1 (4, 4, 4, 4, 4, 4, 4, 4) or A B A B^1 (8, 8, 8, 8). MELODIC RELATIONSHIP: The overall character of this tune, with its modulation to the dominant at the close of the first strophe, seems to give evidence of its 19th centruy origin, not necessarily secular.

2. "You've made a slight mistake, Sir,
   I'd like for you to know,
   This is the express office, Sir,
   And not the town depot."
   "You do not understand me, Sir,"
   With trembling lips he said,
   "He's not coming here as a passenger,
   But he's coming to us dead."

3. Just then a whistle pierced the air,
   "The Express!" someone cried,
   Then with trembling, stumbling steps,
   The old man stepped outside;
   Just then a casket in a box
   Was lowered to the ground,
   It was an eager, anxious crowd
   That quickly gathered round.

4. "Don't handle him so roughly, boys,
   For that's our darling Jack.
   He left us just as you are now,
   Look how he's coming back;
   He's broken his poor mother's heart,
   As partings always do,
   Thank God he died a hero's death
   While with the boys in blue."

124. SOUTHERN HOME

This rather over-sweet song was sung, if I am not deceived, in eastern Kentucky in the 1930's. It could have been later. The surprise to me is that it is not in the many collections examined. The evidence suggests that the rover pining out his heart for his southern sweetheart and shack is a hobo who has been "most everywhere" and is now heading down the line.

The song was sung by a Methodist minister, Raymond Earlywine, Greenup County, in 1961 to James E. Porter, one of my folklore students.

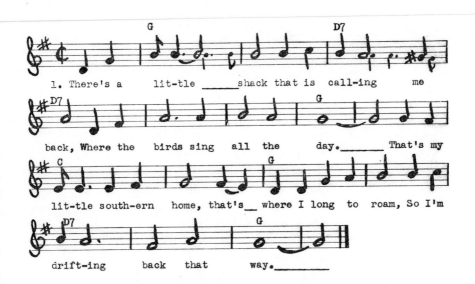

SCALE: Heptachordal (g (g#) a b c d e f#) Inflected Scale.   MODE: Major; Plagal.   RANGE: d' - c" (Minor 7th).   TONAL CENTER: G. PHRASE STRUCTURE: A B C D (4, 4, 4, 4).   MELODIC RELATIONSHIP: This somewhat cliche tune obviously is of relatively recent origin, apparently secular.

Refrain: (same music as stanza)

I'm a-heading down the line for that southern home of mine,
Never again to roam;
I've been around most everywhere, but there's no place so fair
As my little southern home.

2. And on the southern shore there's a girl I adore,
   She is waiting for me each day;
   She's the sweetest girl in all the world
   That's why I'm drifting back that way.

   Refrain

3. Stanza whistled

   Refrain

125. MY MOTHER'S HANDS

This simple song is not found in the collections examined. I have no idea whether it has any circulation or not, but I will give the facts as gleaned from my informants.

It was sung and taped by Mrs. Doris Breeding of Adair County in 1958. She says she heard it from her mother, Mrs. C. R. Moss, who had learned it from older sisters. Her father says that it was composed and sung by Prof. L. Bandy in his singing schools of Adair County. He was from eastern Tennessee. There are no dates given but Mrs. Moss must have learned it in about 1920.

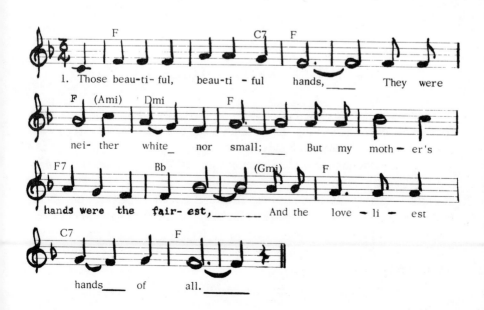

SCALE: Pentachordal (f g a b^b c).   MODE: Plagal.   RANGE: f' - c"
(Perfect 5th).   TONAL CENTER: F.   PHRASE STRUCTURE: A B C
D (4, 4, 4, 4).   MELODIC RELATIONSHIP: This tune is most probably
a contrafactum from a variety of sources, possibly hymnody. If Professor L.
Bandy composed the tune (see Dr. Roberts' notes) inevitably eclecticism crept
in.

2.   My mother's hands, her beautiful hands
    That guided me safe o'er the sands,
    I bless God's name for the memory
    Of Mother's own beautiful hands.

3.   Those beautiful, beautiful hands,
    How they cared for my infant days,
    They smoothed my brow and eased the pain,
    I think I can feel them now.

4.   Those beautiful, beautiful hands,
    I shall clasp them again once more;
    When my feet touch the banks of the Heavenly lands,
    We shall meet on the shining shore.

126. PUT MY LITTLE SHOES AWAY

The story of a little child always tries to draw our serious attention. And
when one is dying and making plans and unselfish requests, we are touched with
the goodness and beauty of childhood.

The piece is found more in circulation than collections indicate. Randolph
(OFS, IV, no. 715) has two texts of 4 and 5 stanzas respectively. Only a few other
scattered evidences appear in folksong literature: Spaeth, WSMML, pp. 25-26,
Neely, TSSI, pp. 257-258. I heard it rather often in the 1920's and 1930's from
records and in tradition. It must have been composed by one of our minstrels
and put on phonograph records. Cf. OFS, no. 707 and NCF, IV, no. 318 (related
themes only).

My version was sung by Mrs. Emma Miracle, Bell County, in 1958.

1. Now come bathe my fore-head, Mo - ther, ___ For I'm grow-ing ve - ry weak. Let one drop of wa - ter, Mo - ther, ___ Fall up - on my burn - ing cheek.

SCALE: Heptachordal (f g a b♭ c d e).   MODE: Major; Plagal.   RANGE: c' - c'' (Perfect octave).   TONAL CENTER: F.   PHRASE STRUCTURE: A B A C (2, 2, 2, 2) or: A A¹ (4, 4).

2. You will do this, won't you, Mother,
Please remember what I say,
You will do this, won't you, Mother?
Put my little shoes away.

3. Soon the baby will be larger,
And they'll fit his little feet,
Won't he look so handsome, Mother,
When he walks upon the street?

4. Santa Claus he brought them to me,
With a lot of other things,
And I think he brought an angel,
With a pair of golden wings.

C. HUMOROUS AND SATIRICAL SONGS

127. CRAWDAD MAN

This is a kind of floating banjo and square dance number, taking its name from the often repeated refrain such as This Morning, Uh Huh, Sweet Thing, Sugar Babe. The rhythm, the tune, and the dialect place it among Black and minstrel collections of the South. Lomax has three related pieces but gives no specific sources (FSUSA, no. 34, ASFS, p. 310). A rather curious title that SharpK admitted into their volumes "Crow-fish Man" (no. 199) is related. A fairly full set of stanzas with refrain is in the North Carolina collection (NCF, III, V, no. 483). See also related texts in ANS, p. 241, REW, p. 124, White ANFS, p. 32, and OSF, III, no. 443. Lawless lists 8 pieces in printed sources.

This item was sung by Crockett Carter of Harlan County in 1958, learned from his father.

1. I got a hook and you got a line, Ho-ney,
I got a hook and you got a line, Babe,
I got a hook and you got a line, Gwine-a
ketch 'em craw-dad dis ol' time, Ho-ney,
Ba-by mine.

SCALE: Pentatonic (e f# g# b c#).   MODE: III; Plagal.   RANGE: b -
c#" (major 9th).   TONAL CENTER: E.   PHRASE STRUCTURE:
A B A^1 B^1 A^2 A^3 C (2, 2, 2, 2, 2, 2, 4) or A A^1 A^2 B (4, 4, 4, 4).   MELODIC
RELATIONSHIP: Cf. OFS III, p. 197 - 198, No. 443 "Sweet Thing," very close.
ABFS p. 310 "Frog Went A-Courtin" – striking resemblance; also, NCF, IV, 4B,
"The Twa Sisters." See "Frog Went A-Courtin" in this collection for an almost
similar melodic line.

In regard to repetition of an idea some pedagogue once said: "It's AAA then go,"
apropos in the rhythmic motives of this four-phrase tune.

2. See'd a feller totin' a sack, Honey,
    See'd a feller totin' a sack, Babe,
    See'd a feller totin' a sack,
    Had all de crawdad he could pack, Honey, Baby mine.

3. Sell my crawdad three fo' a dime, Honey
    Sell my crawdad three fo' a dime, Babe,
    Sell my crawdad three fo' a dime,
    Kin yo' sell yo's as cheap as mine, Honey, Baby mine?

4. What you goin' to do when the pond goes dry, Honey,
    What you goin' to do when the pond goes dry, Babe,
    What you goin' to do when the pond goes dry?
    Sit on de bank an' watch the crawdads die, Honey, Baby mine.

5. Dis is de end of my crawdad song, Honey,
    Dis is de end of my crawdad song, Babe,
    Dis de end of my crawdad song,
    Come on, Honey, better, git along, Honey, Baby mine.

128. IDA RED

A lively banjo piece without definite stanzas, it is used for square dances and
hoedowns in Appalachia and the Ozarks. It is not so wide-spread in distribution
as "Cindy" and "Shoo Fly." With the passing of the old-time parties and barn
dances in the country it has lost some of its usefulness and popularity.

See Halpert, **et al, Check List,** Archive of American Folksong (1942, p. 181) for recordings from Ohio, Virginia, Kentucky, and California. Some other scattered references are these: NCF, III, no. 448, "I Got a Girl" (one short text, V, tune); OFS, III, no. 442; TSCF, no. 74; a listing in FSSUS, p. 231, no. 228; and ABFS, pp. 110-111 (from the Texas Bottoms). Lawless lists 13 in print.

The piece was recorded by Mary S. Nelson in 1959 from the singing of Mrs. Mary Wright, both of Greenup County.

SCALE: Pentatonic (g a b d e).   MODE: III; Plagal.   RANGE: d' - b' (Major 6th).   TONAL CENTER: G.   PHRASE STRUCTURE: A B C B^1 (2, 2, 2, 2) or A B (4, 4).   MELODIC RELATIONSHIP: This lively little tune is vernacular in the realm of hoe-down and square dance.

*Refrain:
Ida Red and Ida Blue
And I'm in love with Ida too.

2. Ida Red she ain't no fool
    She can put a saddle on a humped-back mule.

280

3. I'll buy me a horse and make me a sled,
   And nobody rides but Ida Red.

4. Sold my horse and bought me a wagon,
   To keep little Ida's feet from draggin'.

5. Down the road and across the creek,
   See my little Ida twice a week.

6. I asked little Ida to be my wife,
   She said, "No sir, not to save your life."

7. Down the road and across the creek,
   Can't get a letter but once a week.

8. Ida Red and Ida Blue,
   I'm a plumb fool about Ida too.

9. Ida Red she ain't no fool,
   She's big as an elephant, stout as a mule.

10. Down the road 'bout a mile and a half
    Can't see Ida but can hear her laugh.

*Refrain after every stanza or two.

129. SHOO FLY (Cindy)

Although my informant called this string of "Cindy" verses "Shoo Fly" because of the refrain, the piece is easier identified by the dual name. Another help is the fact that other sets of stanzas in collections are called "Massa Had a Yallar Gal" and "Eliza Jane."

NCF, III, no. 404, has 5 versions of "Cindy" and V has 3 tunes (G by a different singer). The headnotes to the texts and tunes give a dozen references (BKH, 172; FSSH, 434; JAF 54: 168), most showing the popularity of the piece in Appalachia and the South. NCF, III, no. 406, has 3 versions of "Massa Had a Yaller Gal," V has one tune (C). Again the headnotes cite White (ANFS, 152-

153), who traces the song to minstrel songbooks of the 1850's, especially in Alabama. TNFS, 66-68, cites versions from Louisiana, South Carolina, and Kentucky. NCF, III, nos. 436 and 437 have a text each of "Eliza Jane II"; V has 2 tunes, one by a different singer. See FSSH, no. 169, "Eliza Jane" (4 versions), no. 170, "Cindy" (2 versions), and no. 171, "Massa Had a Little Yaller Gal" (one text).

The present piece was sung in 1959 by Mary Wright, with banjo, for Mary S. Nelson, both of Greenup County.

LIVELY

SCALE: Heptachordal (c d e f g a b).   MODE: Major.   RANGE: c'-c''
(Perfect octave).   TONAL CENTER: C.   PHRASE STRUCTURE: A B //
A^1 B^1 (4, 4, // 4, 4).   MELODIC RELATIONSHIP: This tune is probably
found in the old books of minstrel song; but the editor has not observed it among
any of his bibliography.

Measure 5 shows the usage of synaloepha – combining of adjacent vowels –
a normal idiom of folk singers.

Note how the numerous tonal iterations are balanced off with descending scale
cadences.

* Probably intended to be sung F.

2. I took her to a black smith shop
    To get her mouth made small,
    She turned around a time or two,
    And swallowed shop and all.

    Refrain

3. My gal she's got religion,
    She's a Methodist thru and thru,
    And I've just about made up my mind
    To be a Methodist too.

    Refrain

4. I asked my gal to marry me,
    She said I'll see you later,
    Then she mashed my nose all over my face
    With a great big Irish pertater.

    Refrain

5. I went to see my darlin'
    She was standin' in the door,
    Her shoes and stockings in her hand,
    And her feet all over the floor.

    Refrain

6. I went to see my darlin'
    They asked me in for supper,
    I stumped my toe on the table leg
    And run my nose in the butter.

    Refrain

7. She hugged me and she kissed me,
    She called me sugar plum,
    She threw her arms around my neck
    And I thought my time had come.

    Refrain

130. GOIN' DOWN TOWN

This Negro piece, apparently from the South, is a rowdy number used for hoedowns and square sets. White (ANFS, pp. 178) and Lomax (FSNA, no. 270) trace it to ante-bellum minstrel shows and perhaps into earlier Negro folk roots. After the War Between the States the Negroes had their forty-acres-and-a-mule dream and celebrated their freedom with a small crop of cotton or tobacco. The piece has later taken on stanzas from "Cindy," "Old Joe Clark" and others in the hands of Southern Mountain whites in their fun and dancing. See nine texts and four tunes in NCF, III, V, no. 415; other references are **KySyll**, p. 20; OSC, pp. 60-62 (Ky); JAF, 22: 249 (N.C.); FSSUS, p. 231 (Ky.).

The present text was sung in 1959 by Warren Wright for Mrs. Mary S. Nelson, both of Greenup County.

SCALE: Heptachordal (d e f# g a b c#).   MODE: Major; Plagal.
RANGE: c#' - b: (Minor 7th).   TONAL CENTER: D.   PHRASE STRUC-
TURE: A A B C // A^1 A^2 B^1 C^1 (2, 2, 2, 2, // 2, 2, 2, 2) or A B // A^1 B^1 (4, 4,
/ / 4, 4).   MELODIC RELATIONSHIP: Cf. NCF, V, No. 415 "Lynchburg
Town," four versions.

The character of this rather jaunty and trite tune is entirely compatible with the
text, somewhat reminiscent of the numerous play-game and nursery tunes; however its roots are attributed to Negro folksong and minstrelsy. The singer began
with the refrain.

Refrain (varation):

To go down town,
Goin down town,
Tobacco's sellin for fifteen cents,
Goin to take my tobacco down.

2.   Mama sent me to the store,
She told me not to stay,
But when I saw those pretty girls,
I could not get away.

Refrain

3.   I went to see my darlin'
She was standing in the door,
Her shoes and stockings in her hand
Her feet all over the floor.

Refrain:

4.   I hooked my mule up to a sleigh
And took her for a ride,
I asked her if she'd marry me
As we rode side by side.

Refrain

5.   Hold tight, little darlin
Quit actin like a fool,
I got no time to kiss you now,
I'm busy with this mule.

Refrain:

6. Watch that mule go down the road,
   He's got his ears laid back,
   Hold you seat, little darlin'
   He' gonna jump the track.

   Refrain

7. Sleigh bells a'ringing,
   Snow fallin' fast,
   Got my mule in the harness now,
   Got him hooked at last.

   Refrain

8. Goin' to buy myself a big cigar,
   Goin' smoke it on the street,
   Going say hello and wink
   At every pretty girl I meet.

   Refrain

9. Goin' to buy myself a walking cane,
   Goin' to buy myself some candy,
   Goin' to buy myself a high silk hat
   And spend the rest for brandy.

131. DON'T LET THE DEAL GO DOWN

This piece is largely made up of the shoe-my-feet stanzas of Child no. 76, with a gambling and hobo framework. It was popularized in phonograph records in the 1920's and 1930's by the North Carolina Ramblers and the Delmore Brothers (CMUSA, pp. 48, 121), but it is not now found in many collections. Its title varies with the more memorable lines, such as "High-topped Shoes" in NCF, II, no. 301 (2 variants), V (2 tunes, one by a different singer), and "Last Gold Dollar," in the listing of FSSUS (p. 227, no. 181). For other related texts see OFS, IV, no. 671, and KFR, 1960, 131.

The present text was collected by Mrs. Sopha Keeney from the singing of Negro Bill Williams in 1959, both of Greenup County.

Don't let the deal go down,_____ Don't let the
deal go down,_____ Don't let the deal go down,____ 'Til the
last gold dol-lar is gone. 1. Been all a-round this
whole wide world,___ I been down in Mem-phis, Ten-nes-see, And
a-ny old place I hang my___ hat, Here is
home sweet home ___ for me.

SCALE: Heptachordal (f (f#) g a b c d e) Inflected scale.   MODE: Plagal.
RANGE: d' - d" (Perfect octave).   TONAL CENTER: F.   PHRASE
STRUCTURE: A B A B[1] // C B[2] A[1] B[1] (2, 2, 2, 2, // 2, 2, 2, 2) or A A[1] //
B A[1] (4, 4, 4, 4) Reprisenbar.   MELODIC RELATIONSHIP: The singer
commenced this song with the refrain. The harmonic implications of the tune,
traveling counterclockwise through the circle of fifths, and its ragtime rhythms,
denote that it is perhaps of relatively recent vintage. The tune is actually built
of two scales; F major and G major. It embraces a tonal dichotomy, and also
some characteristics of ragtime music.

2.   Where'd you get those high-topped shoes,
     And the dress you wear so fine?
     I got my shoes from a railroad man,
     An' my dress from a driver in the mine.

     Refrain

3. Baby, who's gonna shoe your pretty little feet,
   And who's gonna glove your hand,
   Who's gonna kiss your rosy cheeks,
   An' who's gonna be your man?

   Refrain

4. Oh, Momma, shoe my pretty little feet,
   Momma, glove my hand,
   An' sister kiss my rosy cheek, and
   I don't need no man.

   Refrain

132. WATERMELON ON THE VINE

This song in praise of the big melon is obviously a minstrel piece, composed by whites to dramatize the Negro taste. It has not appeared very far North; in fact I find it in only two collections: Listed by Davis (FSV, p. 337), and given a few notes by Belden and Hudson (NCF, III, nos. 454, 465, and 468), V, 454, 465, one tune each). I have heard it and have another text from McCreary County, Kentucky.

The present short version was sung by Mr. Stanley Whitt for Lena Ratliff and daughter Geneva Cox, all of Morgan County, in 1960.

1. Oh, talk a— bout your ap— ples, peach— es and your plums,

Talk a- bout your co- ney when Sun- day comes, Oh,___
give me,___ give me, how I wish you would, Oh, that
wa- ter- mel- on smil- in' on the vine.

SCALE: Hexatonic (a b c# e f# g#). MODE: Plagal. RANGE: c#'-c#''
(Perfect octave). TONAL CENTER: A. PHRASE STRUCTURE: A B C
D (2, 2, 2, 2). MELODIC RELATIONSHIP: NCF, V, No. 454b has aspects
of both tonal and rhythmic similarities.

Stanza 2, reference to "white folks" would indicate that this piece is of black
provenience; however, both the tonal material of the tune, as well as the phrase-
ology of the text, indicate "white" origin – possible for minstrelsy.

2. Oh, the white folks are foolish, hain't got no sense,
    Don't see the watermelons smilin' through the crack in the fence,
    Oh, give me, give me, how I wish you would,
    Oh, that watermelon smilin' on the vine.

133. OLD JOE CLARK

Barely discernable lines of this song can be traced to the 1840's in England
where they were old in Children's games and rhymes. Some of the stanzas and
directions for play parties have been collected in this country (Botkin, p. 269).

But with the coming of the American banjo this song has put on new and vigorous growth as a good old hoedown and square dance piece. It has a good stomp, and new stanzas can easily be added to old Joe's rascality. This dance version of text and tune is omnipresent in Appalachia (NCF, III, V, no. 86, 6 texts, 7 tunes, 2 by different singers) also in the Ozarks (OFS, no. 533). I wonder if it could have a specific source or individual adaptation. For instance, when I was teaching folklore and collecting in southeast Kentucky, many students from Clay County declared that the song originated in that county. They related that an old Negro banjo picker by the name of Joe Clark became an institution of folk music by making up dance pieces and by serving as the subject of pieces made up on him. "Old Joe Clark" they said was the most popular one on him. Further inquiry might have been fruitful but I did not get to do it. The head note in NCF lists it from Va., Tenn., Miss., Texas, Okla., Ark., Missouri, Indiana. It was recorded in the 1950's by Charlie Bryan (Lawless pp. 51-52).

These few stanzas (out of some hundred or more) were sung by Bill Williams (Negro) to Sophia Keeney, Greenup County, in 1959.

SCALE: Heptachordal (e f# g# a b c # (d#) d). Inflected scale.   MODE: Plagal; Major with D-sharp; Mixolydian with D-natural.   RANGE: c'#-d#' (Major 9th).   TONAL CENTER: E.   PHRASE STRUCTURE: A A^1 A^2 B //C D C^1 B^1 (2, 2, 2, 2, // 2, 2, 2, 2) or A A^1 // B B^1 (4, 4, // 4, 4).   MELODIC RELATIONAHIP: Variants of this tune are numerous: NCF, V, No. 86, versions C and G bear close resemblance. In most all variants, however dissimilar in tonal material, the idiom of the flatted seventh is common. Here (again) is to be observed a modal dichotomy in the inflected scale — D and D#.

2. Old Joe Clark's a dirty old dog,
   Tell you the reason why,
   He tore down the old rail fence,
   So his cows could eat in my rye.

Refrain

3. I went down to Old Joe's house,
   Old Joe was layin' in bed,
   Run my finger in Old Joe's throat,
   An' pulled out a terrapin's head.

Refrain

134. ROCKY ISLAND

An obvious barn and square dance number, "Rocky Island" has the repetitions of stanzas and refrains we find in "Cindy" and in "'Liza Jane." Yet it has its own consistency and theme centering in the Rocky Island retreat, wherever that is. I have been able to find only one song with this title and that is in KFR, 1961, 63-64 from the Combs collection listed in FSSUS, p. 230, no. 212, from Kentucky. There is a somewhat similar piece in TSCF titled "Icy Mountain."

The present piece was recorded in 1954 from Buell Kazee, who learned it in the early 1900's in Magoffin County. He has been mentioned often as the recorder of some 53 numbers for Brunswick in the 1920's and 1930's.

SCALE: Pentatonic (g a b d e).   MODE: III; Plagal.   RANGE: d' - b'
(Major 6th).   TONAL CENTER: G.   PHRASE STRUCTURE: A A^1 A^2
B (3, 3, 2, 2) or A A^1 (6, 4). The prolongations in measures 3 and 6 are probably
the result of performance prerogative.   MELODIC RELATIONSHIP: The
provenience of a simple hoedown tune such as this would be pure guess work at
best.

Measures 3 and 6 indicate internal incrementation.

2. Get up on the mountain,
    Mountain so high,
    Hang my head in the eagles' nest
    And hear the little ones cry.

3. Goin to Rocky Island,
    Goin away I know,
    See my Cindy darling,
    Ho-a-honey-ho.

4. Get up on the mountain,
    Hoe a little cane,
    Make a little sorghum
    To sweeten old Liza Jane.

5. Peaches in the summer time,
    Apples in the fall,
    If I don't get the girl I want,
    I won't have none at all.

6. Ho-a-honey ho,
    Ho-a-honey ho
    Goin to Rocky Island
    Ho-a-honey ho.

7. Get upon the mountain,
    Give my horn a blow,
    Hear my Candy darling
    Sing ho-a-honey ho.

8. Ho-a-honey ho,
    Ho-a-honey ho,
    Get on Rocky Island
    Ho-a-honey ho.

135. PAP'S OLD BILLY GOAT

A song on the same subject but not close in either text or tune is given by Spaeth (REW, pp. 157-158) as composed and made popular in the 1870-1890 period by Harrigan and Hart. A version of this number has been collected in North Carolina (NCF, III, no. 514). Davis lists a title and first line from Virginia (FSV, p. 151).

It has not been collected widely despite the recording of it that I heard in eastern Kentucky in the 1920's. This text was sung in 1959 by Henry Keeney for his wife Sophia, both of Greenup County.

1. Dad brought home a great big bil-ly goat,
Mom she washed 'most ev—'ry day, She hung her clothes out
on the line, That dad—goned old goat he came that way.

SCALE: Hexachordal (c d e f g a).   RANGE: c' - c'' (Perfect octave).
TONAL CENTER: C.   PHRASE STRUCTURE: A A B C (2, 2, 2, 2) or:
A B (4, 4).

2. He jerked down that red flannel shirt,
   You ought to have heard those buttons crack,
   But I'll get even with that son-of-a-gun,
   I'll tie him across the railroad track.

3. Well, I tied him across the railroad track,
   And the train was a-comin' at a powerful rate,
   He coughed up that old red shirt,
   He flagged down that darned old freight.

4. I went into the depot and bought me a ticket,
    Walked right in and I sat right down,
    Stuck my ticket in the brim of my hat,
    The dad-goned wind blowed it out on the ground.

5. Conductor come around and said gimme your ticket,
    Or you'll be left on the railroad track,
    I'll get even with that son-of-a-gun,
    Got a one way ticket and I ain't a-comin' back.

136. GROUND HOG

This humerous hunting song is found in most states touching Appalachia and almost nowhere else. An exception is in the Ozarks (OFS, III, no. 413) where southern mountain people migrated in the westering period of the early nineteenth century. There is no definite clues as to its age, except what Lomax says (FSNA, p. 251): "Chasing a little old innocent woodchuck is satirical and anti-climatic to earlier frontier bear-hunting." He quotes a stanza from David Crockett's time about catching a bear because "they loved bar-meat cooked and fried." I have experienced some excitement in digging a whistle-pig out of his hole, but nothing to compare with the Crockett style.

Selected references are in NCF, III, no. 221, 9, V, 5 tunes; the headnote lists the song in Virginia, West Virginia, Kentucky, North Carolina, Georgia, Ozarks, and Tennessee. Others are in FSS, no. 176; WVCS, no. 41; SSSA, pp. 5-6; and a few more in Kentucky: **KySill**, p. 38, LT, p. 30, FSSUS p. 220, TSCF, no. 86. Lawless lists 26 instances of the number in print.

The present item was recorded in 1959 by Mary S. Nelson from the singing of Warren Wright, both of Greenup County.

1. Shoul-der up my axe, whis-tle to my dog,___

Shoul-der up my axe, whis-tle to my dog,_____

Go-in' up the hol-ler to catch a ground hog,___

ground hog._____

SCALE: Heptachordal (f g a b♭ c d e♭).　　MODE: Mixolydian, Plagal, although the Ecclesiastic mode appears somewhat anomalous in this prosaic setting. RANGE: c' - c'' (Perfect octave).　　TONAL CENTER: F. PHRASE STRUCTURE: A B A B[1] A B[2] C (1, 1, 1, 1, 1, 1, 2) or A A[1] A[2] B (2, 2, 2, 2).　　MELODIC RELATIONSHIP: NCF, V, No. 221 C.

The significant tonal element in this tune is the lowered seventh scale degree, characterizing the overall scale pattern as Mixolydian mode.

2. Two in rock, one in a log,
   Two in rock, one in a log,
   I heard him whistle an' knew he was a hog,
   Ground hog.

3. Run here Sal with a ten foot pole,
   Run here Sal with a ten foot pole,
   And twist this ground hog out of this hole,
   Ground hog.

4. I took the pole and twisted him out,
   Took that pole and twisted him out,
   Good God almighty ain't a ground hog stout.
   Ground hog.

5. Took him home and tanned his hide,
   Took him home and tanned his hide,
   Made the best shoe string that ever was tied,
   Ground hog.

6. Dig, old Tige, as hard as you can tear,
   Dig, old Tige, as hard as you can tear,
   The meat's good to eat, the hide's good to wear,
   Ground hog.

7. The meat's in the cupboard, the hide's in the churn,
   The meat's in the cupboard, the hide's in the churn,
   If that ain't ground hog, I'll be durned,
   Ground hog.

8. Little piece of corn bread laying on a shelf,
   Little piece of corn bread laying on a shelf,
   If you want any more, you can sing it yourself,
   Ground hog.

137. THE LITTLE BLACK BULL

The piece is closely related to a more widely reported song titled "The Old Gray Horse Came Tearing Out the Wilderness" (NCF, III, no. 174, and OFS, II, no. 271). Randolph has a one-stanza text with the same title though not the same lines as the present one. Since Scarborough found many related items in her Negro study (TNFS, p. 13) we surmise that it is a Southern Negro number. It is indeed somewhat related to a Negro love triangle "Bald Eagle" in my eastern Kentucky collection (TCFS, no. 66). See also ASB, p. 102; APS, 268; JAF, 56, 102; FSV, 260-261 (listed only, from Civil War times).

This piece was recorded by Mrs. Virginia Holmes in 1958 from the singing of her husband, who grew up in Butler County. He in turn had heard it from his father in about 1900.

1. The lit-tle black bull came down the mount-ain,
Un-cle John-nie Hoo-zie, The lit-tle black bull came
down the mount-ain Long time a - go.

SCALE: Hexatonic (g a b d e f#). MODE: Plagal. RANGE: d'-b'
(Major 6th). TONAL CENTER: G. PHRASE STRUCTURE: A B A^1 C
(2, 2, 2, 2) or: A A^1 (4, 4). MELODIC RELATIONSHIP: If the song has
Negro origins, as Dr. Roberts surmises, there is no trace of the Negro idiom in
the tonal material.

2. He shook his tail and jarred the waters,
   Uncle Johnnie Hoozie,
   He shook his tail and jarred the waters
   Long time ago.

3. He pawed the dirt in the heifers' faces,
   Uncle Johnnie Hoozie,
   He pawed the dirt in the heifers' faces
   Long time ago.

138. I LOVE MY ROOSTER

This is a curious version of a very popular song for children, usually called
"The Farmyard." In it most of the animals and fowl of the farm are imitated
cumulatively. Children like to make the animal sounds, the faster sung the
better. In his **Games and Songs** of 1903, pp. 115-116, W.W. Newell traces the
type over several centuries in European singing. For other related pieces see

SharpK, no. 218, OFS, III, no. 352, 4 texts; NCF, III, no. 124 (5 reported, one and portions printed), V, 3 tunes; FSV, p. 187; **KySyll;** LT, pp. 6-13; DD, pp. 156-157; AMS, p. 77; FSF, pp. 418-419.

My version is short and not fully cumulative, although it may have been longer. It was sung and recorded in 1957 by Mrs. Nan Jones, Knox County.

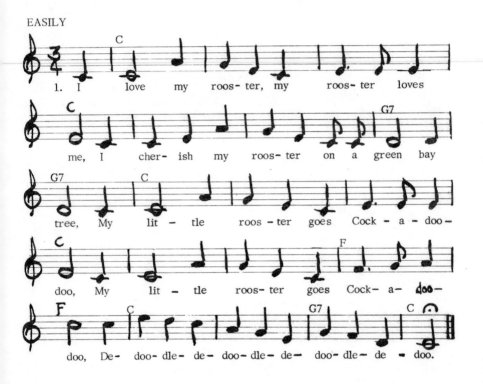

SCALE: Hexachordal (c d e f g a).   RANGE: c' - e" (Major 10th).
TONAL CENTER: C.   PHRASE STRUCTURE: A A^1 A A^2 B (4, 4, 4, 4, 4).
MELODIC RELATIONSHIP: The tune is obviously an offspring of "The Campbells are Coming." Three versions of this song are contained in NCF, V, No. 124, with entirely different tonal and rhythmic settings.

2. I love my duck, my duck loves me,
    I cherish my duck on a green bay tree,
    My little duck goes quack, quack, quack,
    My little rooster goes Cock-a-doo-doo.
    De-doodle-de-doodle-de-doodle-de-doo.

3. I love my cat, my cat loves me,
    I cherish my cat on a green bay tree,
    My little cat goes meow, meow, meow,
    My little rooster goes Cock-a-doo-doo,
    De-doodle-de-doodle-de-doodle-de-doo.

4. I love my pig, my pig loves me,
    I cherish my pig on a green bay tree,
    My little pig goes oink, oink, oink,
    My little roster goes Cock-a-doo-doo,
    De-doodle-de-doodle-de-doodle-de-doo.

139. MY SON JOSHUA

This humorous number has some features of a traditional song. My informant knew the text and the tune well, clicking her tongue at the "Giddap" refrain line. But to date I have been able to find only a single parallel, in—of all places, Frank Shay's **My Pious Friends and Drunken Companions**, pp. 64-65. It was collected and sung by Margaret W. Evans of Greenup County in 1959.

RAG TEMPO

1. My son, Josh- u- a, went to Phil- a- del- phi- a;

Would- n't do a day's work if he could.

He smokes ci-ga-rettes like the oth-er fel-lows do;
What he's a-com-in' to ain't no good. Well,
I'll be swan, I must be get-tin' on,
Gid-dap, Na-po-le-on, it looks like rain. Well,
I'll by-gosh, that's an aw-ful big____ squash.
Stop when you're ov-er by the farm a-gain.

SCALE: Heptachordal (f g a b (b♭) c d e).   MODE: Major*; Plagal.
RANGE: c' - c" (Perfect octave).   TONAL CENTER: F.   PHRASE
STRUCTURE: A B A C // D B D C^1 (2, 2, 2, 2, // 2, 2, 2, 2) or A A^1 // B
B^1 (4, 4, // 4, 4,).   MELODIC RELATIONSHIP: This song is most likely of
American origin. Its lilting rhythms of dotted-eighth and sixteenth notes are
peculiarly suggestive of ragtime music.

* Although this is theoretically a mixed mode it most certainly does not possess
the character of the church modes (Ionian and Locrain); this tune is most certainly associated with contemporary harmony, with the B-natural effecting modulation to the dominant. The editor is arbitrarily classifying it as basically major.

2. I met lots of men, allus got the best of them;
   I met a couple on the Boston train.
   I said, "Howdy do," they said "How're you?"
   Stop when you're over by the farm again.

Refrain:

Well, I'll be swan, I must be gettin' on,
Giddap, Napoleon, it looks like rain.
Well, I'll be switched, the hay's not pitched.
Stop when you're over by the farm again.

140. JUST ANYTHING

This slight little item has not come into the collectors' nets and therefore must not now be in active tradition. The only other text that I have seen is in the Randolph collection (OFS, III, no. 449, titled "Anything").

My singer reported that Mrs. Ellen Rice, a blind singing woman of her community, upon being asked to sing something, mentioning no definite title, would come forth with "Just Anything." I collected the item from Mrs. Mildred D. Webb, Greenup County, in 1959.

SCALE: Hexachordal (g a b c d e).   MODE: Plagal.   RANGE: c' - b'
(Major 7th).   TONAL CENTER: G; circular tune.   PHRASE STRUC-
TURE: A B A^1 B (2, 2, 2, 2) or A A^1 (4, 4).   MELODIC RELATIONSHIP:
There seems to be a marked affinity between the character of this whimsical
and obscure tune and its title.

Note the fusion of the phrases with the common tone, D.

2. My little song is quite complete,
    I think by rights I deserve a treat,
    My usual drink is brandy sling,
    But now I'll take just Anything.

141. LITTLE BLACK MUSTACHE

A modern American stock song, it has been inspired by the slick and fickle
ways of the dark villain of early movies. It has gained wide circulation by
renditions in music halls, barber shops, and by recordings made in the late 1920's
by a very popular singer Vernon Dalhart (CMUSA, p. 58). This may be the
recording that I heard on records in the 1920's. It has been kept alive mostly in
the South. Randolph collected three texts, one dated 1927 (OFS, no. 402);
Henry found two variants in the 1930's in Appalachia (FSSH, no. 96); and there
is one is FSSUS, pp. 180-181. The most complete parallels are in NCF, II, IV,
no. 202. Lawless lists 16 instances of it in print.

The present number was sung and taped in 1958 by Linda Giles from Boyd
County.

MODERATELY

life. I thought the time would sure-ly come that I would be his wife. His pock-ets they were filled with gold, and Oh, he cut a dash, With a dia-mond ring, a watch and chain, and a dar-ling black mus-tache. Oh, that lit-tle black mus-tache, that lit-tle black mus-tache; Ev-'ry time I think on it my heart beats quick as a flash; That lit-tle black mus-tache, that lit-tle black mus-tache: But you must know I've lost my beau with the lit-tle black mus-tache.

SCALE: Heptachordal (d e f# g a b c#).   MODE: Major; Plagal.
RANGE: a - d" (Perfect 11th).   TONAL CENTER: D.   PHRASE
STRUCTURE: A A^1 B A^2 // C D C E (4, 4, 4, 4, // 4, 4, 4, 4) or A B // C C^1
(8, 8, // 8, 8).   MELODIC RELATIONSHIP: For an entirely different musical
setting see NCF, IV, No. 204A. A significant aspect of the above tune is its wide
intervallic skips, frequently to the octave. The piece shows a very interesting
structure, a well-known phenomenon, structurally speaking, namely, showing how
the end of one phrase is fused with the beginning of the next.

2. One day there came a sour old maid,
    Who owned her weight in gold,
    She wore false teeth and had false hair,
    And was forty-five years old.
    The cruel lad deserted me
    Just for the old maid's cash,
    And now you know I've lost my beau
    With the darling black mustache.

    Refrain

3. And now they live just across the street,
    In that great mansion home,
    She married him for his black mustache,
    He married her for her gold.
    Young girls, remember my sad fate,
    And do not be too rash,
    But let alone the stylish chaps
    That wear a black mustache.

    Refrain

142. JUICE OF THE FORBIDDEN FRUIT

This recent satirical song of the stage has not been collected very widely and not before the 1890's. Some of the "drinkers" named in various texts—Blaine, Oscar Wilde, Cleveland, Frank James—lived through the turn of the last century. See Belden, BSM, p. 441, and OFS, III, no. 403 (2 texts and tunes). There is an instance of the song in the **Texas Folklore Society Publications** (1927): 199-200.

My performer, a woman of about 60, said she distinctly remembered learning the piece in Breathitt County in about 1904. She was helping Uncle Joe and Calvin stem tobacco in the barn and they let her overhear this song. She also sang several old Child ballads and others. It was given to me in 1961 by Mrs. Stella Byrd Brooks.

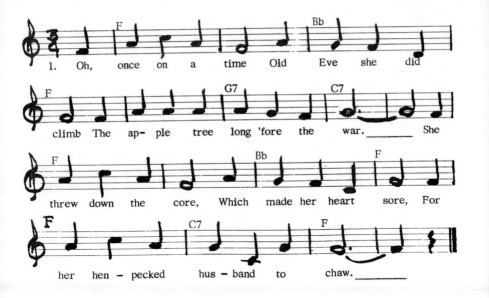

1. Oh, once on a time Old Eve she did climb The apple tree long 'fore the war._____ She threw down the core, Which made her heart sore, For her hen — pecked hus — band to chaw._____

SCALE: Pentatonic (f g a c d).   MODE: III; Plagal.   RANGE: c' - c"
(Perfect octave).   TONAL CENTER: F.   PHRASE STRUCTURE: A B
A C (4, 4, 4, 4) or: A A^1 (8, 8).

2. And ever since then
   All manner of men,
   The blind, the lame, and the mute,
   The bankers and clerks,
   Politicians and Turks,
   Drink the juice of the forbidden fruit.

3. Old Henry Ward Beecher,
   The Sunday School teacher,
   Drinks what he calls sassafact root.
   But it's all the same
   If it had its right name,
   It's the juice of the forbidden fruit.

143. BRYAN O'LYNN

This bald satire has appeared in collections on both sides of the Atlantic, usually in the humorous and nonsense sections. For his notes to a Missouri text Belden (BSM, pp. 501-502) pushes the origin of the piece back to sixteenth century England, when the English made fun of the Scottish for uncouth clothing and make-shift living. Later it began, like the Irishman jokes, to be applied to the Irish character. There is one stanza in Halliwell's **Nursery Rhymes** (p. 34) and six stanzas in his **Popular Rhymes** (p. 271). The longest instance, eleven quatrains, is in SharpK, no. 151, from Kentucky. Randolph (OFS, no. 471) gives evidence of the song in Kansas in the 1870's. Aside from my text there are no refrains in the published versions except a one-line "Larry-ho-ho, ho-larry-ho" in Belden's "Tom Bo-lin."

Another Kentucky version was printed by Evelyn K. Wells in **The Ballad Tree,** page 167. She comments on it as a song for the nursery and gives her source as a woman Elizabeth Niniard of Harlan County, who had learned it from Henry Harris. It was reprinted in a Calendar "A Year of Song," for August 1952, Pine Mountain Settlement School. Lawless lists 6 instances of it in print. The present piece was recorded by Sophia Keeney in 1959 from the singing of Orin Nelson, both of Greenup County.

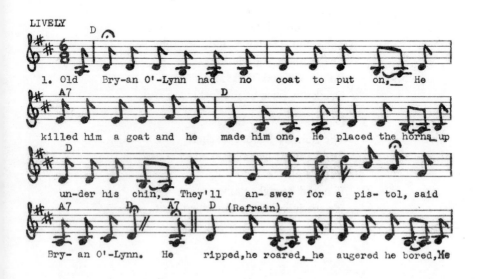

LIVELY

1. Old Bry-an O'-Lynn had no coat to put on,__ He
killed him a goat and he made him one, He placed the horns up
un-der his chin,__ They'll an- swer for a pis- tol, said
Bry- an O'-Lynn. He ripped, he roared, he augered he bored, He

306

slashed, he lashed,___ he board-ed the pen, To
call up the Dev-il, said Bry-an O'-Lynn.

SCALE: Hexatonic (d e f# a b c#).   MODE: Plagal.   RANGE: a - d"
(Perfect 11th).   TONAL CENTER: D.   PHRASE STRUCTURE: A B A C
// A A¹ C¹ (2, 2, 2, 2, // 2, 2, 2) or: A A¹ A² (4, 4, 6).   MELODIC RELA-
TIONSHIP: Note the predominant iteration of the tonic, D, throughout.

There is a trace of word-painting on the final line: "To call up the Devil–––."
and actually in the whole refrain. Cf. SharpK, II, No. 151, for another version.

2. Old Bryan O'Lynn had no watch to keep time,
    He got him a turnip, he scraped it out fine,
    He placed a cricket up under its skin,
    Now start up your tickin', said Bryan O'Lynn.

    Refrain

3. Old Bryan O'Lynn had no pants to put on,
    He killed him a sheep and he made him one,
    He put the hairy side out and the smooth side in.
    Lay close to me, mutton, said Bryan O'Lynn.

    Refrain

BIBLIOGRAPHY AND KEY TO THE NOTES

ABBB   Laws, G. Malcolm, Jr. **American Balladry from British Broadsides.** Bibliographical and Special Series (BSS), vol. 8. Philadelphia: American Folklore Society, 1957

ABFS   Lomax, John and Alan Lomax. **American Ballads and Folk Songs.** New York, 1934

ABTSNE   Flanders, Helen, T. P. Coffin, and B.K. Nettl. **Ancient Ballads Traditionally Sung in New England.** 4 vols. Philadelphia: University of Pennsylvania Press, 1960-1964

AFSS   Wilgus, D.K. **Anglo-American Folksong Scholarship Since 1898.** New Brunswick, New Jersey: Rutgers University Press, 1959

AFTS   Chase, Richard. **American Folk Tales and Songs.** Signet Book. New York: New American Library, 1956. Reprint by Dover, 1971

AMS   Richardson, Ethel P. **American Mountain Songs.** New York: Greenburg, 1927; reprint, 1955

APS   Botkin, Benjamin A. **American Play-Party Song.** Lincoln, Nebraska, 1937; Reprint ed., New York: Frederick Ungar, 1963

ASB   Sandburg, Carl. **The American Songbag.** New York, 1927

BAS   Bronson, Bernard H. **The Ballad as Song.** Berkeley: University of California Press, 1969

BB   Niles, John Jacob. **The Ballad Book of John Jacob Niles.** Boston: Houghton Mifflin, 1961

BBM   Barry, Phillips, Fannie H. Eckstorm, and Mary W. Smyth. **British Ballads from Maine.** New Haven, 1929

BFSSNE   **Bulletin of the Folksong Society of the Northeast.** BSS, vol. 11. Philadelphia: American Folklore Society, 1960

BFSSW   Moore, Chauncy, and Ethel Moore. **Ballads and Folk Songs of the Southwest.** Norman: University of Oklahoma Press, 1964

BKH   Fuson, Harvey H. **Ballads of the Kentucky Mountains.** London, 1931

BMMK   Thomas, Jean. **Ballad Makin' in the Mountains of Kentucky.** New York, 1939. Reprint by Oak Publications, 1964

BMNE   Flanders, Helen H. and M. Olney. **Ballads Migrant in New England.** New York, 1953

BS   Williams, Cratis D. **Ballads and Songs.** Microcard ed., Series A, no. 15. Lexington, 1937. Reprint by Microfilms, Inc., West Salem, Wisconsin.

BSI   Brewster, Paul G. **Ballads and Songs of Indiana.** Indiana University

	Publication, Folklore Series, no. 1. Bloomington: Indiana University Press, 1940
BSM	Belden, Henry Marvin. **Ballads and Songs Collected by the Missouri Folk-Lore Society.** University of Missouri Studies, XV. Columbia, Missouri, 1940; reprint, 1955
BSNA	MacKenzie, W. Roy. **Ballads and Sea Songs from Nova Scotia.** Cambridge, Mass., 1928
BSO	Eddy, Mary O. **Ballads and Songs from Ohio.** New York, 1939
BSSM	Gardner, Emelyn Elizabeth and Geraldine J. Chickering. **Ballads and Songs of Southern Michigan.** Ann Arbor, 1939
BSSN	Greenleaf, Elizabeth B. and Grace Y. Mansfield. **Ballads and Sea Songs of Newfoundland.** Cambridge, Mass., 1933
BT	Wells, Evelyn K. **The Ballad Tree.** New York: Ronald Press, 1950
BTBNA	Coffin, Tristram P. **The British Traditional Ballad in North America.** Pub. of the American Folklore Society, BSS; vol. II, Philadelphia, 1950. Revised ed., 1963
CC	Haun, Mildred. **Cocke County Ballads and Songs.** Master's Thesis, Vanderbilt University, 1937
CDF	Korson, George. **Coal Dust on the Fiddle.** Philadelphia, 1943. Reprint ed., Detroit: Folklore Associates of Gale Research, 1965
Child	See ESPB
CMUSA	Malone, Bill C. **Country Music: U.S.A.** Memoirs of the American Folklore Society (MAFS), no. 54. Austin: University of Texas Press, for the American Folklore Society, 1968
DD	Thomas, Jean. **Devil's Ditties.** Chicago, 1931
EFSSA	See SharpK
ESPB	Child, Francis James. **The English and Scottish Popular Ballads.** 5 vols. Boston, 1882-1898. Reprint ed., New York: Dover, 1965
ETSFF	Burton, Thomas and Ambrose Manning. **East Tennessee State University Collection of Folklore: Folksong.** Johnson City, Tenn.: East Tennessee State University Press, 1967
ETWVMB	Cambiaire, C. F. **East Tennessee and Western Virginia Mountain Ballads.** London, 1935
FFA	Lawless, Ray M. **Folksingers and Folksongs in America.** Rev. ed., New York: Duell, Sloan and Pearce, 1965
FFI	Stout, Earl J. **Folklore from Iowa.** MAFS, no. 29. Philadelphia, 1936
FSA	Gordon, Robert W. **Folksongs of America.** National Service Bureau Publication, 1938
FSE	Lloyd, A. L. **Folk Song in England.** New York: International Publishers, 1967

FSF   Morris, Alton C. **Folk Songs of Florida.** Gainesville: University of Florida Press, 1950

FSKH   Combs, Josiah. **Folk-Songs of the Kentucky Highlands.** New York, 1936

FSKM   McGill, Josephine. **Folk Songs of the Kentucky Mountains.** New York, 1917

FSM   Hudson, Arthur P. **Folk Songs of Mississippi and Their Background.** Chapel Hill, North Carolina, 1936

FSMEU   Combs, Josiah. **Folk-Songs du Midi des Etats-Unis.** Paris, 1925. Revised and enlarged ed. by D. K. Wilgus. Austin: University of Texas Press for the American Folklore Society, 1967

FSNA   Lomax, Alan. **The Folk Songs of North America in the English Language.** New York: Doubleday, 1960

FSNE   Greig, Gavin. **Folk-Song of the North-East** . Peterhead, Scotland, 1909. Reprint ed., Detroit: Folklore Associates of Gale Research, 1963

FSS   Cox, John Harrington. **Folk-Songs of the South.** Cambridge, Mass., 1925. Reprint ed., Detroit: Folklore Associates of Gale Research, 1963

FSSH   Henry, Mellinger E. **Folk-Songs from the Southern Highlands.** New York, 1938

FSSUS   **Folksongs of the Southern United States.** See FSMEU

FSUSA   Lomax, John and Alan Lomax. **Folk Song: U.S.A.** New York: Duell, Sloan and Pearce, 1947

FSV   Davis, Arthur Kyle, Jr. **Folksongs of Virginia: A Descriptive Index and Syllabus.** Durham, North Carolina: Duke University Press, 1949

FTM   Hudson, Arthur P., G. Herzog, and H. Halpert. **Folk Tunes from Mississippi.** New York, 1937

GSAC   Newell, William Wells. **Games and Songs of American Children.** New York, 1883, 1903. Reprint by Dover, 1963

IFMUS   Nettl, Bruno. **An Introduction to Folk Music in the United States.** Detroit: Folklore Associates of Gale Research, 1962

JAF   **Journal of American Folklore.** Philadelphia and Austin, 1888-

JFSS   **Journal of the Folk-Song Society.** London, 1899-1931

JHFS   Chappell, Louis. **John Henry: A Folklore Study.** Jena, Germany, 1933

JHTD   Johnson, Guy B. **John Henry: Tracking Down a Negro Legend.** Chapel Hill: University of North Carolina Press, 1929

KFP   **Kentucky Folk-lore and Poetry Magazine,** 1927-1931

KFR   **Kentucky Folklore Record.** Bowling Green, Ky., 1955—

KMFS   Wheeler, Mary. **Kentucky Mountain Folk Songs.** Boston, 1937

KySyll   Shearin, Hubert and Josiah Combs. **A Syllabus of Kentucky Folk Songs.** Transylvania Studies in English II. Lexington, Ky., 1911

LT   Wyman, Loraine and Howard Brockway. **Lonesome Tunes: Folk Songs from the Kentucky Mountains.** New York, 1916

MM   Eckstorm, Fannie H. and Mary Smyth. **Minstrelsy of Maine.** Boston, 1927

MTBV   Davis, Arthur Kyle, Jr. **More Traditional Ballads of Virginia.** Chapel Hill: University of North Carolina Press, 1960

NAB   Laws, G. Malcolm, Jr. **Native American Balladry: A Descriptive Study and a Bibliography Syllabus.** BSS, vol. I. Philadelphia: American Folklore Society, 1950. Revised ed., 1964

NCF   **The Frank C. Brown Collection of North Carolina Folklore.** 7 vols. Vols. II and III edited by Arthur P. Hudson and H. M. Belden; vols. IV and V edited by Jan P. Schinhan. Durham: Duke University Press, 1952-1961

NGMS   Flanders, Helen H., Elizabeth F. Ballard, George Brown, and Phillips Barry. **The New Green Mountain Songster.** New Haven, 1939. Reprint ed., Detroit: Folklore Associates of Gale Research, 1965

NM   Bruce, J. C. and J. Stokoe. **Northumbrain Minstrelsy.** New Castle, England, 1882. Reprint ed., Detroit: Folklore Associates of Gale Research, 1965

NWS   Odum, Howard W. and Guy B. Johnson. **Negro Workaday Songs.** Chapel Hill: University of North Carolina Press, 1926

OAM   Green, Archie. **Only a Miner: Studies in Recorded Coal-Mining Songs.** Urbana: University of Illinois Press, 1972

OFS   Randolph, Vance. **Ozark Folksongs.** 4 vols. Columbia, Missouri : State Historical Society of Missouri, 1946-1950

OSC   Lomax, John A., Alan Lomax and Ruth Seeger. **Our Singing Country.** New York: Macmillan, 1941

PSL   Korson, George. **Pennsylvania Songs and Legends.** 2 vols. Philadelphia: University of Pennsylvania Press, 1949

PTWH   Campbell, John F. **Popular Tales of the West Highlands,** New ed., 4 vols. Paisley and London: Alexander Gardner, 1890

REW   Spaeth, Sigmund. **Read' em and weep: The Songs You Forgot to Remember.** New York, 1926; reprint, 1959

RF   Ralston, W.R.S. **Russian Folktales.** London, 1873

SBS   Roberts, Leonard. **Sang Branch Settlers: Folksongs and Tales of a Kentucky Mountain Family.** MAFS, vol. 61. Austin and London: University of Texas Press, 1974

SCB   Smith, Reed. **South Carolina Ballads.** Cambridge, Mass., 1928

SCSM	Scarborough, Dorothy. **A Song Catcher in Southern Mountains.** New York: Columbia University Press, 1937
SCW	Silber, Erwin. **Songs of the Civil War.** New York: Columbia University Press, 1960
SFC	Ritchie, Jean. **Singing Family of the Cumberlands.** New York: Oxford University Press, 1955. Reprint ed., New York: Oak Publications, 1963
SFSEA	Jackson, George P. **Spiritual Folk-Songs of Early America.** New York, 1937. Reprint ed., New York: Dover, 1964
SG	Thomas, Jean. **The Singin' Gatherin.'** New York, 1939
SharpK	Sharp, Cecil J. **English Folk-Songs from the Southern Appalachians.** 2 vols. Edited by Maud Karpeles. London: Oxford University Press, 1932, 1952; 1960 in 1 vol.
SHMC	Walker, William. **Southern Harmony and Musical Companion.** New York, 1939
SMF	Hudson, Arthur P. **Specimens of Mississippi Folklore.** Ann Arbor, Michigan, 1928
SSSA	Henry, Mellinger. **Songs Sung in the Southern Appalachians.** London: Mitre Press, 1934
TBFWV	Cox, John H. **Traditional Ballads and Folk-Songs Mainly from West Virginia.** New York, 1939. Reprint ed., BSS, no. XV. Austin: University of Texas Press for The American Folklore Society, 1964
TBV	Davis, Arthur Kyle, Jr. **Traditional Ballads of Virginia.** Cambridge, Mass., 1929. Reprint ed., Charlottesville, Virginia: University of Virginia Press, 1970
TFS	Owens, William A. **Texas Folk Songs.** Publications of the Texas Folklore Society no. XXIII. Dallas: University Press in Dallas, 1950
TFSB	**Tennessee Folklore Society Bulletin.** Murfreesboro, 1935-
TKMS	Wyman, Loraine and Howard Brockway. **Twenty Kentucky Mountain Songs.** Boston, 1920
TNFS	Scarborough, Dorothy. **On the Trail of Negro Folk-Songs.** Cambridge, Mass., 1925
TSCF	Roberts, Leonard. **Tales and Songs of the Couch Family.** Microcard edition, Series A, no. 30, UK-18. Lexington, Kentucky, 1959. Reprint ed., Microfilms, Inc., West Salem, Wisconsin, 1963
TSSI	Neely, Charles. **Tales and Songs of Southern Illinois.** Menasha, Wisconsin, 1938
TSSO	Fowks, Edith. **Traditional Singers and Songs from Ontario.** Detroit: Folklore Associates of Gale Research, 1965
TTCB	Bronson, Bertrand. **The Traditional Tunes of the Child Ballads.** 4

	vols. Princeton, New Jersey: Princeton University Press, 1959-1972
Type	Aarne, Antti and Stith Thompson. **The Types of the Folktale**. 2nd revision, FFC, no. 184. Helsinki, Finland, 1961
UCDG	Roberts, Leonard. **Up Cutshin and Down Greasy**. Lexington, Kentucky, 1959. Basic contents reprinted in **Sang Branch Settlers** (q.v.)
VFB	Flanders, Helen H. and George Brown. **Vermont Folk Songs and Ballads**. Battleboro, Vermont, 1931
WVCS	Gainer, Patrick W., Leonard Roberts, **et al**. **West Virginia Centennial Book of 100 Songs**. Charleston, WV, 1963
WSMML	Spaeth, Sigmund. **Weep Some More, My Lady**. New York, 1927
WVF	**West Virginia Folklore** Publication of the West Virginia Folklore Society. Edited by Ruth Ann Musick. Fairmont, WV, 1950-1967

Index of Titles and First Lines of Songs

Titles are in boldface